WITH FLYING COLORS

Confessions of a NavCad

WITH FLYING COLORS

Confessions of a NavCad

Col. R.L. Upchurch
USMC (Ret)

Library of Congress Number: 99-91944
ISBN #: Hardcover 0-7388-1426-1
Softcover 0-7388-1427-X

This is a work of fiction. Names, characters, places and incidents either are the product of the author's imagination or are used fictitiously, and any resemblance to any actual persons, living or dead, events, or locales is entirely coincidental.

This book was printed in the United States of America.

To order additional copies of this book, contact:
Xlibris Corporation
1-888-7-XLIBRIS
www.Xlibris.com
Orders@Xlibris.com

TO PROVIDENCE

Acknowledgements

There are many people who helped me write this story. Foremost is my wife, Providence, a former stewardess, English teacher, and school counselor. She is my proofreader, sounding board, and morale booster, and she kept me focused when I wanted to shuck the whole project and head for the golf course. Terry Cline, the novelist and probably one of the greatest storytellers of all time, taught me how to get started. Marie Durden sketched and painted the flag waving, carefree cadet on the book cover. My fellow tour guides at the National Museum of Naval Aviation added to my experiences with their endless stream of sea stories. When a group of retired naval aviators gather to share their tales about "flying by the seat of their pants," the difference between fact and fiction gets more than a little clouded. Therefore, any resemblance my characters have to any actual persons, living or dead, is purely coincidental, if not impossible. And thanks to all my friends and family who read my manuscripts and offered encouragement and constructive criticism: Joe and Gussie, Bill and Nita, Fred and Susan, Miles and Mimi, Vernon and Barbara, Michael and Knight, and Randy and Mary. As in all novels about aviation, the greatest contribution has been from the countless pilots who earned their wings *With Flying Colors*. God bless them all.

Chapter 1

I was never one to venture recklessly into the unknown. Accordingly, when the car turned into the little airport that morning my body responded with a low order tremor. At age 10, I was young enough to be plenty scared and old enough to want to hide it. Shoving my sweaty hands deep in my pockets I turned my head hoping to find Willy at least a little jumpy. He was jumpy all right, but not as I had expected. Willy normally moved like a lethargic snail, but my summer companion was bouncing around in the back seat like a hound on the way to the hunt. Ryan parked the '36 Ford convertible in the shadow of a large oak tree and killed the engine.

Willy leaped over the side, took two steps toward the airplane and stopped. "Watch'a wait'n for, Tommy? C'mon!" he called, waving his hand.

Ryan tossed his cigarette in the grass, stomped on it, and slammed the door. "Let's go, twerp, I don't have all day."

"I'm coming," I muttered, fumbling with the handle.

I stood in the shadow of the old oak and stared at the little Aeronca Champ squatting in the tall Kentucky grass. It didn't look much like an airplane—more like a winged orange crate with tandem seats, two wheels, and a propeller. And the engine couldn't have been larger than one of those two-cycle bangers that powered a motorbike. While Ryan loosened the tie-downs Willy and I walked around the airplane pointing at the wings, tail, propeller, and fuselage. They were the only parts we could identify. Shading my eyes, I leaned my forehead against the clouded, celluloid window. All the levers, gauges, and buttons made me think I was staring into the snaggletoothed mouth of a man-eating dragon. I swallowed hard, convinced that I would never come back from this ride alive.

* * *

Although my home was a factory suburb of Detroit, Michigan, I spent most summers on Uncle Trevor and Aunt Connie's farm in Bullhead County, Kentucky. Dad said the county was named for all the bullheads—what I called catfish—feeding at the bottom of the ponds and creeks near the Ohio River. I figured the county was named after the attitude of its inhabitants. Dad wanted me to experience the hard work he did and satisfaction he had on the old Fitzgerald farm where he grew up. I obediently, but reluctantly obliged.

Willy Rumford lived on the farm a half-mile up the road. Willy was a miniature clone of his dad, Fulton Harley Rumford. With his teeth chomping on a hay stalk, straw hat tilted forward on his brow, and callous hands tucked into the bib of faded overalls, he was from Fulton's loins, no doubt about that. Maybe Willy didn't have his dad's sour disposition, but he came close. Emma Rumford figured that sending Willy over to play after finishing his chores would be neighborly. Fulton Rumford thought it was foolishness. "That boy's got 'nough to do," he grumbled, "without entertainin' any city kid on a summer holiday." Two or three times a week, however, when Fulton went into Paducah to trade his dairy products for feed and fertilizer, Emma sent Willy to visit. She never came with him. In fact, she never went anywhere.

Willy would never play the games I liked, such as catch with almost anything, climbing trees, or sliding down hay piles. "Pa says them things'r kid stuff," he said while sucking the juice out of a weed stem. "Says they're *un-pro-ductive.*" So we engaged in the productive activities Fulton approved of, such as rooting out and spearing rats from the creek bed, knocking crows off the corn stalks with Willy's .22 rifle—a near impossible feat for a city shooter like me—and occasionally sneaking off and smoking sun-cured corn silk while we did what Willy called, "pole bobbing for bullheads."

Fulton Rumford did allow me, however, to join them at hay baling time, purely to gain another pair of hands free of charge, I figured. Being nine months older, corn fed, and hard worked year round, Willy tossed bales in the wagon like they were empty egg cartons. Fulton drove the tractor and I sat behind him on the baler, feeding in the binding wires, a job he said was "meant for them whose bodies is less favored by the Almighty."

Sitting on the baler's kidney-throbbing seat, choking on dust and hayseeds while feeding in wires one at a time was throat-grabbing miserable, to say nothing of how that machine would gobble up my arm like a limb in a wood chipper should I become a tad careless. I envied Willy working with the neighbor men loading the hay wagon, out of range of the dust cloud and Fulton's watchful eyes.

Willy was already showing a tendency to be broad shouldered and thick chested, with a head to match. He was also clumsy. More often than not he had a bruise here or a scrape there, from splitting and stacking wood or falling off the barn's hay lift, he said. As for me, I tended to be shy, lanky, and nondescript. My hair was not blonde, brown, nor black, but sort of hazel, like my eyes. Aunt Connie said I reminded her of the scarecrow in her vegetable garden: sad-eyed, thatchy crown, fence-picket thin, and not much company. On top of all that, she said, I was alien to the way of farming.

After baling up an entire hay field Fulton allowed us to take a couple hours off and dip our cane poles and dusty bodies in the bullhead pond. Sometimes while watching our bobbers drift on the murky surface I'd make fun of Willy's bib overalls and his down home dialect. He'd retaliate by expressing sympathy in his slow, maundering voice for anyone not privileged to be raised in rural Kentucky.

"Truth be known, Tommy, we usually don't really care much for yur kind. Like Pa says, ya have to wear a belt to hold up yur coveralls, yur low-cut shoes bare yur ankles for snakes and sticky burs, and ya leave yur head bare for the sun ta fry. But I try to be Christian tolerant. Twern't yur fault ya weren't reared in Kentucky."

Willy would pause to take a drag from his corncob pipe and

exhale a dark cloud that smelled like smoldering skunk hair. "No ailin' wished," he'd say with a shrug. "We just don't cotton much to outsiders, that's all. Besides the funny way ya dress yurselves, Pa says y'all are *un-pro-ductive*. Can't tell the difference 'tween sweet and white taters, can't squeeze a drop from a cow's tit, and yur even 'fraid to scoot a hen from 'er nest sose you can fetch her eggs. Besides that," he'd add with a twitch of his nose, "well, y'all talk awkward."

"Like you don't talk *awkward*, yourself," I'd scoff. "Half the things you say down here ain't even in the dictionary. And if you didn't slobber grease and butter down your chin when you eat fried chicken and corn on the cob you wouldn't have to wear a stupid bib attached to your stupid blue jeans."

Overkill such as that would usually get me in trouble. We'd soon be wrestling on the bank, playfully at first, then tempers would flare and one of us would get in a good lick. That would be Willy. The other would go home teary-eyed—me usually—lagging behind the victor basking in his moment of triumph. Again, that would more than likely be Willy.

Back at the Rumford farmhouse, Fulton would beam through his three-day beard and give Willy a playful, but smarting smack on the head. "Don't cotton to fight'n, boy," he'd say, looking at me out of the corner of his eye, "but since ya already done it, ya made me proud by getting the best of that city kid."

I'd hang my head low and walk up the road to our farm, working hard to regain my composure before I got there. In a few days we'd be back at the pond, engaging in more fishing, more bantering, and sometimes more wrestling.

* * *

I left Willy peering in the Aeronca's cockpit and stepped away to watch Ryan release the tie-down ropes. Ryan wore his uniform khakis and brown shoes, the clothes he preferred for flying after he came home from the war. His scuffed, leather flight jacket reeked of sweat, oil, and aviation gasoline. In 1944, when he dropped out of college to join the Army Air Corps, his face was as smooth as the silk on a dime store pillow. Now his face showed the effects of flying 85 missions over Germany in his P-47 Thunderbolt. Worry lines fanned away from his lonely, blue eyes, a few reversing course to dig deep furrows in his forehead and there was a slight tremor in his fingers when he held his cigarette.

Chauffeuring kids on the ground or in the sky was not Ryan's favorite pastime. He lit another cigarette and grumbled further displeasure at the task curtly assigned by Aunt Connie. "I ain't a whuppin' baby sitter," he mumbled while untying the rope on the left wing. With his cigarette dangling from the corner of his mouth, he curled the tie-down rope around a cement block half-buried in the sod.

When Ryan stepped around the tail and worked on the other wing tie-down I whispered in Willy's ear. "Doesn't look very sturdy, does it?" I reached up to feel the fabric covering a drooping aileron.

"Don't touch that!" barked Ryan over his shoulder. I yanked away my hand as though I'd touched a hot stove. "Picked her up last month for a song and a smile and I don't want you twerps poking holes in her before we even get airborne."

"She's a little smaller than I figured, Ryan, but she's a real beauty, ain't she Willy," I said, nudging my companion for his endorsement. He nodded his support, eyes big and shiny as hubcaps.

"She may be small," replied Ryan, "but she's big enough to get us where nothing else matters." He gestured toward the sky. "Up there you're as close to heaven as you're gonna get without buying the farm." He walked around the tail, wiggling the rudder and elevator, inspecting wires, massaging a patch or a dent.

"What'cha mean, Ryan? You already live on a farm," Willy said, squinting his eyes against the morning sun.

"Pilot term," he replied. "Means crashed and burned—bought

a burial plot on the old farm. Pilots buy the farm. Everybody else just plain dies."

I stared at his profile wondering how the man I idolized could talk about death like it was a real estate transaction. Ryan's blue eyes, light brown wavy hair, chiseled nose, and strong jaw gave him rough good looks, but he was impatient and irritable with 10-year old kids. When he turned toward Willy and me, I self-consciously lowered my eyes, resting them on his left shoulder.

I wanted to change the subject. Talking about dying, when I was about to go up for my first airplane ride, didn't sit too well. "That your outfit in the Air Corps?" I asked, pointing to the colorful unit patch on his sleeve.

He stared at the patch for a second, stuck his thumb between the loose threads holding the piece of frayed embroidery, and ripped it off his leather jacket. "Here, you take it, Tommy—a souvenir of your first flying lesson." He shoved the faded patch in my hands, a white number eight bracketed by two yellow wings. It was the insignia of Jimmy Doolittle's Eighth Air Force. With mouth agape, I held it like a precious gem.

"Gosh, Ryan, thanks." I turned and gloated at my scowling, summer companion.

"What about me?" asked Willy, his lower lip pushed out in protest.

"Tommy's family. I'm afraid he's my last hope to carry on the Fitzgerald flying tradition." Ryan sighed. "To be honest, though," he said jabbing at me with his forefinger, "if he don't fly an airplane better'n he drives a tractor, he ain't gonna be a lot of hope."

Just because I ran the tractor into the barn the previous week he thought I couldn't do anything right. Well, it was the first time I'd driven anything at all, let alone a big tractor. Still, to Ryan I was the inept, pesky cousin from the big city: ignorant, clumsy, and always getting in his way.

"You ever get scared?" I asked. What a dumb question, I thought immediately. Ryan broke the meanest bronco at the Bullhead County Fair. When he slid off the spent, glistening animal, panting and snorting its surrender, Ryan had swaggered out of the corral like he'd been on a bike ride.

"Only when I take up twerps," he grumbled. "Never can tell what a little kid will do when he gets in an airplane, especially a city kid." Now it was Willy's turn to gloat. Ryan dropped his cigarette butt in the dirt and ground it out angrily with his heel. "Instead of chauffeuring you twerps, I should be in Paducah, interviewing for that job," he mumbled.

* * *

Earlier that morning when Ryan was eating a late breakfast after milking, Aunt Connie saw Willy and me staring curiously at a photo stuck to the icebox. It was Ryan standing proudly in front of his recently purchased Aeronca Champ. Staring didn't mean we were aching to go flying, at least in my case, but I guess she took it as such.

"Ryan," she said while pouring him more coffee, "the boys are achin' to go up for a plane ride. Why don't you take 'em up this morning? They need something to do besides bouncing around this house all day."

Willy took it one step further. "Yeah, Ryan. You could give us flying lessons. How about it?" Willy had looked at me for support. Even though I had no desire to take the controls of a flying machine, I nodded my head.

"Please, Ryan," I said in a voice I hoped sounded sincere, but not convincing.

Talking through me as though I were invisible, he looked at Aunt Connie and shook his head. "Can't do it Ma. I gotta go to Paducah and check out that job at the radio station." He wiped the buttermilk off his mouth with his wrist, then sopped up the last of the egg yolk with a biscuit.

"Go to Paducah tomorrow, son. The boys need to get out. I'll call Emma and make sure Willy's got her blessing. Since Fulton went with your pa to the auction at Mayfield, I don't reckon she'll mind."

While Aunt Connie was on the phone, Ryan finished his breakfast. He may have been home from the war, but until he broke away on his own he still answered Aunt Connie's beck and call. When Emma Rumford gave the OK, Ryan frowned his disappointment and downed the rest of his buttermilk.

"C'mon twerps, 'fore the day heats up."

When Ryan grudgingly agreed to take Willy and me up for our first airplane ride, I had no choice but to go along. He was my idol. Besides, Willy would never let me forget it if I chickened out.

* * *

Ryan unsnapped the engine cowling. "With little twerps like you hanging around, it's lucky we pilots have guardian angels," he muttered, using his fingers to wipe the oil off the dipstick. He popped it in and out of the engine, then held it in the sunlight.

"You believe in angels?" I asked, surprised at this revelation.

He squinted at the oil level before he answered. "Well, some pilots have dreams where they can fly like a bird," he said replacing the dipstick. "In their dreams they stick out their arms and loop, roll, hover, or just sail through the sky without a care in the world. They consider those dreams a preview of a pilot's heaven, thinking that when they buy the farm they'll spend eternity soaring with the eagles. They also figure that if they happen to see a mortal pilot up there in trouble, why not pull along side and lend a hand—maybe even adopt him. After all, they got nothing better to do. I suppose you could call that being a guardian angel, don't you agree?" I nodded. "Now, I'm not saying I believe that stuff, but I will admit that I got out of some tough scrapes over Europe where there wasn't any logical explanation. Either I got some help, or I was damn lucky." Ryan closed the cowling. He pointed at me and jerked his thumb toward the Aeronca's cockpit.

"OK, twerp, get in. And remember, don't touch anything unless I say so." I ducked my head under the wing and climbed into the front cockpit. While Ryan secured my seat belt he shouted over his shoulder. "We'll be back in half an hour, Willy. Then it's your turn." Willy snatched up a tall weed, stuck the stem in his mouth, and plopped down next to the oak tree.

Ryan leaned across my lap, adjusted the throttle and mixture, and pointed to a little switch in front of my left knee. "When I say 'contact,' turn that switch all the way to the right, got it?"

"O-OK," I said, trying to hide my anxiety.

Ryan backed out of the cockpit and moved to the front of the airplane. After rotating the propeller twice he peeked around the engine. "Contact!" he yelled.

With two shaky fingers, I clicked the magneto switch to the right. "Contact!" I yelled back.

Ryan flipped the propeller blade downward and backed away. The engine sputtered, then the four little cylinders rattled like the tractor on a cold morning. He climbed in the rear cockpit and secured the flimsy door with a hook fashioned from a coat hanger wire. As we taxied toward the windsock I waved at Willy. He thumbed his nose, pulled his straw hat over his eyes and lay back against the tree.

We made a wobbly take-off and circled the airfield in a steady climb to 3000 feet. After demonstrating how to turn, climb, and descend, Ryan told me to take the controls. Deathly afraid of moving a muscle lest the rickety craft fall from the sky, I closed my eyes and swallowed hard. When I opened them the control stick swayed in front of me like a cobra ready to strike.

"Come on, cousin, go ahead and take it. We ain't got all day!"

Exhaust stung my eyes and waves of nausea surged through my body. Only a fool, I told myself, would have begged to do something this terrifying.

"Just take it in your right hand and I'll talk you through a couple of maneuvers," Ryan yelled over the noisy engine.

Hoping to delay taking the controls a while longer I turned my head and yelled that I couldn't hear. Ryan shouted something back and a few seconds later the only sound was the wind whistling through the idling propeller. Fresh air cleared the exhaust

804-UPCH

from the cockpit and the airplane entered a smooth, gradual descent.

"OK, cousin," he said patting my shoulder, "I've pulled the throttle back so you can hear me. Now take the stick or I'm going back and get Willy. Hell, it's so easy a monkey could do it."

Still frightened, but revived by the sudden quiet and fresh air, and especially the threat to go back for Willy, I inched my right hand forward and placed it on the rubber grip, eyes closed, afraid to breathe.

"To go up," Ryan said calmly, "pull the stick back a couple of inches. I'm gonna add a little power."

I opened my eyes and took a deep breath. "Like this?" I said, yanking the stick backward. The airplane pitched up, then dropped abruptly like we had fallen off a cliff. My stomach rushed upward, pushing a sour ball up my gullet.

"Whooooa, I have it," said Ryan with a nervous laugh. I let go and the control stick snapped forward, then moved to the center position as Ryan maneuvered the little airplane out of its stall and back to level flight.

"Take it easy on the controls, Tommy. This ain't a stallion we're riding. It's more like a skittish pony. Try it again."

Gosh, I hate this, I told myself. I wrapped my hand around the stick's handle and pulled back until the aircraft entered a shallow climb. When I relaxed back pressure the nose lowered and I floated upward in my seat as if I were descending in a fast elevator. I grinned like a Cheshire cat.

"That's a little better," said Ryan. "I'm gonna add more power and get us back up a ways so you can try it one more time."

After climbing 1000 feet he gave me the controls and I tried a few turns, improving with each maneuver. Ryan talked me through glides, climbs, and turns. Beaming with confidence, I decided to be a little more daring. Forgetting I was holding a skittish pony, I yanked the stick back and to the left and pushed right rudder, throwing the aircraft out of balanced flight. The Aeronca bucked like a bronco, then snapped to the right. The nose dropped through the horizon and we entered a tight, shuddering spiral toward the earth. Frightened and confused, I pushed my right foot forward and held the stick all the way back in a death grip.

"Oh-oh, Tommy, we're in a spin! Hold on tight!"

Assuming he meant hold on to the stick, I gripped it in both hands, fighting Ryan's efforts to correct my mistake.

"Dammit, let go!" he yelled.

I released the stick, but my foot was still frozen on the rudder pedal. White, green, and blue silhouettes flashed by my windscreen as though I was plummeting toward the earth in a runaway merry-go-round. I floated up against my safety belt, then smashed down into my seat, held by some invisible force that paralyzed every muscle in my body. I felt pressure against my right leg.

"TOMMY, GET OFF THE RUDDER!"

When I unlocked my right knee the rudder pedal rammed against my foot, the stick popped forward and back, stopping between my knees. The engine stalled and the smell of gasoline, sweat, and fear invaded the cockpit. I lowered my head and let my breakfast spew forth unrestrained. A surge of negative g caused my second spasm of vomit to stop in midair, splatter against the door window, and ricochet into the rear cockpit. Ryan slapped away half digested eggs and gravy while he fought to pull the little aircraft out of its violent descent toward the Kentucky farmlands. I lifted my head just in time to see bright green foliage rushing toward my windscreen.

"HANG ON, WE'RE. . . . "

Ryan's shout was interrupted by a loud CARRRUNCH! Leaves and branches grabbed the windows like claws of hungry, green monsters. I knew we were dead. But suddenly blue sky and sunlight filled the cockpit. Miraculously, the flimsy little aircraft was flying again. While wiping yellow slime off my face I peered out the window at the wooded landscape dropping away from our leaf-encrusted landing gear.

"Phew, that was close," sighed Ryan. "Those saplings couldn't have been more than a few feet high." He gently steered the buffeting aircraft toward the airstrip. "We're going home, and if I see your hand get near that stick I'm gonna break it off and beat you over the head with it." He could have saved his breath. I was too terrified to move a finger.

After we landed Ryan got out of the cockpit and used his bandanna to wipe his chest free of my breakfast. I used an oily rag to clean myself, and then helped him pull twigs from the fabric and struts of his beloved Aeronca Champ. He caressed each dent and puncture as though they were wounds on his only child. Willy ran toward the airplane, eyes flashing.

"WOW!" he shouted. "When I saw you doing a tailspin o'er that field yonder, I thought you was goners for sure." He ducked under the wing to peek in the cockpit. "Hey, what hap. . . . " Wrinkling his nose, he backed away from the airplane. "YUK! You puked, you rotten crud! How'm I gonna get in that seat with yur puke all o'er it?"

"We won't be going up, Willy," said Ryan picking splinters out of a deep gash in his propeller. "Tommy got a little adventurous and my airplane is gonna need some repair work before she flies again."

Willy's eyes darted from Ryan to me, eyebrows touching the bridge of his nose. "What'ya do up there, ya ignorant nose wart? You ruin't ever'thing!" Holding his nose with his left hand, Willy pushed me backward with his right.

"Nothing," I answered, shoving him back. "And I'm not a nose wart."

Tears in his eyes, Willy screamed in my face. "You are, too! Yur a wart . . . a ignorant, pukey, nose wart. My only ever chance to do sumthun' like this and you broke the plane. Now I won't ever get my ride."

With both hands he pushed me again, this time putting all his weight behind it. I lost my balance and fell backward in the grass. Leaping up, I charged recklessly, shoving him into a wing strut, already bent from its collision with the trees. Willy grabbed me around the neck and we were soon engaged in a rolling, squeezing, pinching, pounding, kid fight under the wing of Ryan's wounded aircraft.

By the time Ryan yanked us up by our collars we both had tears streaming down our cheeks. When my eyes cleared I was surprised to see a nasty mouse growing under Willy's left eye and blood oozing from a split lip. In all our previous scrapes I had never put a mark on him.

"Knock it off, twerps, before you total my airplane!" Holding us at arm's length, Ryan dragged his wildly swinging charges clear of his precious Aeronca.

"Willy," he said, shaking him by the collar, "you'll get your turn when I get my plane fixed. As for you, Tommy Fitzgerald, I swear the Almighty doesn't have enough angels to keep me out of harm's way when you're around."

"I'm sorry about your airplane," I sobbed while wiping a trickle of blood from my nose. "Let me try again. I know I'll do better next time." I wasn't thinking next week when he fixed his airplane. More like next year or the year after.

"Uh-uh," he said. "Some people are born to fly and some aren't. I think you best keep your feet on the ground. I'll look for someone else to carry on my legacy."

"I'll do it," offered Willy, wiping fresh blood from his mouth. "Let me be yur legacy. I can fly better'n him any day."

"You're not family, you dumb hillbilly," I said. "Only family can carry on a legacy."

Willy swung at me so hard he would have thrown his arm out of joint if he hadn't gotten it tangled in Ryan's flight jacket. I ignored the fists flailing by my face and stared at the disappointment in my cousin's eyes.

"Someday I'll show you I'm not a twerp," I whimpered. "Someday I'll be a pilot. Just you wait and see."

Willy stopped swinging and sneered through his red, snotty nose and half closed eye. "You, a pilot? Yur nuts, nose wart. First you run his plane in the trees, then you puked all over it. You'll never be a pilot," he said thumbing his chest, "but I will!"

Still holding us stiffly at arms' reach, Ryan pulled us toward his dusty Ford convertible waiting dutifully at the edge of the airstrip.

* * *

When we arrived in front of Willy's farmhouse Ryan watched him walk up the drive. "You know, Tommy?" he said. "Willy's pa ain't gonna take too well to him getting bloodied by you today."

"What do you mean? Willy's usually the one who whips me."

"I mean Fulton Rumford figures when his boy comes home whupped, especially by a city kid, he deserves another whuppin' as punishment for losing. That's just the way it is in some families."

I watched Willy pause and take a deep breath before he walked up his porch steps. "That's stupid. I can't see how farmer Rumford would do that," I said softly. As much as I disliked Fulton Rumford, I couldn't imagine him beating up his own devoted, hard working kid.

"Stupid or not, that's the way it is. If you ever grow up you'll learn not all families are like ours. That is if you ever grow up." Ryan slapped his Ford in gear and we headed down the road toward the Fitzgerald farm.

I didn't see Willy until Saturday when I ran into him and his dad at the Oxbow Feed Store. Willy tried to avoid me, but I cornered him behind the grain sacks. Besides the shiner I gave him, he had two ugly bruises on his jaw and his arm was in a cast from his palm to his elbow.

"What happened to you? I know I didn't do all that," I said pointing at his cast.

He fumbled with the soiled plaster a second, then straightened up emitting his usual aura of arrogance. "Thars truth to yur words, nose wart," he said proudly. "You couldn't do this if my hands were bridled behind my backside. I done fell off the hay lift, that's all."

"Again? Gosh, Willy, you're so darned clumsy."

"That you back there, Will? Get on out here, boy!"

We peeked around a pile of empty gunnysacks at Fulton Rumford standing with his huge hands on his hips, blocking the light coming through the doorway.

Willy's eyes flicked back and forth between me and his dad and his bruised lower lip began to quiver. "G-Gotta go, nose wart." He darted around the sacks and tried to squeeze through the doorway, but Fulton grabbed him by the cross strap on the back of his overalls.

"I tole you not to go wanderin' off, boy," he grunted while cuffing Willy on the side of his head. "Now git in the truck." He shoved his son out the door and returned to the counter.

* * *

That was the last time I saw Willy Rumford. The creek flowing between the two farms was no longer a place to explore and root out farm pests; it was a line of demarcation. I spent the remaining two weeks of my stay mulling over my misadventure in Ryan's Aeronca and his obvious disappointment in my performance. I could not have been more shattered when he exiled me from his sacred airspace. As far as Willy was concerned, well, he acted like a bullheaded jerk when he called me an "ignorant nose wart." For once I made him pay.

Ryan got the radio job in Paducah. He and Uncle Trevor carved out a narrow airstrip on the 20 acres that abutted the Rumford farm to accommodate the little Aeronca Champ on weekends and holidays. Aunt Connie wrote us that every Saturday when Ryan flew over the farm and lined up along the creek to make his landing, Willy snuck down to the airstrip and met him.

"Poor Willy," she wrote. "He'd follow Ryan half way up to the house, begging for the ride he missed the day Tommy had the mishap in the trees. But Ryan wouldn't do it without his pa's say-so, seeing Fulton got so upset the last time. Knowing he would never get his pa's permission, Willy would stick his hands in the bib of his overalls and kick stones all the way home.

"One Saturday when Fulton was in Paducah," her letter continued, "I called Emma and asked her to send Willy up to the house. Ryan was home for the weekend and I'd have him give the poor boy his ride. Ryan didn't want to do it at first, afraid Willy'd get excited and mess up like Tommy did. But when they got in the air Willy flew the airplane pretty good. In fact, Ryan said he flew like a born pilot. When they got back they was both grinning like bulls on breedin' day, 'bout as tickled as men can be, I reckon."

Tickled to *death* would be more like it, I thought reading her letter. Fulton Rumford would have killed Willy for sure if he'd ever found out. Probably Mrs. Rumford as well. But her words really hurt, I mean Ryan saying Willy was a born pilot and all. When settled in school I tried to keep my mind on things besides my shameful performance in Ryan's airplane. But my near fatal ride was as impossible to forget as a big zit on the end of my nose. Ryan's curt dismissal that day and the news about Willy's successful flying lesson all but destroyed my fragile preadolescent ego. From that day forward I elected to nestle in my comfortable zone of familiarity, avoiding anything the least bit adventurous.

Chapter 2

I could not stop shivering. Mt. Pleasant, Michigan, was noted for its severe winters, but this was the coldest day Central Michigan College had suffered in decades. It was cold enough to give the snowflakes those razor-sharp edges that crunch under your feet like broken glass. With my head buried in the collar of my quilt-lined jacket and my hands deep in my pockets, I hobbled across the campus like a turtle on its hind legs.

I was on my way to my favorite class, Sociology 205, a.k.a., Courtship and Marriage. The extracurricular lab work was great. Male and female Sociology 205 students liked to pair up and experiment with some of the professor's theories, such as the role of sexual intimacy in dating. So far it was the only course I'd put to use in the 18 months I had been a student on Central's campus.

Courtship and Marriage notwithstanding, I was fed up with the college routine: puerile fraternity beer parties followed by debilitating hangovers; boring lectures with endless note taking; and fruitless, all-night bull sessions. Although I had aspirations of playing college football and basketball, my mediocre performance in Class C high school athletics proved woefully inadequate for college. I didn't even survive the first cut in both sports, just two more failures to add to the many I'd piled up as an adolescent. My life was going nowhere. I looked at my watch. Just enough time to grab a steaming cup of coffee at the Student Union.

VAROOOOOOM.

"What the hell was that?" somebody yelled. Clumps of icy snow plummeted from the pine trees, showering students running for cover along the sidewalks. I peered through the pine boughs and saw four tightly packed silhouettes zooming toward the bright,

804-UPCH

ice blue sky. Arcing right in a graceful wingover maneuver, the four jets reversed course and formed a solid, silent mass of navy blue streaking toward me at tree top level.

VAROOOOOOM.

Again snow showered us from above. And again the jets pulled straight up, blocked the morning sun for a split second, and disappeared behind a fluffy winter cloud. For several seconds the jets' echo rumbled across the horizon like distant thunder. I wondered what brought on this little air show over our remote, nondescript institution of higher learning. A few students pointed east, voiced their annoyance or admiration, then resumed their journey to the far points of the campus.

Stomping my feet on the large CMC letters inlaid on the Student Union's doormat, I eyed the clusters of students sipping hot drinks and sharing gossip or lecture notes. A couple of fraternity brothers hustling a pair of Zeta Taus waved a greeting, more out of duty than an invitation to join them. I never could figure out why they admitted me, Mr. Mediocrity, in their Tau Kappa Epsilon chapter. Last year must have been a slow one for TEKE pledges, I surmised. I pointed at my watch and mouthed, "Class." There was no time to chitchat.

Waiting to pay for my coffee gave me a minute to survey the noisy cafeteria for new exhibits. On most days everything from corporation recruiting to cigarette companies passing out complimentary four smoke packets occupied the perimeter tables in the cafeteria. My eyes focused on a banner emblazoned with the big yellow letters, FLY NAVY, hanging above a table stacked with brochures. Behind the table a dashing naval officer engaged several male students in animated conversation. Nearby, admiring coeds watched his every gesture over the rims of their coffee cups.

"So that's it," I mumbled. "This morning's air show was this guy's overture." For years I had avoided anything that resembled flying. Even the sight of Ferris wheels made me uncomfortable. But when I recalled those jets streaking over my head at speeds near the speed of sound I had a feeling of detachment as though I were in one of those cockpits smiling down at myself cowering under the pines.

"Ahem. . . . " grunted the cashier, fingers vigorously rubbing her thumb. Snapping out of my daydream, I dropped a dime in her palm and it slammed shut like a Venus flytrap. While sipping coffee my eyes again homed in on the Navy display. I wondered if it was curiosity or was I unearthing a long suppressed desire to master the beast that almost killed me nine years ago.

It had been years since I thought about my childhood pledge to prove my aeronautical adroitness to my cousin, Ryan. He was now a successful disk jockey in Kentucky, still flying and still adamant about my keeping my feet on the ground. Occasionally we exchanged letters and when I wrote him that I was going to college he answered with some bad news.

> Dear Tommy, Glad you're going to college. Hang in there and get a degree. Sorry to have to tell you this, but Willy's pa was killed in a barn accident a few weeks ago. I don't know how Emma and Willy can run the place without Fulton. She's so frail and keeps to herself all the time and I don't think Willy wants to be a farmer. There's another problem. Ma says Fulton didn't leave Emma any insurance. Nice guy, that Fulton. By the way, I bought another airplane, a four place Stinson. Now that Fulton's not around to object, I've given Willy a few more flying lessons. I'm amazed at how well he handles the controls. He's a natural. Good luck in college. Ryan.

I had difficulty mourning for Fulton, but I was sad for Emma and Willy's loss. So Willy was still impressing Ryan with his flying skills. Big deal. I guess Ryan forgot my own promise to be a pilot someday. Then again, that silly vow was uttered in a fit of frustration when I was very young. Ryan probably wasn't even listening. Yet I had to admit I couldn't think of anything more exciting than being in one of the jets I saw that morning. I decided to mosey on over and take a closer look.

While working my way through the tables I thought about Willy Rumford and that grass airstrip in Kentucky. I assumed that Willy was running the old homestead and probably married to a large-boned farm girl with a kid hanging on each breast. He sure as hell wouldn't be in college—or would he? When I thought of my hayseed summer companion sitting in some university classroom with his hands stuck in his bib overalls I had to chuckle. Nah, I thought, shaking my head. College would be too "citified" for Willy Rumford.

"Hi," I said casually as I approached the display table.

The dapper Navy pilot flashed a Hollywood smile and thrust his hand forward. "I'm Lieutenant Mark Goodsen. Welcome to the exciting world of naval aviation."

When we shook hands I detected the faint, masculine aroma of Old Spice cologne, as though it was automatically dispensed during handshakes. He asked me to sign a roster, "to form a mailing list," he said.

"Why not?" I picked up the ballpoint pen next to the clipboard and scribbled my name.

The officer spun it around and peered at my scratchy handwriting. "Thomas Q. Fitzgerald. And the Q is for. . . . ?"

"Quinton, and I go by Tom," I said.

He nodded and began a well-rehearsed sales pitch. "As you can see, Tom, naval aviation offers a young man everything he could ask for: prestige, adventure, an exciting career, and the opportunity to serve his country." He handed me one of the brochures. "The training is challenging," he said pointing to a photo of a cadet sitting in a Navy SNJ Texan trainer with an instructor leaning over his shoulder, "but it leaves plenty of time for socializing with the local natives." Grinning broadly, he flipped the brochure over and pointed to a photograph of a cadet in a white dress uniform escorting a lady to a formal dance. Underneath was a photo of two guys frolicking on the beach with a bevy of girls in skimpy bathing suits.

"I get the message," I said. That message was that learning to fly is an adventure and Navy wings of gold are the key to the hearts and other anatomical parts of amorous females. The nearby table of doe-eyed admirers batting their eyelashes at this Adonis in navy blue confirmed that assumption.

"So, how'd you like to fly jets?" Lieutenant Goodsen pointed his finger at my chest. "Believe me, it's the most thrilling thing you'll do in your lifetime."

"Sounds interesting," I said.

The Lieutenant winked at the girls sitting nearby. They tittered in unison and thrust their bobbing heads into the center of the table like hens in the barnyard sharing a kernel of attention.

Thumbing through a brochure I paused at a photo of a jet landing on an aircraft carrier. "Can I get in this program without landing on one of these boats?" I asked meekly. "It looks pretty scary."

His broad smile faded momentarily, then returned, as though he had just reminded himself that I was merely a landlubber displaying my ignorance of the sea. "Uh, Tom. That's a ship, not a boat," he said quietly.

"Oh, right, a ship," I replied.

"Good. Now, operating from aircraft carriers is what sets naval aviators apart from other pilots. If all you can operate from are concrete runways you might as well be in. . . . " leaning forward he whispered with obvious disdain, " . . . the *Air Force*." He straightened up and smoothed his blouse. "It's well known that those who wear Air Force blue are afraid of aircraft carriers. That's why their wings are second place silver instead of blue ribbon gold like these," he said touching his left breast. "And that's why they're called pilots and we're called aviators."

I'm not so sure about that fear part, I mused. Ryan was in the Air Force's former self, the Army Air Corps, and he wasn't afraid of anything, with the possible exception of flying with me. On the other hand, if this officer's boasts were legitimate and naval aviation was the greater challenge, Ryan would have to be impressed. And there was Willy and his pledge to become a pilot. The first thing I would do after finishing training would be to visit Willy Rumford and flash my gold wings in his face.

Noting the gleam in my eye, the Lieutenant placed his hand on my shoulder and grinned his anticipation. "I have a feeling you want to be among the nation's finest," he said, pulling out an application and laying it on the table in front of me.

Feeling his magnetic eyes drawing me into his world of adventure, I shifted my gaze to the gold wings over his rainbow of decorations and down to the dotted line on the application. I needed to think, so I pointed at my watch. "It's time to go to class," I said weakly. "I may be back later."

"Fine," he said. "I'll be here until sixteen hun—uh, four o'clock." He turned and with his arm outstretched, greeted another student thumbing through a brochure. "Hi, there. I'm Lieutenant Mark Goodsen. Welcome to the exciting world of naval aviation. . . ."

When I approached the exit I stared at the full-length mirror next to the cashier's counter. I hadn't changed much in 10 years. I was still a lanky kid with a crop of hair like weathered straw, a protruding chin, a trace of post-adolescent acne under his jaw, and slouching, narrow shoulders. I turned around and caught the confident Lieutenant "Adonis" maneuvering his hands over the table in a mock dogfight, while curious guys and awestruck coeds watched attentively. For an instant I saw my body in his uniform, but the door flew open and a gust of January air jolted me back to reality. This is ridiculous, I thought. We're a hundred worlds apart. I turned up my collar and carefully negotiated the icy steps to the sidewalk leading to Warner Hall and Sociology 205.

Mouthing an apology to Professor Anderson for being tardy, I tiptoed to my seat in the back row. She scowled, then resumed her timely lecture: Making a Commitment. After settling into my desk my mind wandered. I still hadn't chosen a major because there was nothing in the catalog that stirred my interest. Not that it mattered anyway, since I would soon be out of money. I wanted to break away and do something exciting—yet not too exciting—that didn't require money to get started and paid well. I conceded that I was asking for a lot. But this flying program might be the answer—lots of adventure and it wouldn't cost me one dime. All right, so it's more adventurous than anything I'd ever done, but who knows? Maybe it's not as scary as it looked in the brochures. And Ryan said he wanted someone to carry on his legacy. Granted, that was before I almost wrecked his airplane, but this was one way I could prove to my hotshot cousin that I could do something as well as he could—maybe better. After all, he never landed on a boat—I mean a ship. When I snorted at that satisfying thought several heads jerked in my direction, including Professor Anderson's.

When the professor resumed her lecture I also resumed my argument with my alter ego. Are you nuts? I asked myself. Whenever you think about flying—which isn't very often—you get arctic chills and jungle sweats. I stared at my hands. Already they were shaking as if I had palsy. I told myself that I needed a better reason to do this than a childish desire to prove something to my cousin and a Kentucky yokel. If I failed, and that was a good possibility, I'd spend the next few years recovering from another dismal failure. Why not just go back to Detroit and work in one of the auto factories until I was drafted. When I got out of the Army I could save a few bucks and with the GI Bill, that would be enough to continue my education. Or maybe I should forget college and join my high school buddies in their bowling league world of blue-collar bliss.

While doodling airplanes on my note pad I cursed my dismal existence and my lack of courage to change it. My pencil lead snapped, punctuating a pregnant pause in the professor's lecture. She scowled at me and several classmates turned to glower their support. I half-smiled an apology and withdrew another pencil from my plastic pocket protector.

Think back, I told myself, when you were flying Ryan's Aeronca

Chapter 3

Walking into the Student Union I decided it was time to shift my life out of neutral. With quivering fingers I picked up the US Government ballpoint pen and signed on the dotted line. After a beaming Lieutenant Goodsen shook my hand, he placed my letter of intent with two others in his briefcase and assured me I'd hear from him soon.

Three weeks later I was in the Grosse Ile Naval Air Station Training Facility, struggling through a two-day battery of aptitude tests. After passing the written portion Saturday afternoon, the yeoman informed me the physical exam Sunday morning was the only remaining obstacle. I hoped my body was in better condition than it looked.

When I reported to the dispensary a corpsman at the front desk told me to strip down to my shorts and join a line of examinees. "While you're waiting," he said, "fill out this form."

The dispensary was cool but the odor of sweaty, male bodies permeated the passageways. We walked from room-to-room in our undershorts, holding our clothes in one hand and our medical history form in the other. The robots in white jumpers and bell-bottoms barked instructions.

"Form," snapped the corpsman, shoving a hand across the counter while holding a test tube of amber liquid against the overhead light. He grabbed the medical form from my hand and replaced it with a half pint-sized milk bottle. "Bring me a urine sample," he ordered as he placed my form on a stack six inches high.

I discovered that urinating on command is like trying to whistle with a mouth full of peanut butter. After straining for a few anxious moments I squeezed out a trickle of the precious fluid and carried it back to the corpsman. He frowned at the skimpy specimen and placed it among several other bottles, some with labels and some without. Then he pulled out a piece of rubber tubing and syringe and told me to sit down. While he fumbled with the syringe I stared at the wall and bit down on my lower lip trying to ignore the size of the needle about to penetrate my pale, tender skin.

After two near misses he mumbled from the corner of his mouth, "First time I didn't hit a gusher on the first strike. Your veins are skinny, like your arms."

When finished he overlapped two bandages in the crook of my elbow to cover the three puncture holes. Finally, after recording the results of the lab work next to my height, weight, and vital signs, the corpsman returned my form and directed me to a line of bodies in the passageway.

GONG, GONG, GONG.

The deafening alarm was followed by an announcement on the PA. *Now hear this; now hear this. Flight surgeon and duty corpsman report to south exit immediately, I say again . . .*

"What's that about?" I asked a sailor scurrying down the passageway.

"Crash at the end of the runway," he yelled over his shoulder.

I backed against the wall to make room for a doctor and corpsman lugging bags with Red Cross markings. When they had passed I joined the long line of examinees nonchalantly reading magazines or working crossword puzzles. Listening to the fading siren wailing like a cat in a far away alley, I began to shiver. Strange, I thought, that no one seems concerned about an aircraft accident right here on the airfield. With crossed arms I hugged my shoulders trying to squeeze out the image of the crashed airplane. The sailor next in line turned from his Mickey Spillane novel and looked at me curiously.

"This place is really cold," I said with a half smile and a shrug.

He stared at me another few seconds, grunted, and returned to his reading.

The flight surgeon was a mousy looking guy with a receding hairline and fingernails bitten to the quick. Resting on the tip of his nose was a pair of those funny looking, half moon glasses for reading only. When it was my turn he faced me and peeked into all of my upper orifices with his pointed flashlight, then slapped a cold stethoscope against my chest, peered at my sunken breast bone, then slapped it against another spot, then another. Next, he told me to drop my shorts, turn my head, and cough. I barked in the ear of the guy next to me and flinched when the doctor's icy fingers probed my groin for a lump of dangling intestine. Shorts still around my knees, he told me to stand on each foot and hop three times. Convinced I wouldn't topple over, he told me to turn around, bend over, and spread my cheeks. Aided by a small flashlight, he peeked in the only orifice remaining unexplored and checked for anything that didn't belong there. Satisfied that my anal sphincter was flawless, a requirement for all Naval Aviators (so says the Air Force), he scratched something indecipherable in the "approved" box and told me to pick up my form at the dispensary administration desk in 30 minutes.

When I completed my final piece of paperwork that afternoon, the yeoman told me everything was in order and that I should expect orders to Pensacola sometime during late June or early July.

"By the way," I said curiously, "what happened to the pilot that crashed earlier?"

"He bought it," the yeoman said with a shrug.

"Bought it?" I asked.

"You know, bought the farm, buried himself in a smoking hole, crashed and burned, busted his ass."

"Oh, yes," I said, faintly recalling Ryan's use of the term the day we almost "bought it" in his Aeronca.

"The guy was flying an AD Skyraider," explained the yeoman. "That's one of those big, unforgiving prop jobs and he let it stall on approach. You don't stall a Skyraider on approach. That's the great circle route to the farm."

"Great circle?" Again I was puzzled. What did the great circle route on a globe have to do with an airplane crash.

"Yeah, the shortest distance between two points—life to death in one easy step. Hell, they couldn't find enough pieces to fill the body bag." He returned to his typing with hardened indifference.

I had no idea what an AD Skyraider was, other than it had a propeller instead of a jet engine. I made up my mind right there, however, that if I became a pilot I would do everything possible to stay out of the cockpit of "big, unforgiving prop jobs." It was going to be jets or nothing. With my track record, more than likely it would be nothing.

When I returned to Central I told my friends and professors I would soon be off to seek my destiny. I wasn't sure where I would be a year hence, but when fall rolled around, Thomas Quinton Fitzgerald would not be seen roaming the timeworn halls of Central Michigan College. That night I sat at my desk and wrote a short letter to Ryan, being careful to mask my anxiety.

> Dear Ryan, Guess what your cousin, Tommy, will be doing this summer—learning to fly! Not just any flight training, the US Navy kind. You know, on aircraft carriers. I've spent most of my life floating around aimlessly, so I might as well float around on one of those ships and fly off it as well. Ha-ha. What do you think about that, land-bound flyboy? Your flattop cousin, Tom.

On July 1st I sat in the Grosse Ile administration building waiting to pick up my orders to Pensacola. In my back pocket was Ryan's response to my letter, hardly an inspiration for success. He was now an assistant manager of a radio station in Louisville, Kentucky, but periodically would broadcast the farm news or report traffic from his brand new V-tailed Beech Bonanza. His attitude about my flying skills, however, had not changed.

> Dear Tommy, You must have been drunk to do such a stupid thing as quit college to try and fly with the Navy. It's been many years since you tried to wreck my Aeronca Champ, but my advice to stay out of airplane cockpits still stands. Since I'm the one who took you up on your first airplane ride, I will blame myself if you end up buying a plot on the old farm and I don't mean Dad's. Don't do this, please! Your guilt-laden cousin, Ryan.

What's he talking about? I thought. He did the very same thing in 1944. Granted, there was a war on, but he did quit college to join the Army Air Corps. Determined not to let Ryan's lack of confidence in my abilities get me down, I stuffed the letter in my pocket and picked up a magazine.

While waiting for my orders, another recruit named Ron Warden introduced himself. About six feet tall, slight build, wearing khakis and a crew cut, Ron was another Joe College who ran out of money. After a few minutes of conversation we concluded that if the Navy would take two liberal arts guys like us, pilot training couldn't be much of a challenge.

Ron was a little on the nervous side, punctuating his sentences with eye blinks—one for commas and two for periods—and constantly flicking the ash off his cigarette, even if there was none. By the time his Lucky Strike was half-smoked it looked like a butt salvaged from a poolroom ashtray. I didn't know how all that tension would play in the cockpit of an airplane, but he was a modest and friendly sort, so we got along fine.

To keep us occupied while he prepared our orders, the chief yeoman gave us a stack of directives outlining the 18 months at flight training. We browsed through the material, periodically asking questions that demonstrated our ignorance about the Navy. Excited about a passage in the regulations, Ron flicked his mangled Lucky Strike, laid it on the ashtray, and held the manual in both hands.

"Hey, Tom," he called, blinking his eyes once, "remember when I said I needed a new watch before we left for flight training? Well, not anymore because they give us a watch when we get to Pre-Flight School." Double blink.

I was engrossed in the section about swimming requirements. They were extensive and my aquatic skills were marginal at best. I managed to squeak through my college lifesaving course, but when the swimming coach handed me my Red Cross certificate he whispered in my ear, "Promise me you won't try to save somebody, Fitzgerald. I'd hate to see two people drown."

"What are you talking about?" I mumbled, trying to concentrate on my reading. Ron picked up his cigarette, *flick, flick, flick*, returned it to the ashtray, picked it up and flicked it one more time as if he'd miscounted, and put it back.

"Geez, smoke it or douse it!" I mumbled.

"Huh?"

"Nothing. What'd you say about watches?"

Ron pointed to a line in the order he was reading. "It says here we get a free watch when we check in."

Anything free got my attention. "What do you mean, we get a free watch?"

"It says right here, 'Every cadet should expect a watch the first week after he checks in.'" He looked up, blinked twice, and smiled.

"Seems funny they'd give everybody a watch when they walk in the door," I said. "Anyway, just about everybody has a watch." I examined the Bulova wristwatch I won at a high school raffle three years earlier, then returned to my reading. The first swimming requirement was a full mile, wearing the khaki, multi-pocket coveralls called a flight suit. I doubted I could swim a mile, even with a life preserver strapped on my back.

The Chief looked up from his desk. "Excuse me, gentlemen, those aren't watches you wear. Those are watches you stand."

"What do you mean, 'stand'?" I queried.

"Yeah," added Ron. "Why would you stand on your watch?"

blink, blink, blink . . . flick, flick, flick. A thin trail of smoke rose from the carpet and he ground it out with his heel.

The chief sighed. "Look. Aboard ship the day is divided into six watches." He held up his fingers and counted. "Midnight to four, four to eight, eight to noon and around again to midnight. The order that NavCad Warden is reading simply means that you'll be put on a list to stand a watch as soon as you check in. It's like guard duty, only at a desk. You'll learn more about that stuff when you get to Pensacola." NavCad was an acronym for Naval Aviation Cadet.

"You mean they don't give us a wristwatch?" Ron whined.

"When you finish flight training you get a silk scarf, aviator sunglasses, and a new leather flight jacket," said the chief, "so maybe they'll give you a wristwatch, too. But they aren't gonna pass out all that neat stuff until you get your wings. Too many cadets wash out . . . one out of three I think . . . or is it two out of three?" He winked at his subordinate.

"Oh, at least three out of four," answered the yeoman, smiling from his typewriter.

The chief's comment made me think of Charlie Bunsen, my high school chemistry and math teacher. A former naval officer, he wasn't exactly supportive when I told him I was going to Pensacola. "Thomas," he said shaking his head in disbelief, "you could barely pass chemistry and you slept through trig. How in blazes are you going to get through something as demanding as Navy pilot training? You'll wash out with the first week's laundry." Bunsen placed his hand on my shoulder and said softly. "Try for Marine Corps rifleman. If it has to be the Navy, maybe a cook or a deck hand. But forget about flying. That's way out of your league."

My cousin Ryan, my swimming coach, and my teacher. Why in the hell am I doing this, I thought, when so many of my mentors don't believe I can make it? I shuddered at the humiliation of coming home a failure. I could never do that. Like a fledgling eagle, I was about to take my first leap off a cliff and it was either fly or die trying. There would be no turning back.

* * *

"No wristwatch. Damn!" mumbled Ron as he went back to his reading. *blink, blink, blink; flick, flick, flick.*

While we waited for the Chief to finish our orders Ron invited me to ride with him to Pensacola in his 1942 Mercury convertible. We could split expenses. It sounded like a good idea and we agreed to meet at a convenient location in Farmington, 10 miles west of Detroit.

A week later my parents drove me to our rendezvous point. My father, a gunner's mate on an armored cruiser during World War I, seemed unmoved that I chose his old service, but he did offer me the benefit of his wisdom. Rarely did he utter more than two consecutive sentences, so I listened carefully.

"Son, don't speak to your superiors unless they speak to you first. Second, never step forward when they ask for volunteers. Most important, play it straight and keep your record clean, because it will follow you 'til the day you die."

For my dad, that was an oration. Then he asked a question. "You sure you want to do this, son? It's not too late to reconsider." I nodded. Like my mentors, my dad's faith in my ability to succeed in this endeavor was guarded at best.

From the start, my mother had not embraced my decision. Besides expressing disappointment about my dropping out of college, she reminded me how she carried a bag and washcloth whenever we traveled. Her memories of cleaning me up after I got deathly sick in automobiles, streetcars, and trains were still vivid. Her son doing something involving more motion than all those things put together seemed to be a foolhardy adventure.

"Mother, I haven't been carsick in ten years," I said trying to reassure her.

"Maybe so, but whenever you go up in one of those airplanes, carry a bag in your lap anyway. You could put it on a string and carry it around your neck so your hands would be free. Your teacher will understand." She put her hand on my forearm the way she always did when she was trying to make a point. I patted her arm like I always did when I wanted her to know I understood.

"Don't worry, Mother. I'll be fine. And they're not teachers, they're flight instructors." I turned my head to look down the highway and thought, I'll puke inside my shirt before I'll walk around with a barf bag hanging around my neck.

"Oh, son, I found this on your dresser. I thought you might have forgotten to pack it." Mother handed me Ryan's patch, the one he gave me before my ill-fated ride in his Aeronca. I massaged the faded threads with my thumb.

"As a matter of fact, I did intend to bring it," I said. "When Ryan gave it to me eight years ago he said something about carrying on his legacy. I thought I'd take it along as a good luck charm."

"That's nice, Tommy. He would be proud that at least you tried." Mother pulled out a Kleenex and dabbed at her eyes.

I was relieved to see Ron's Mercury appear on the far side of the highway. The top was down and a cloud of smoke billowed from the tail pipe as he slowed to make a U-turn. He stopped at the curb, bounced out of the driver's seat, and killed his Lucky with a series of flicks before shaking hands with my parents. I grabbed my Samsonite one-suiter and transferred it to Ron's trunk where it joined a cardboard valise, an old set of golf clubs, a slightly warped tennis racket, and a case of recycled oil. I kissed my mother's wet cheek, shook my dad's hand one more time—noting his grip was tighter than usual—then climbed into the convertible, slamming the door twice before it latched. As we pulled into traffic I didn't look back. I knew they would be standing there long after we were out of sight.

Chapter 4

At noon on July 16th, Ron drove across the Bayou Grande Bridge and stopped at the main gate of NAS Pensacola. Marine sentries dressed in starched khaki impervious to humidity and perspiration checked every car in a courteous, but resolute manner. A shiny globe and anchor adorned each white helmet and large, brass belt buckles reflected images of approaching cars. The toes on their spit-shined shoes sparkled like sapphires. These guys looked nothing like the sailors that casually waved us through the gate at NAS Grosse Ile.

When the Marine demanded identification Ron did the talking. "Sir," he said proudly, "we're aviation cadets reporting for duty. Could you direct us to where we check in?"

The corporal placed his face two inches from Ron's nose. "I'm not a sir!" he growled, resting his right index finger on his two chevrons. He glanced at the traffic backed up behind us and held out his hand. "Let me see your orders."

After fumbling in my manila packet for several seconds I found my orders, passed them to Ron and he handed both sets to the sentry who was impatiently tapping his fingers on the car door. "Here you are, si. . . . " Ron clamped his lips, catching the sir just before it got out.

The sentry scanned our orders, periodically glancing at the lengthening line of cars behind us. After verifying our claim to be NavCads he gave us a map of the air station, thumped a finger on the square marked, Cadet Indoctrination Battalion, and waved us through the gate. We turned left in front of a deep blue F9F Panther jet mounted on a concrete pedestal. Under the cockpit in large gold script were the words, *Blue Angels.* Looking over my shoulder, I studied the sleek aircraft and turned to Ron.

"What's a Blue Angel?"

"I think it's a movie with Marlene Dietrich," he said. "Maybe they named that airplane after her, she being a sexy movie star and all." Ron held his cigarette out the window and flicked the ash, which immediately bounced off the balmy Pensacola air and landed in his lap. Barely escaping two head-on collisions, he slapped wildly at his crotch until the smoldering lump fell on the floor mat, already scarred with numerous burn holes. After unsuccessfully trying to suck life into his dead Lucky Strike, he crammed the limp butt in his overflowing ashtray.

"Seems logical," I said.

Ron pointed at the manicured golf course on our right. I looked at the foursomes lugging their bags along the fairways and nodded with disinterest. I had never set foot on a golf course in my life. I pointed to a row of warehouses and aircraft engine test stands on our left. The backs of several khaki uniforms huddled around the controls of a mounted radial engine. Running at full power, its roaring cylinders pounded my tender eardrums.

While we drove toward the cantonment part of the air station known as mainside, I heard the drone of aircraft. I looked up at a formation of six yellow SNJ Texans, the same as those pictured in the brochures. The aircraft peeled off for their landing approach to Chevalier Field, the circular airdrome on the eastern edge of NAS Pensacola. I felt my nose tingle—aviation gasoline. The pungent odor pulled me backward to an Aeronca cockpit full of gas fumes and vomit, tailspinning over a little airstrip in Kentucky. I shook my head and concentrated on the map.

While passing a grassy parade field we blinked at the sunlight reflecting off shiny, stainless steel scabbards. Cadets carrying swords on their shoulders like fishing rods were practicing a ceremony under the watchful eyes of Marine Corps drill instructors. Ron stopped the car, giving way to a cadet formation crossing the street to enter a building with "Academics" printed above the entrance.

Toting bulging, leather book bags, they climbed the steps and rhythmically shuffled through the building's double doors. There wasn't a smile in the crowd.

Another formation of iron-jawed cadets clad in khaki shorts and navy blue T-shirts jogged toward a line of old seaplane hangars on Pensacola Bay. The map indicated that two of the hangars served as gymnasiums for physical fitness classes.

I directed Ron around a corner and pointed to a parking spot in front of a two-story, brick structure spanning an entire block. Polished granite steps led to a screened porch with a blue and gold sign over the door reading, "Indoctrination Battalion, US Naval Air Training Command." I recalled the chief's warning that through those portals passed thousands of aviation cadets and that three-fourths never made it, washing out or quitting somewhere along the way. The thought of failure induced a momentary shiver, in spite of the 95-degree heat.

Ron turned off the ignition. "I guess we'd better check in," he said. When my door opened the old Merc let out a loud groan, drawing the attention of two sailors walking along the sidewalk. They slowed their pace curiously eyeballing the vintage convertible, not the two befuddled NavCads checking in for duty.

Ron lifted the trunk lid. I grabbed my Samsonite and he removed his belt-bound valise and his tennis racket.

"Maybe you should leave the racket here, at least for now," I said. "We're supposed to be student pilots, not tourists."

"One of the brochures showed cadets playing tennis," he said taking a practice swing. "This shows 'em I came prepared. I'll bring the clubs in later."

I nodded agreement and allowed the trunk lid to fall, wondering if I would be out of place without a tennis racket or golf clubs. We climbed the granite steps and when we opened the screen doors I detected the pungent odor of brass polish and floor wax. Two rows of five-inch naval gunfire shells linked by ropes painted with several layers of white enamel formed an aisle between the assembly areas on each side of the lobby. I learned this was the quarterdeck, likened to the official reception area at the head of a gangway aboard a ship. We approached a door with "Administration" painted on the frosted glass and paused. The building was surprisingly quiet. Reluctant to break the silence we entered without knocking.

The only sound was the whir from the two ceiling fans hanging overhead. Three metal desks were arranged in a V. A NavCad wearing a white brassard with BSOOD sewn in bold black letters sat at the point. His nose was stuck in a loose-leaf binder labeled, *BSOOD Watch Instructions.* I nudged Ron, pointed at the words on the binder and whispered, "Ask him when you get your new watch." He grinned and nudged me back. We soon learned that BSOOD stood for Battalion Student Officer of the Day.

Marine Corps noncommissioned officers (NCOs) occupied the two desks behind the BSOOD. The NCO on the left with three chevrons and two rockers on his sleeves—technical sergeant—had to be well over six feet tall. Cantaloupe biceps and a bulging neck strained the seams of his military-creased, tropical worsted shirt. Four rows of ribbons above two silver shooting badges, one with crossed pistols and the other with crossed rifles—expert ratings, crowned his left breast pocket.

From his white sidewall haircut to his glistening double-soled shoes, everything about this man was tight and aligned. The wire stay holding his collar points rigid as arrowheads forced the knot in his khaki tie to protrude as though it were a grotesque appendage to his Adam's apple. A clasp with a Marine Corps emblem secured the tie precisely half way between his third and fourth shirt buttons. Small scars on his eyebrows, cheekbones, and jaw resembled teardrops of white paint against his smooth, tanned skin. I wondered if they were from combat or fist fights. I had seen many movies about the Marine Corps. Not one featured a sergeant who looked anywhere near as Marine-like as this guy.

I wondered how he could be so tight and seem so relaxed. With his right hand the tech sergeant rested his coffee cup on the blotter covering the center of his desk. The desk was empty except for an ashtray, a chromed Zippo lighter lying neatly on top of a fresh pack of Camels, and a perfectly blocked Smokey-the-Bear drill instructor's hat. His left hand held the *Pensacola News Journal.*

The corporal sitting at the other desk was just as squared away, but short and stocky, his bulky frame suggesting he pumped iron in his spare time. His left breast displayed one row of ribbons and a rifle shooting badge shaped like the Maltese Cross, the emblem for sharpshooter. He lit a cigarette while studying some sort of roster. Behind their desks was a door with "Officer in Charge" painted in large block letters on the opaque glass.

Unlike the tailored, pressed tropicals worn by the Marine NCOs, the BSOOD's baggy new khakis had totally surrendered to his sweat and the summer humidity.

"Hi," he said softly, still not broken from his civilian ways. "May I have your orders, please?"

"Sure," we chimed in unison. I handed him my orders. While Ron fumbled in his manila envelope, the BSOOD thumbed through his instructions for the page about processing incoming NavCads.

The tech sergeant's eyes peered over the top of his newspaper. He laid his coffee cup and paper on the desk, pushed himself away from his swivel chair, and strolled toward us, hands clasped behind his back, the steel caps on his heels clacking on the tiled deck. I nudged Ron, but his head was buried in his manila envelope. The big NCO stopped directly between us, put his hands on his hips, and rocked up and down on the balls of his feet.

"What's yur names, turds?" he said looking from one of us to the other.

Ron pulled out his orders, looked at me momentarily, and then at the tech sergeant. We opened our mouths but no words came out.

"I SAID, WHAT'S YUR NAMES, TURRRDS?"

"W-Warden, R-Ronald W." Ron's squeak was 10 decibels below and an octave above his normal voice.

"F-Fitzgerald, Thomas Q., sir," I said, cringing at my error.

He placed his face an inch from my nose, an oak tree hovering over a pussy willow. The scalp under his crew cut turned bright red and his carotid arteries twisted under the skin of his thick neck like those skinny balloons you make into little animals. I got a whiff of after-shave, strong coffee, and cigarette smoke.

"Now, do I look like a friggin' officer to you . . . TURRRD?"

"No, well, uh. . . . " I pulled in my head like I was a turtle under attack.

"Then don't call me, sir! I'm a tech-ni-cal ser-geant!" he said slowly, "Tech-ni-cal Ser-geant Flan-a-gan."

I guess Ron thought he would ease the tension when he tucked his tennis racket under his arm and extended his hand. "Glad to meet you, Sarge."

Tech Sergeant Flanagan's face turned from bright red to purple. After locking his eyeballs on Ron's outstretched hand, he shifted his gaze to the tennis racket. He pulled the racket from under Ron's elbow and held it by the tip of the handle like it was the tail of a dead rat.

"Can you friggin' believe this?" he growled with disgust, showing the foreign object to the corporal. He motioned us to follow behind him. Timidly we followed the big tech sergeant as he swaggered out of the admin office and through the quarterdeck. He yanked open the screen door and hurled the racket over Ron's convertible toward the empty field beyond, as though it had been fired from a 105 howitzer. When it started the back side of its trajectory it was a twirling speck against the cerulean, Florida sky.

"Wow!" Ron whispered. "What an arm."

Hands back on his hips, Flanagan stared at Ron's crumpled, old Mercury and shook his head. He turned around, jabbing his thumb over his shoulder. "Does that junk heap belong to one of you, turds?"

"Uh . . . m-me, Sergeant," muttered Ron.

"That's TECHNICAL sergeant, turd. After ya meet the Cap'n, get it over to the cadet parking lot." He pointed at a fenced area kitty-cornered from the Indoc Battalion. "Over there's the only authorized space for Indoc NavCads to park their cars. Once it's there it's off limits 'til yur outta Indoc, unnerstand, turd?"

"Yes, Technical Sergeant," Ron whimpered.

"And when ya move that heap, retrieve yur toy from that field and throw it in the GI can." He pointed to a large trash barrel across the street. "The admiral don't like litter on his air station, 'specially civilian litter." When Flanagan walked past me I reached back to my college ROTC training and snapped to what I remembered was the proper position of attention.

"Fitzgerald, I bet you were in ROTC," he said as he returned to his desk without looking at me.

"Yes, Technical Sergeant," I answered proudly. "Army."

"Army," he mumbled while snapping open his newspaper. "It figures."

After we were checked in and had a quick lesson on how to report to an officer, Flanagan took us to meet the Officer in Charge, Captain Janek Perkaski. The OIC was a stocky Marine officer with a pencil thin mustache that gave his youthful face the maturity to go with the chest full of ribbons under his gold wings. The captain seemed like a nice enough guy—for a Marine, that is. At least he was more cordial than the brute in the front office.

After the captain's welcome aboard, Ron moved his car, retrieved his tennis racket and with reluctant obedience dropped it in the GI can. Flanagan nodded his approval and turned us over to the BSOOD for linen issue and assignment to our cubicle. We were now official members of NavCad Pre-Flight Class, 29-54.

The BSOOD introduced us to our two roommates and hastily departed. Danny Hartwood stepped forward and volunteered to teach us how to make our bunks, with emphasis on the importance of hospital folds and pulling the spread tight enough to bounce a quarter. A lanky, loose-jointed farm boy from Nebraska, Danny was nearly as tall as I, but weighed no more than 150 pounds with dirty feet and a full sweat. When he walked, his limbs wobbled as though he were dangling on a puppeteer's strings. His face had far too many worry lines for a 19-year-old, but his infectious smile exuded unusual warmth.

Our other roommate was a short, burley Texan named, Stan "Stump" Fowler. He was slightly bowlegged and his face was round like his body. With his shoes neatly placed under the foot of his bed, his clothes arranged in his open locker according to bulk—sport coat, shirts, pants, ties—and a bunk as tight as a snare drum, obviously he was a guy who was attuned to the military way. Stump briefed us on the daily routine, starting with the frequent PA announcements to muster on the quarterdeck, as though he had been doing it all of his life.

"First," he said, pointing to the doorway, "you run everywhere you go. When you hear a '*click*' over the PA system, that's the BSOOD keying the microphone to announce, 'Class 29, muster on the quarter-deck immediately!' Whoever hears the click first dashes to the doorway and the rest of us follow in close trail. Then we sprint down the passageway to the quarterdeck. Got it?"

"Got it," said Ron and I together.

The first time "Class 29, muster. . . . " blared through the PA we joined the wild stampede in the passageway. Since my bunk was nearest the door, it didn't take but a few summons on the PA to learn that it was either get out first or get run over by my roommates.

At the end of the second day I flew through the door, arms flailing as I struggled to make the turn. Another cadet, Reed Gallagher, was approaching at full speed from my right. A head shorter than I, his face slammed into my bony shoulder with a *SPLAT* echoing all the way down the passageway. Blood shot out of his nose onto the spotless walls and freshly scrubbed deck.

"Are you OK?" I yelled while pausing to massage my bruised shoulder.

Holding his bleeding nose with one hand, Reed motioned with the other to press on toward the quarterdeck. Neither of us wanted to suffer Flanagan's wrath for holding up muster. Flanagan chewed out the entire class for being so slow anyway—we were never fast enough—and then made us all do 50 push-ups for getting blood on his clean quarterdeck. After muster, Corporal Manzione took Reed to sickbay where a doctor set and bandaged his broken nose.

When we were dismissed the BSOOD told me to report to Flanagan for a special assignment. My bowels threatened a sudden attack of diarrhea, the usual reaction when summoned to the admin office. When I walked in he was standing by his desk.

"Fitzgerald," he said, massaging his brick-like chin, "didn't you say you had Army ROTC training?"

"Yes, Technical Sergeant," I said, relieved that I was not being chewed out for some obscure infraction of the rules. "Two years. I was a corporal when I left college to come down here."

"A *corporal*? That's very impressive, Fitzgerald." Flanagan turned toward Corporal Manzione. "Hear that, Manny. Fitzgerald was a corporal, just like you." Manzione rolled his eyes and went back to his reading. "Well, Fitzgerald, it just so happens we need a competent person to handle an important detail. Interested?"

"You found the right man, Technical Sergeant Flanagan," I said, beaming.

"Good. It's the kind of job where Army ROTC training could come in handy. Corporal Manzione, would you please brief this Army ROTC corporal on his duties as noncommissioned officer in charge of the garbage detail?"

"Why sure, Technical Sergeant Flanagan. I'd be glad to," answered the smiling Corporal Manzione. Flanagan sat at his desk, picked up his *Pensacola News Journal*, and flipped to the sports page.

After Manzione briefed me on my new duties I walked dejectedly back to my cubicle, remembering my father's warning to never volunteer and KEEP YOUR MOUTH SHUT.

* * *

We had much to accomplish in the two weeks of Indoc: tennis ball haircuts, field days (house cleaning), uniform issue, more field days, close order drill, book bag issue, inspections, physical fitness, a lot more field days, and learning how to speak Navy.

Before we received our uniforms Flanagan marched us to the Navy Exchange—the base department store known as the PX—and gave us a list of items to purchase including brass polish, brown and black shoe polish, adhesive tape, and an order slip for a personalized name stamp. Later that afternoon we marched to Air Station Supply where we were issued a complete set of service khaki, dress blue, and dress white uniforms. We carried them back to our cubicle then used the boxes to pack our civilian clothes. After stacking our boxes on the quarterdeck to ship home, Flanagan told us to get our khaki uniform, shoes, and brass ready for a uniform inspection at 0600 (six a.m.) the next morning.

Flanagan emphasized that we could use only brass polish and elbow grease to remove every fleck of the black paint protecting the belt buckles and belt tips. No abrasives were allowed. When taps sounded our uniforms were not even close to being ready for inspection. The only spaces lighted after 2200 (ten p.m.) were the heads—toilets—and the admin office. When all was quiet we sneaked in the head, sat on the commodes, and polished our brass until our blistered fingers ached, occasionally relinquishing our seats to cadets who wanted to use them for the purpose for which they were intended.

Only the former enlisted sailors and Marines got any sleep. The rest of us worked all night and ended up with barely passable brass and some awful attempts at spit-shines, a task that seemed to require a Midas touch. Wrapping a piece of T-shirt around one finger tip, we dabbed it in the wax polish, then rubbed it over the shoe hoping to produce a tough, mirror-like shine. What many of us produced was a glow as glossy as a soap bubble, but also as durable. At 0200 Danny Hartwood proudly held up two glistening shoes that would impress the Queen's Guard. Unfortunately when he took them for a test walk it looked as though he was kicking up puffs of fairy dust. After one lap around the cubicle, his Navy oxfords shed their entire luster and were as dull as when he pulled them out of the box. Without batting an eye, he grabbed his polish and headed back to the head for another try.

At 0559 we were in our baggy new uniforms, waiting at our doorway for the familiar warning over the PA system. Before the mike button's echo ricocheted down the passageway I was halfway to the quarterdeck. Corporal Manzione took muster and Flanagan walked up to the first cadet, Stump Fowler. Flanagan stared at the front of Stump's belt buckle, gleaming like18 carat gold. He pulled the top of the buckle toward him, leaned forward, and examined the back. It was black as coal. He looked in Stump's bloodshot eyes and released the buckle, letting it smack against the top trouser button. Flanagan said nothing. He lowered his head and stared at Stump's oxfords, globs of wax sticking to the leather like mud on a tortoise shell. Poor old Stump had worked until dawn, but he just couldn't get it right.

Flanagan raised his head, his snarling lips two inches from Stump's nose. "Who took a dump on yur shoes, Cadet? Yur wearing official US Navy property and ya let some guy crap on it." The dark stains under Stump's armpits spread like ripples on a pond.

"Yes, si . . . I mean, uh, no one crapped on my shoes, Technical Sergeant."

"Yur wrong, Cadet Fowler. Yur shoes are covered with smelly, ugly crap, and what's worse, it looks like civilian crap. Tell you what. Since yur new, I'll get it off for ya this time." Could he really tell civilian crap from Navy crap? I wondered.

His chin held snug against the knot in his necktie Stump mumbled, "Thank you, Technical Sergeant."

Flanagan lifted his heel and placed it squarely on the toe of Stump's right foot and while leaning forward, ground his steel cleat into the soft, new leather. After doing a similar job on the left shoe, he thumped his right index finger on Stump's chest. "How'n the hell are ya gonna fly a plane if ya can't dress yourself, Cadet Fowler?" growled Flanagan while pounding Stump's breastbone. "Ya got one hour to square away that disgusting belt buckle and those crappy shoes. Now, get off my quarterdeck."

Eyes moist, Stump limped down the passageway. Twenty-five cadets soon followed, me included. The few who passed the inspection—mostly ex-enlisted—went from cubicle-to-cubicle giving tips on how to polish brass and spit-shine shoes. Later that morning I told Stump I was sorry he had to absorb most of Tech Sergeant Flanagan's wrath when our uniforms were in no better shape than his.

"Thanks, Fitz, but you needn't worry about me," he said cheerfully. "This is all part of earning those coveted gold wings." He stopped rubbing his shoe and looked out the window. "One day I'm gonna be on a carrier flying the lead strike on a Russian target. I'll be fighting for this country, just like my father did in WWII and Korea." Somberly, he returned to the task of polishing his shoe. "He was shot down when the Marines landed at Inchon," he said nodding his head toward the window. "Pop's buried on the west end of the air station in Fort Barrancas Cemetery." He stopped working on his shoes and stared at the deck. "I know it sounds silly, but sometimes I feel him watching me."

"Perhaps he is," I said smiling. "I've heard that some pilots believe when they die they spend eternity flying around the sky helping out mortal pilots in trouble, sort of like guardian angels. Maybe your dad's gonna be yours."

"I'd like that," said Stump flashing a broad grin. He wrapped his wet polishing cloth around his finger, and dipped it in the can of Kiwi. He rubbed it on carefully, blew on the freshly applied polish, and compared it with the other shoe that still bore Flanagan's heel print on the toe. "You know what, Fitz?" he said holding them up together. "Flanagan was right. My shoes did look like I'd stepped in a cow patty."

The first day Flanagan considered our uniforms marginally presentable he marched us down to the pier to see the training aircraft carrier, USS *Monterey*, CVL 26. It was docked at the air station while waiting for the next qualification period in the Gulf of Mexico. Running 600 feet at the waterline, the *Monterey* was the biggest ship I had ever seen.

"Take a good look at her, girls," bellowed Flanagan. "Believe it or not, some of you turds'll land a plane on that flight deck. The rest'll already be washed out and chippin' paint off some old tub in the Brooklyn Navy Yard. For them who make it to graduation, eventually a ship even bigger'n this'll be yur home away from home."

I looked up at the mammoth vessel and tried to imagine putting an airplane on her long flight deck. That's a lot of runway, I thought. Maybe my worries about landing aboard ship were ill-founded. Remembering the washout rate, I looked left and right in the formation, wondering which of my classmates would last long enough to see that flight deck through the windscreen of a SNJ Texan. I had doubts that I would be among the fortunate few. When we returned to the barracks I had time to write another letter to my cousin.

> Dear Ryan, Well, the first week of Indoc training was a nasty one but at least I'm still here. Today I saw an aircraft carrier up close, the USS *Monterey*. What a huge ship! It has to be longer than the airstrip where you landed your Aeronca. I only hope I'll be here long enough to see what it's like to land an airplane on her flight deck. From what I hear, primary flight training is really rough and a lot of guys don't even make it through Pre-Flight. I'm scared already and I haven't even been close to an airplane. Tell Aunt Connie and Uncle Trevor I said Hi. Your NavCad cousin, Tommy

Chapter 5

After completing our second week of indoctrination Tech Sergeant Flanagan gave us our final inspection and marched us down Turner Street to the Second Cadet Battalion, our home for 16 weeks of ground school. Ron Warden was assigned a room across the passageway, but Danny, Stump, and I moved in with Vince Fabrizio, a carefree, second generation Italian from New Paltz, New York. He was a head shorter than Danny and me and about as tall as Stump without the bow in his legs. When he laughed the narrow gap between his front teeth and the pinprick dimple in his chin opened like caverns, making a chuckle spread into pure jubilation. Vince walked leaning forward about two degrees as though he couldn't wait to find out what was up ahead. I liked to think of Vince as the eternal optimist.

Danny Hartwood constantly had problems, usually because of his literal interpretation of every rule and regulation, a dangerous habit for a military man. The first time he stood his first 2400 to 0400 watch, when 0400 came around he stretched his long, angled frame and went to bed. The only problem was that he didn't wake up his relief at 0345 as he was supposed to do. Danny thought "relief" meant leaving at the end of his watch and getting one blessed hour of sleep before reveille. It wasn't long before the NavCads referred to Danny Hartwood as "Dufo," a fictitious bumpkin a popular stand-up comic used in his routine during the early 1950s.

Our daily schedule rarely varied. After a 0500 reveille we showered, shaved, and shined our brass, then prepared our rooms for morning inspection. At 0555 we grabbed our book bags and hurried behind the barracks to assemble for the 0600 formation. Class

29 was Delta Company of the Second Battalion. Derrick Gardner, a scrappy Brooklyn-born hustler, was the adjutant. He began morning routine by reading the Plan of the Day.

"Ba-TAL-ee-on! AH-ten-HUT!" (pause) "Plan . . . of . . . the Day . . . United States Naval School . . . Pre-Flight." Derrick scanned our faces to ensure all cadets had their eyes straight ahead. "The Plan of the Day's got—uh, it contains both official and unofficial matter and all you's guys—uh, you's personnel—are responsible for knowledge of its contents. PA-raaade-REST!"

While we were at the position between "attention" and "at ease," Derrick stumbled through all announcements, then he gave us the thought for the day. That day the order stated, "Use the right tool for the job," but Derrick got confused and said, "Use your tool for the right job." The battalion commander then turned us over to our respective company commanders. Our company commander, Pete Zarek, a former Marine Corps staff sergeant, turned around and issued his first movement order of the day.

"UP, BOOK BAGS. . . . "

Moving as one, we leaned over and grasped the handles of our large leather satchels. Hunched over like a formation of arthritic old men, we waited for the command of execution.

"TO!"

Each cadet hoisted his bag of textbooks, notebooks, plotter, navigation computer, slide rule, and a regulation-crammed looseleaf binder.

"Riiiight . . . FACE!"

We faced the direction of the mess hall.

"FOR-ward . . . MARCH!"

With the cumbersome book bags pulling our shoulders toward a 10-degree right list, we marched off to morning chow. After a speedy, but nutritious breakfast, we marched the two blocks to the academics building.

Pre-Flight was divided into four sections: Academics, Military, Survival, and PFT (physical fitness training). We marched everywhere. Even changing classes in the academics building, we shuffled in column like a line of convicts at Alcatraz. The first class was Principals of Flight (aerodynamics), then on to Meteorology, Engines, Naval History, and finally my bugaboo—Navigation.

My math background was minimal and when the instructors tossed us the formulas and coefficients for determining brake horsepower, lift, drag, thrust, plus weight and balance, I struggled. I managed to muddle through everything but Navigation. Plotting the course of a moving aircraft somewhere in the ocean to a ship that constantly changed its course and speed was beyond my meager powers of computation. I was even more confused when the instructor threw in the voluminous tables used for celestial navigation. Learning these skills required meticulous attention to detail, something in which I had rarely indulged before arriving at Pensacola. How I wished I had stayed awake in Bunsen's trig class. Each night from 1900 to 2100, 18 cadets, including Ron Warden and myself, received extra instruction called "stupid study." I was helped in celestial navigation, and Ron, who hadn't seen a science class since ninth grade, was tutored in aerodynamics.

After noon chow our DI gave us two hours of rifle drill on the grinder—three acres of asphalt behind the barracks. Following rifle drill, Pete Zarek marched us to one of two locations. On Monday, Wednesday, and Friday we reported to one of the old seaplane hangars for physical fitness training and Tuesday and Thursday to Swim Tank #1 for water survival.

During our second week of Pre-Flight we were on the way to the PFT hangar when Pete ordered us to march in place to allow another cadet formation to pass in front of us on its way to Swim Tank #1. While the formation marched by, a scowling cadet on the outside rank glanced in my direction. He was lean and hard like a lumberjack. His angry eyes locked on me for a moment then snapped forward, glued to the back of the cadet 30 inches in front of his chest. He swung his arms stiffly along his sides, fists clenched, muscles tense. Something about him looked very familiar. Must be someone I knew back at Central, I thought, recalling that at least two other guys had signed up when I did. I'll surely run into him sooner or later. Whoever he was, he either didn't like my looks or he wasn't too happy about being at NAS Pensacola. I redirected my thoughts to the miserable two hours ahead of me in the gymnasium.

PFT started with a half hour of calisthenics and ended with a two-mile run in a figure-eight around two seaplane hangars. In between we learned the basics of boxing, wrestling, and hand-to-hand combat to instill self-confidence and enhance our survival skills, so they said. At our first session we lined up in front of a line of 15-inch high platforms, placed a pencil and 3 x 5 card on the deck along side us, and waited for the signal to start the dreaded Step Test. This couldn't be any worse than climbing a steep stairway, I thought, eyeing the wooden cube in front of me.

At the first blast of an electric horn, I stretched my left leg to step up on the high platform and knew immediately this was not going to be easy after all. I followed with my right foot, stepped down with the left foot, and followed it with the right foot, grateful to be back on the deck even for only one second.

BEEP, beep, beep, beep; BEEP, beep, beep, beep. After only two minutes my chest burned and my thighs screamed in agony. While struggling to keep pace with the horn I cursed the Navy, my PE instructor, the world, but mostly myself for asking to be here in the first place. Some cadets lasted only a few dozen beeps before falling on their knees and barfing up their noon meal.

The horn blasted away for what seemed like an hour, but was only about five minutes. When the last *beep* echoed across the steel rafters I leaned over and grasped my knees while sucking in large gulps of air. My legs were numb and my head pounded like a pile driver.

"Cadets, snap to and take your pulse!" the PE instructor screamed over his bullhorn.

We struggled upright and in accordance with the lieutenant's instructions, recorded our pulse rate in the first of three squares on our cards. The remaining two squares were for midway through Pre-Flight and the day we graduated. I tried not to think about those two additional sessions with the electronic beeper. The poor souls who dropped out were marked for extra PFT, sort of a stupid study for out of shape cadets.

The water survival classes included a mile swim wearing flight suit and socks, training in life saving procedures, underwater escape from burning oil, feet-first leaps from a towering platform—to simulate a carrier deck—and the notorious Dilbert Dunker. The Dunker was an airplane cockpit that rolled down 35-foot rails, slammed into the pool, flipped upside down, and sank half-way to the bottom. Our task was to escape from the submerged cockpit and swim to the surface.

"The key to your surviving this little ride," the instructor told us in his loud, patronizing voice, "is do nothing until the bubbles clear. That will take several seconds, so don't panic and try to egress immediately."

I had to think about that for a moment. If that was an airplane sinking in the ocean it could go down a long way in six seconds.

"Remember, you're weightless down there," he continued, "and with foamy water swirling around your face it's easy to get disoriented. When the bubbles clear and you've figured out which end is up, unlatch your seat belt, shoulder harness, and oxygen mask. When you're free of all restraints, pull yourself from the seat, push away from the cockpit forty-five degrees to the left of the nose of the aircraft . . . " he thrust his left fist toward his ten o'clock position for effect, " . . . and swim to the surface. If you get in trouble a diver will pull you out. That's all there is to it, cadets," he added with a broad grin.

The chief pointed at me and I slowly climbed the ladder to the platform. While a sailor strapped me in the bucket seat I stared at the pool two stories below. I felt lightheaded, as though I were teetering on the edge of a cliff. My eyes watered from the chlorinated atmosphere and my respiration accelerated from a lope to a gallop. I expected to swallow half the pool when I hit the water.

A buzzer blasted above my head and the Dunker clattered down the steel rails accelerating like a roller coaster. When it hit the water it flipped upside down sending a miniature tidal wave toward the opposite end of the pool and dropped below the surface. After movement stopped I opened my eyes to a swarm of bubbles the size of Ping-Pong balls. Following the chief's instructions, I waited until the eddies dissipated. Already my lungs cried for oxygen.

When the bubbles cleared I unhooked my safety belt, shoulder harness, and oxygen mask. I paused to orient myself, gripped the windscreen, and pushed my body out of the cockpit—and immediately tried to swim through the bottom of the pool. After bouncing off the cement I turned around and ran into the safety diver checking to see if I was hurt. When I showed him a thumbs up he backed away, giving me room to swim to the surface. As I burst clear, delicious oxygen filled my lungs and I swam to the side of the pool.

Ron Warden leaned over the edge and asked softly, "How'd it go, Fitz? Is it as bad as it looks?"

"Piece of cake," I said throwing him two thumbs up.

Ron grinned nervously, blinked twice, and shuffled back in line while I remained in the warm water until my trembling subsided.

That afternoon the mail included a letter from Ryan.

> Dear Tommy, You're actually there? I hoped you were kidding about this idiotic attempt to do something you're not cut out for. I saw hundreds of guys get washed out, even when there was a war on, and they went home forever humiliated. Those guys, by the way, had more flying talent than you do. I'm sorry you're wasting all that effort for a lost cause, but you've made your bed so you will have to lie in it. By the way, if by some miracle you hang around long enough, you'll find those ships look a lot smaller from the air than they do in port. I'm sure the Navy has a procedure to drop out of flight training with minimum embarrassment. Find out what it is and do it as

> soon as possible. At least it won't count as a wash out. More importantly, you'll still be alive. Your counseling cousin, Ryan.

"Screw you, Ryan," I muttered while folding his letter. "If the Dilbert Dunker couldn't get me to quit, you sure as hell won't."

* * *

When Ron and I were finally released from stupid study we joined my roommates for a trip downtown to celebrate. First stop was the San Carlos Hotel on the corner of Palafox and Garden Streets, the favorite gathering spot for Pensacola's cultured class. Passing through the tall, mahogany doors I was bathed in the fragrance of the lobby's tropical greenery. Thick woven carpets muffled our footsteps as we ambled between ornate tables and wicker divans bearing hallmarks of the finest southern craftsmen. I ran my hand over the rich, brocade tapestry covering the high-backed chairs framing each square, marble column. Being from a blue-collar family that struggled through the depression, I had never set foot in any hotel, let alone one as wondrous as the San Carlos. After exploring the exotic rooms off the mezzanine we descended to the lobby and strolled past the check-in desk. I nodded at the bell captain. He didn't nod back.

At the north end of the lobby we passed through tall French doors and stepped onto the ceramic tile in the spacious taproom. Our steel-capped leather heels announced our presence and momentarily interrupted the quiet, dignified atmosphere the distinguished guests preferred when conversing over mint juleps.

"I smell old money," whispered Vince.

"What's 'old money'?" asked Dufo.

"Money they haven't earned," Vince said softly. "It's inherited—passed down. It's a term you probably wouldn't hear in Nebraska."

"We pass down old farms," retorted Dufo, "but they barely

produce new money, let alone the old kind."

A few gentlemen turned their heads toward our whispers, but quickly returned to their discussions of local stock averages or the upcoming regatta in Pensacola Bay. Regardless, it was nice to be noticed in such courtly surroundings, if only for a brief moment of indifference.

NavCads, of course, did not sip mint juleps. We guzzled the affordable Spearman's Ale, brewed and bottled in Pensacola to satisfy the thirsts of common folk such as NavCads and sailors. The grizzled, black bartender welcomed us with a warm smile.

"What'll it be, gentlemen?" he said, with the same courtesy he extended to a guest carrying a walking stick and a fat wallet. In a few seconds five green bottles of Spearman's Ale and five frosted mugs were lined up in front of us. When Ron did his nerve-rattling, cigarette-flicking the bartender dumped the mangled butts, wiped out the ashtray and replaced it with a smile and a nod. That wonderful old gentleman understood how everyone, even lowly NavCads, needed to be treated like someone important now and then. After two bottles of ale we pooled our resources to leave the bartender a modest tip and left the San Carlos via the taproom exit to Palafox Street.

We took a bus to Pensacola beach and spent the remainder of our Saturday lounging on the sand. While ogling the girls parading up and down the beach we talked about how it would be to fly jets in the fleet. My roommates chatted about the future while I mentally retraced our steps through the San Carlos. Wouldn't it be nice, I pondered, to spend a night at that marvelous old hotel sharing my bed with one of these tanned, long-legged beauties? Rapt in my fantasy, I lay back on the sand and drifted off to sleep.

* * *

Few things depressed me more than being in a bare-knuckled fight. The ones I had were probably split down the middle in wins and losses, but whether I walked away or crawled, I'd spend the next few days cursing myself for being so stupid. While at college, a fraternity brother on the college boxing team offered to give his fellow TEKEs free boxing lessons. When it was my turn I told him I was more interested in how to avoid getting hurt than how to inflict pain on the other guy. He agreed to give me pointers on blocking punches, but citing the old adage, "the best defense is a good offense," insisted he add a few basics about the jab, right cross, left hook, etc. His lessons helped me enough to raise my confidence a little, but I never had a desire to box in a real match.

Again forgetting my father's advice, I made the mistake of checking "yes" next to "boxing experience" when I filled out the personal information sheet during Indoctrination. The one thing I did learn from my boxing lessons was that I had a low threshold for pain. I thought if the PT instructors knew I had some experience they might allow me to skip boxing classes and the accompanying discomfort. My ploy didn't work and when the first Pre-Flight smoker rolled around, a night of camaraderie and pugilistic competition between battalions, I lived to painfully regret that "yes" on my info sheet.

A week before the smoker Staff Sergeant Lopez, our Battalion DI, called me to his office. I admired Lopez. Unlike the recruits the DIs handled in Marine boot camp, most NavCads had two to four years of college and many considered themselves prima donnas. Although his formal education was limited, the Puerto Rican-born Lopez was street-smart, had a natural instinct for how to get the best out of people, and was a poster-worthy Marine. When I stepped into his office he was holding a battalion roster.

"Fitzgerald, we need a heavyweight to balance our program in the smoker next week. You've done some boxing so you're elected." He leaned back, wiggling his pencil between his fingers, daring me to dispute the assignment.

The word, "heavyweight," seemed ludicrous in my case. I may have met the 175-pound, weight minimum, but those pounds were distributed more in bone than muscle. Somehow I had to get him to change his mind.

"B-but, Staff Sergeant Lopez!" I stammered. "I only had a few lessons in college—never any bouts. I-I don't think I'd represent the battalion well."

"Oh, shut up, Fitzgerald. I hate whiners." He pointed to my form with his pencil. "You checked this box so you're our heavyweight. Look on the bright side. Win or lose, you get a seventy-two hour pass for participating. Cadet Gardner is boxing middleweight and will fill you in." He picked up a roster, a signal that the conversation was finished.

Walking back to my room I considered the prospect of the three-day pass. I met a gorgeous girl at the beach the previous weekend and was hoping that with some wining and dining, she might become my San Carlos fantasy. How bad could it be, anyway? The bout lasts three rounds. I can surely keep away from a guy for a mere nine minutes.

The night of the smoker I sauntered into the gym thinking about the three wonderful days with a southern belle whose body rivaled Jayne Mansfield's, not about whom I would have to fight that night. Marine and Navy officers on the Pre-Flight staff occupied the front row seats surrounding the ring while the cadets sat behind them in rows, 25 deep. Our DIs passed out cigars as we walked in and a cloud of smoke hung over the brightly lighted ring like the haze over a battlefield. I watched as the fighters flung their 16-ounce gloves at each other as though they were having pillow fights. Nobody seemed to be getting hurt and after the first three bouts I felt confident I could escape this engagement with minimum damage.

Bad assumption. My opponent from the Third Battalion turned out to be a YMCA Golden Gloves contender right out of the steel mills in Gary, Indiana. Charles Haley was a couple of inches shorter than I, but weighed a hefty 210 pounds to my 181. While waiting for the starting bell I stared at his glistening, ebony body, arms like rump roasts hanging from broad, thick shoulders. I knew this was not going to be any pillow fight.

Derrick Gardner, who fought his match to a draw, slapped my

shoulder and said, "Just box 'em, Fitz. He looks pretty strong. Ya shouldn't slug it out with a guy who's built like a musk ox."

Pretty strong? I thought, staring at my opponent. That's one hell of an understatement. The fight had not even started and the little confidence I had in my boxing skills had already evaporated.

During the first round we danced around the ring, jabbing here and there, both of us occasionally trying a right cross or left hook. He gave me a couple of good shots, but I shook them off. Early in the second round I surprised myself when I landed a solid combination, my right catching him squarely on the nose. He blinked twice and backed away, blood trickling over his upper lip. My confidence roared back and my fellow Battalion II cadets chanted with delight.

"TOM-MEEE—BATT THREE'S HIS-TOR-EE!"

Caught up in the excitement, I pelted him with more lefts and rights. He leaned against the ropes, covering his face with his mammoth gloves. Aha! I thought. I've got him.

Derrick was shouting above the din. "No, no, Fitz, back up, back up! He's faking!" But I ignored Gardner and pounded away, pulverizing his 16-ounce gloves while not scoring one blow to his body.

It didn't take long for my arms to grow heavy, exactly what Haley was waiting for. When my barrage diminished to love taps he counterpunched, putting those beefy shoulders behind each blow. I tried to block his punches but it took a major effort just to keep my gloves above my waist. The bell sounded the end of the second round. Now the cadets in the Third Battalion were doing the chanting.

"BATT TWO'S—ALL THROUGH—CHAR-LEE—WINS IN THREE!!"

Derrick jumped in my corner shaking his head. "Fitz, ya walked into his trap. How do yur arms feel, pal?"

"Like these gloves are full of concrete," I moaned.

"Ya got a round apiece. Just stay away from the guy." He shrugged. "Maybe he'll get tired and you'll get another good shot."

He flashed a sympathetic grin and after patting me on the back, gave my shoulders a quick massage. I had a few seconds of blessed rest remaining and I turned to survey the mass of chanting faces supporting my opponent or me. Through the smoky haze I saw a familiar face in the fourth row, the same NavCad I spotted in the formation headed for the swim tank. He was not chanting, just staring at me coldly, a sneer working its way out of the corner of his mouth. The bell rang. As I stood, Derrick grabbed the leg of my stool.

"Let him come to ya, Fitz," he shouted in my ear. "If he drops his right use yur left hook. It's yur best punch." Gardner patted my back and stepped out of the ring.

Haley didn't tire like I'd hoped. While he pounded me at will I countered with a few shots to his body. Occasionally I threw a left jab through his guard, hoping to start another nosebleed. No luck. For the remainder of the round I used my waning energy to block the blows threatening my decapitation.

Third Battalion went wild, screaming at Haley to score a knockout or at least knock me down. I was too stubborn to oblige. Luckily he didn't connect with any body blows. A good shot would have doubled me over and cleared the way for an uppercut or right cross that would have ripped my head clear off my shoulders. Regardless, I was getting the beating of my life.

Mercifully the bell signaled the end of the third round. Both battalions cheered so loudly I could barely hear Derrick giving me instructions to look unhurt while the judges compiled their scores. I knew it wasn't even close. Haley won a unanimous decision and we went back to the locker room. I sat on a bench while Derrick congratulated me for not getting knocked out. After removing my gloves he carefully cut the tape from my swollen hands and departed to catch the last two fights.

Totally exhausted, I pushed myself up from the bench, leaned into the mirror, and surveyed my battered face, moving my head back and forth searching for a spot that wasn't turning blue. Feeling like I'd been trampled by the running bulls of Pamplona, I put my hands behind me and lowered my body slowly back to the bench, hoping not to aggravate the thunder behind my eyes. Charles Haley came around the corner on the way to the shower. Other than a slight swelling under his nose, I couldn't detect a mark on his body.

"I gave you everything I had, Fitzgerald, but you wouldn't go down," he said, shaking his head. "Man, for a skinny white guy, you can really take the punishment." He stuck out his hand and smiled. "Friends?"

How generous, I thought as I stood up and accepted his hand. Then I made a stupid comment. "I'm no boxer, Haley. Perhaps it would be different in a street fight where there's no rules." I held his hand and stared into his dark eyes.

"Perhaps," he said, his smile fading. He gave my hand a final shake and walked to the shower.

I sat on the bench, then lay back and closed my eyes over my throbbing head wondering how I could have been so dumb. His comments were gracious and I had to challenge him to a street fight. What the hell was I thinking? Besides my incivility, my street fighting skills were no better than my boxing skills. I heard him turn on the water. Maybe I should apologize, I thought sheepishly. When he walked out of the shower stall a few minutes later I stood up.

"Haley, can I ask you a question?"

He folded his arms across his broad chest and waited, as though bracing for another challenge. "I suppose."

"Where'd you learn that maneuver on the ropes? I walked into it like a hound charging a wounded grizzly."

His broad grin instantly melted the ice between us. "The old rope trick," he said, dropping his arms and leaning back against a sink. "It was at the Golden Gloves tournament in Louisville a year ago. While I was lifting weights, a kid about twelve or so pounded a heavy bag a few feet away. He was like you, tall and skinny . . . no offense," he said smiling.

"None taken," I said wincing at the pain pounding against my forehead.

"Anyway," he said, "this big guy walks by him—I dunno, maybe he's two or three years older—and makes some comment about the kid hitting the bag like an old lady. 'Oh, yeah?' the kid says. 'How about goin' a few rounds with this old lady?' The guy sneers and says, 'Sure, punk, why not? A good lesson wouldn't do you any harm.' They go at it and when the big guy gets him against the ropes the kid covers up just like I did." Haley first acted the big guy, then the skinny kid, then turned and played the big guy again, his hands popping jabs and swinging hooks.

"The big guy hammers the kid real hard and I'm about to get up and stop it, until I see all he's hitting is the kid's gloves, so I hesitated. Pretty soon the big guy gets tired and drops his hands. From nowhere left jabs ram the guy's face like a jack hammer, POW-POW-POW." Haley popped his left fist about a foot from my face. "The big guy's eyes go glassy and, BAM-BAM, the kid slams him with a left hook and a right uppercut that came all the way from the canvas. The guy falls to his knees, his eyes roll up like a mama doll's, and KER-PLOP, he lands flat on his face. The kid sneers and leaves the ring, never looking back. Never saw anything like it. His name was Cassius. Cassius Cray, or Clay—something like that."

"Well, it was good tactics," I said, tapping his meaty shoulder. "You really did a number on me. I think I'd better pass on that street fight." It was the closest I could come to an apology without sounding wimpy.

Haley winked and tapped me back. "Good. I had enough street fighting back in Gary. It ain't fun. See you on the grinder." He walked back to his locker.

I left the gym ashamed of letting down my classmates, ashamed of losing, and especially ashamed of my stupid comment about a street fight. I almost made an enemy out of a pretty good guy and a darn good athlete. Something else bothered me. Who was that guy staring at me from the spectator seats? And why did he seem to be getting so much pleasure from the beating I was taking?

The 72-hour pass began the next day, but with a head that

looked like a bag full of marbles, I was in no shape to woo a lovely lady. I called, hoping for a rain check. "Don't count on it," she said before slamming down the receiver.

On Sunday afternoon I cleaned up and walked across the street to the ACRAC (Aviation Cadet Recreation and Athletic Club). My aching jaw needed the comfort of my favorite cooler, 7-Up over ice cream. I listened with envy to the cadets rehashing their weekend liberty in Pensacola and frowned at the jukebox blaring Bill Haley and the Comets' new hit, *Rock Around The Clock.* That's all I needed, another Haley giving me another big headache. I spotted my boxing opponent sitting alone near a window, staring at Pensacola Bay. I stopped at his table figuring I owed him a 'hello.'

"Hi. I thought you'd be in town using your three day pass," I said, forcing a smile through my bruised lips.

Haley looked at me briefly, then turned to watch a sailboat gliding across the bay. "I'll tell you what, Fitzgerald. Colored guys from Gary, Indiana don't go into southern towns, even Navy towns like Pensacola—if they're smart, that is."

"Why not?" I said, failing to catch the inference. He turned toward me, rolling his eyes at my naiveté. He didn't ask me to sit down, so I didn't.

"Look. You're from Detroit and I'm from Gary, Indiana—the supposedly enlightened north. Those places aren't any Garden of Eden, but they're a long way up from the Deep South. Northern colored folks have a tendency to ignore these people's quaint, southern customs . . . and they have a tendency to take offense," he said with a sardonic grin. "I'm better off right here."

Feeling like I was intruding on his privacy and my mouth too sore to become engaged in a discussion on southern racial relations, I nodded and lifted my hand good-bye. "OK," I said. "It's your weekend. See ya later." I dragged my body to the bar and Charles resumed his vigil out the window.

I ordered a cooler to soothe my sore mouth. As I savored the cold, sweet, sensation sliding past my lips a NavCad tapped me on the shoulder and introduced himself as GW Savage. Like most people, he was a little shorter than I, but about the same weight with broad, drooping shoulders. He had short, curly hair, an Arabic nose, and a rugged complexion.

A few weeks earlier Ron Warden used his drooping cigarette to point him out on the grinder. "See that guy, Fitz? Former UDT—Underwater Demolition Team—you know, a Navy commando. I hear he's one tough bastard." *flick, flick, flick.*

I peered at GW over my 7-UP. This guy had an aura of self-confidence, all right. I waited for him to start riding me about my loss to Haley.

"The judges were wrong. You should have won that fight," said GW, gesturing with his head toward Haley who was leaving the ACRAC. "He was tiring and you proved you could take anything he had to dish out." He reached down and pulled a pack of camels from the inside of his sock. I took note of this practical method to carry cigarettes without having a non-military bulge in the shirt or pants pocket.

"He hit you a hundred times and couldn't put you down; you connected immediately and drew blood."

A hundred times, I thought? No wonder I'm dying.

"And you got in a few good shots toward the end." He tapped out a cigarette and returned the pack to the inside of his sock.

Grateful for his comments, I put my cooler on the bar and managed a smile. "Thanks," I said wincing at a stab of residual pain in my lower lip. "I could use a few comforting words right now."

GW grinned at my discomfort. He took a Zippo lighter from his pocket, opened the top, and flicked the wheel with his thumb, producing an instantaneous flame. "Another round and I'm convinced you would have put him away." He blew a cloud of blue smoke straight up in the air and smiled.

"Or he'd have put me away," I said as I took another sip of my cooler.

He put his head down, then looked up and grinned. "I've had

a few fights in my day. Believe me," he said patting me on the shoulder, "you did fine." He got up and walked toward the exit.

I watched through the window as the former UDT commando crossed the grinder toward his barracks. For some reason my aching body felt much better.

* * *

"Congratulations, Fitz, you made the front page."

It was Tuesday. I was napping on my bunk after the evening meal and Vince had thrown the *Gosport*, the base newspaper, in my face. I opened my eyes and stared at a photo of Charles Haley pounding me with a right cross. The article was titled, "The Best Fight of the Night!" The caption below read, "He took a pounding, but wouldn't go down!" I stared at the photo. When I was a kid I fantasized about seeing my picture on the sports page of some newspaper for doing something spectacular, not for getting creamed in a boxing match.

* * *

The next time I rode the bus the "quaint southern customs" to which Haley referred became shamefully clear. Growing up in Detroit, Michigan, a city with a large population of minorities, I mixed with blacks in school, boy scouts, sports, and in my part-time jobs. As with the Hispanics, Asians, northern Europeans, and fellow Scotch-Irish in my immediate neighborhood, some blacks I liked, some I didn't. Although I knew segregation existed in the south, it was so remote I didn't think much about it. I was about to discover it wasn't remote any longer.

About eight o'clock on a Sunday evening I was on my way back to the air station after a solo trip to Pensacola Beach. I boarded the city bus, dropped my dime in the hopper, and glanced at the empty seat behind the driver. The panel separating the driver from the passenger section would cramp my long legs, so I chose an empty seat two-thirds of the way down the aisle. I placed my gym bag in the overhead rack and dropped my weary body next to the window. It was odd, I thought, that a black lady who boarded with me paid her fare, got off the bus and reentered through the side door. Comfortable in my ignorance, I directed my thoughts elsewhere, failing to notice the curious looks from some of the passengers seated around me. A minute after I dropped in my seat the bus slowed to a walk. Wondering what had happened I looked up and met the driver's eyes staring at me in his large rear view mirror.

"Hey, Navy guy in the back!" he growled. "Get on up here."

There were a couple of sailors up front but I was the only uniformed guy in back. It had to be me he was addressing.

"I said, move up front!" he yelled, still glaring in his mirror.

Most of the white passengers turned around, scowling. I looked for a reserved sign or some indication that I had taken someone else's seat. I met the driver's eyes in the mirror, put my finger against my chest and mouthed, "You mean me?"

"Yeah, you! Come up front or get off the bus." He pulled over to the curb, opening the front door as the bus ground to a halt. "Up front or out," he snarled, pointing to the empty seat behind him and then to the open door.

I looked around at the silent faces, the whites expressing anger, I guessed for the delay I was causing, and the blacks showing no expression at all. The black man sitting behind me leaned forward and whispered in my ear. "Son, you must be from the north. You're sitting in the Negro section. Down here we sit apart." After giving me a friendly pat, he scooted back in his seat.

I finally had the picture. So this was what segregation was all about. I remembered the black lady who paid her fare behind me then got off to board through the side entrance—so she wouldn't insult the white passengers by brushing against them as she made her way to the rear of the bus, I assumed with disgust. I felt humiliated, then ashamed when I thought of the far greater humiliation black people endured on a daily basis. It was move as ordered or walk the eight miles back to the barracks. After thanking the man behind me, I nodded to the angry eyes in the rear view mirror, retrieved my gym bag, and made my way up front. Squeezing past an annoyed lady in the aisle seat, I took the empty space behind the driver. He grunted, ground the transmission into low gear, and pulled back into the right lane of Garden Street.

On the long, quiet ride to the air station I recalled times when discrimination was going on all around me and I didn't even notice. Eating in restaurants, attending the theater, lounging on the beach, or using the restroom, I never thought about the absence of black faces. I recalled the times I sat among friends and how the word "nigger" sailed over my head without the slightest thought of its implication. Whether it's commission or omission, I reminded myself, a sin is a sin. I remembered Haley sitting by himself in the ACRAC, uncomfortable or unwelcome among his fellow NavCads. When you've worn a white face all of your life, I decided, you could never begin to understand what it's like to be a black American.

Feeling depressed about the whole episode, that night I decided to write another letter to Ryan.

> Dear Ryan, Surprise . . . I'm still here! Things are going as well as could be expected in Pre-Flight, but I got sucked into a boxing match at the regimental smoker. Got taught a hell of a boxing lesson by a colored guy from Gary, Indiana—a former Golden Glover. Strangely, a few days later while riding a bus I got another painful lesson. This time it was about racial segregation in the south. Did you encounter discrimination in the Army Air Corps? I don't know why it bothers me so much when so many folks down here accept it as a way of life, even the black people. At least they seem to, anyway. I get the feeling a lot of the whites know it's wrong, but are afraid to try and change it. How can we claim to be a country formed on the premise that all men are equal when we treat a fellow

human being as though he were some lower breed of animal? It just doesn't make sense. On a brighter note, in a few weeks I'll start flight training. I have to admit I'm scared. I keep remembering that wild ride in your Aeronca. Wish me luck. Your anxious cousin, Tom.

* * *

About a month later my roommates asked me if I had ever been to Trader Jon's. I shook my head, so the following weekend Ron Warden and the four of us visited the most famous tavern on the Florida panhandle. After we stepped off the bus in downtown Pensacola we walked south on Palafox toward the wharf. Two blocks beyond the stores, souvenir shops, and cocktail lounges, we entered a misty waterfront area littered with drunken sailors, sleazy bars, tattoo parlors, and greasy spoon grills. Pushing on we encountered a towering wooden plank facade. An upright rectangle of escaping light marked the entrance to Trader Jon's Tavern.

In 1941 Trader Jon was better known as Martin Weissman, the owner of a bar in Key West, Florida. One night, while en route to Las Vegas, Nevada, he stayed overnight in Pensacola. Being a pilot since his teens, he fell in love with the exciting, aviation town on Pensacola Bay. He returned and on December 31, 1941, only 24 days after Pearl Harbor, opened the tavern on South Palafox Street. As a tribute to all naval aviators already in combat and the cadets who would soon join them, he adorned the inside with aviation memorabilia. Over time he accumulated every piece of aviation equipment imaginable and hung it in his tavern.

Wings, rudders, tailhooks, ailerons, propeller blades, instrument panels, control sticks, canopies, wing flaps, and even landing gear swayed precariously from the beamed ceiling. The airplane models dangling above the long bar picked up the drafts from the ceiling fans and zoomed around each other in mock dogfights. Occasionally a loud *CLUNK* announced a mid-air collision, but after a couple of twirls the duo uncoupled to continue their air-to-air combat.

Signal flags, antennas, flight suits, helmets, goggles, Mae West life vests, knee boards, rubber rafts, and poopy (exposure) suits hung from the heavy fish nets draped along the paneled walls. One partition displayed photos of Trader Jon posing with famous aviators, politicians, sports figures, and Hollywood celebrities. An entire wall honored the Blue Angels, the Navy Flight Demonstration Team. Tradition held that you could never call yourself a naval aviator unless you had tipped a few in Trader Jon's.

Once you finished flight training you would not pass through Pensacola without dropping in on Trader, anymore than you would miss dropping in to see a favorite aunt or uncle. He never forgot a name, even if you hadn't been in his tavern in 10 or 15 years. Wearing his Bermuda shorts, flowered shirt, and beachcombers hat, Trader would flash his Jack-o-lantern smile, rush out from behind his bar, and pumping your hand vigorously say, "Why, it's Tom Fitzgerald. Welcome back to Trader Jon's."

While we lounged over one of Trader's heavy, sailor-proof tables, Dufo stopped sipping his draught beer, paused in serious thought, then leaned forward so only we could hear his proclamation.

"I'm worried, guys. I . . . well, I haven't been, uh, hard since I got here." Dufo clinched his lips and sat back in his chair, waiting for us to offer a remedy for his problem.

"Come to think of it," said Vince, "I've been pretty limp myself. Before I came down here I'd wake up with one during the night or at least have a droopy one in the morning when I had to take a leak. But since we started Pre-Flight—nothin'."

"It's got to be the saltpeter," said Ron, *flick, flick, flick.* "They put it in our grits each morning to make sure we don't get so horny we won't be able to concentrate on our studies. I heard it from a guy in Class 28."

"You're crazy," said Stump. "Nobody's putting saltpeter in our food. It's the syndrome, that's all."

We stared at each other wondering what a syndrome was.

"Look," he said leaning forward to share his wisdom, "I read in *Every Man's Magazine* that in WWII the government discovered Marine recruits were so exhausted and preoccupied with hating their DIs, they never got horny. They called it the "Boot Camp Syndrome."

"Then I'm OK?" said Dufo, eyes flashing like crystal.

"Of course." Stump shook his head and took a slug of his beer.

I glanced across the room at Lorna, Trader's voluptuous barmaid. In her usual uniform of short-shorts and a halter-top, she was the fantasy of every NavCad and sailor at NAS Pensacola.

Some of us assigned certain body parts a nickname. In high school, when my member had a habit of growing at the most awkward times, I called it Pinocchio. But it was now the appendage of a future naval aviator, so I chose something in the same anatomical area as Pinocchio's nose, but more macho . . . the horn of a rhinoceros.

"If they're putting saltpeter in my food," I said slowly, "it's not working. Rhino's ready to charge." The guys followed my stare. Together we leered at the cleavage pouring out of Lorna's halter as she leaned over to take a bar order from a group of sailors.

"Same here," said Vince, "Apollo's ascending the Acropolis."

Dufo followed Lorna's every move, a lustful grin creeping across his long face. "Halleluiah! Bronco Bill has fully recovered," he muttered.

"Wow!" said Stump mockingly. "You guys have torpedoed the Navy's scheme to dampen your libido with saltpeter." Then Stump's eyes locked onto Lorna and wouldn't let go. "Even if your suspicions were true," he said with a smirk, "it would take a lot more than a dash of saltpeter to melt the cast iron Texas Panhandle of Stanley Walton Fowler."

* * *

The next day I received Ryan's answer to my letter.

Dear Cousin Tommy, Believe me, the bookwork is the easy part. Remember, you haven't even sat in a cockpit yet. The news that you got your brains scrambled in a smoker didn't surprise me. Sort of follows the pattern. And yes, I've seen the racial thing you talked about. We didn't have any colored guys in our squadron, but we had some in the motor pool. They were damn good mechanics and our squadron was running short. When I asked why they weren't working on our airplanes instead of jeeps the skipper looked at me like I was crazy. On the other hand, there was a squadron with all colored pilots flying Mustangs somewhere in North Africa. A Lieutenant Colonel Benny Davis was the skipper and not a single bomber they escorted was lost. All I can say is that when the red tails—Benny's squadron—jumped the ME 109s over Europe, the Krauts didn't notice if those 50 caliber bullets ramming their backsides were white or black. I reckon this blight in our country will change some day, but like cancer, the cure's a long time coming. In regards to being fearful of your flight training, you definitely should be afraid. After that wild tailspin you got us into over Kentucky, we're both lucky to be alive. It still isn't too late to come home and forget about this nonsense. Please think about it. Your concerned cousin, Ryan.

* * *

Many of us found learning to march difficult, but Dufo had a unique problem. When he marched he extended his long legs farther than anyone else. The effect was a noticeable bounce that threw his timing off, causing him to trip up the cadets in front and behind him. One day Staff Sergeant Lopez saw Dufo's head bobbing above his fellow cadets like he was riding a pogo stick.

"Platoon, HALT!" bellowed Lopez. "Cadet Hartwood, front

and center."

Dufo weaved through the ranks and towering above his angry DI, stood rigidly at attention. "Cadet Hartwood, reporting as ordered, sir."

Lopez pinched his eyes shut, his jaws torqued so tight his cheeks quivered. "Dammit, Hartwood, how many times do I have to tell you I'm not a sir? And why can't you march like everyone else?" Lopez sighed his frustration, put one hand on his hip and motioned around his body with the other. "March around me in a wide circle, but on your heels, not on your toes." He stretched his body until his lips were an inch from Dufo's chin. "Do not allow the balls of your feet to touch the grinder. Do you understand, Hartwood?"

"Yes, si . . . eh, yes, Staff Sergeant."

Dufo began marching in a circle, Lopez turning with him to watch the awkward NavCad clomp along on the backs of his feet. The rest of us observed silently, fascinated at Dufo's lesson in heel marching.

"Heel, heel, heel, heel . . . keep going . . . heel, heel, heel. OK, that's better . . . heel, heel . . . good, goooood! Now again, heel, heel, heel. . . . " Lopez fell in behind Dufo snapping his fingers rhythmically as though he were giving Dufo a dancing lesson. "Now get back in formation and march on your heels, NOT ON YOUR TOES!"

The ordeal made Dufo nervous and Staff Sergeant Lopez was about to learn that this NavCad from Nebraska had a problem we discovered weeks ago and it was a lot more disturbing than marching on his toes. Plus, the more edgy he became, the worse the problem. It was the worse case of flatulence any of us had ever encountered. Dufo usually gave a warning, such as fidgeting with his pencil, moving about in his chair, or shuffling his feet, but we were not always able to escape in time. We couldn't understand how so much stink could come out of such a skinny body. Always the expert on matters of mystery, Ron offered his opinion.

"It's like this," he said. "Dufo's so damn skinny that the air in his system is compacted under tremendous pressure." He squeezed his hands together like he was making a snowball. "So when he farts, it's like tapping a cylinder of mustard gas . . . SHAAABOOM! Out it comes, contaminating everything in sight."

I saw Dufo's fingers twitch and knew his tension was approaching critical mass. When he did an about face, his body betrayed him and a fetid effervescence showered his DI like a polecat spraying a hound dog.

Lopez closed his eyes and his lip curled upward in a futile effort to protect his nostrils. Holding his breath, he raced to the head of the formation. In one long exhale, Lopez ordered us to march double time, leaving Dufo's cloud of gastric mist settling in our wake. Occasionally Dufo bobbed up and down in formation, but that was the last time Staff Sergeant Lopez called him out for a lesson in heel marching.

* * *

Two weeks before we finished Pre-Flight, I was sitting with Ron, Vince, Dufo, and Stump in the taproom of the San Carlos Hotel. While drinking our usual quota of Spearman's Ale and sharing expectations about our first flight in the SNJ Texan, Stump made an observation.

"You know, you're not really a man of the sea until you get a tattoo."

"I don't know," said Vince. "That's one of those forever-type things. Besides, I plan to be a hero someday and I haven't seen many heroes with their arms covered with tattoos."

"I'm with Vince," said Ron, shaking his head. "We're gonna be officers and gentlemen. How can you be an officer and a gentleman and wear a tattoo?"

"How would we know?" asked Dufo. "Officers don't take off their shirts."

"I bet it hurts," I said, wincing at the thought of that big needle darting in and out of my delicate skin.

"Nah," said Stump, "no more than a pinprick. My dad got one when he was a cadet. I've always wanted one and I think it's time." He took a slug of his Spearman's Ale, his mind already made up.

I was unsure at first, but after my sixth beer I decided it would be neat to have a military symbol of some kind engraved on my flesh. Maybe it would give me more of a macho image with the girls and show Ryan I was really into the military thing. But how would my parents react? My mother would probably say she was disappointed in my judgment and remind me that it's a sin to mark up my body. My dad would say very little, if anything. He only spoke when his input was critical. A tattoo on his son's arm would not be considered critical.

I decided it was time to be a man of the sea. "Maybe I'll join you, Stump," I said smugly, proud of myself for making this very "manly" decision. Actually, after the last beer it seemed like a wonderful idea. Dufo signaled he was in with a thumbs up. Vince and Ron were the holdouts.

We paid our bill and unsteadily walked out of the San Carlos bar into a brilliant, violet sunset. Vince said we were all crazy, bade us good night, and joined Ron heading for his old Merc parked near the bus stop. I wondered if I should follow them instead of my adventurous buddies. Nah, I thought with the wisdom of an inebriated 19-year old. I'm going to have my body engraved with a salty symbol of masculinity. I will be a real man of the sea!

Stump, Dufo, and I continued down Palafox Street. When the air reeked of stale beer, cigar butts, and dead fish we figured a tattoo parlor had to be close by. Spotting a faded sign reading, "Body Art," at the end of the wharf, we ducked into Trader Jon's and bolstered our courage with one more Spearman's Ale.

Prior to entering the parlor we watched through the window as the bulbous-nosed, tattoo artist squinted at his work on a sailor's left arm. The artist's shoulders were covered with inky engravings ranging from a skull with a cobra crawling out of one eye socket to a crucifix with, *He Died For Us,* scribbled underneath. An anchor chain was tattooed on a roll of flab protruding between his ink and bloodstained tank top and Bermuda shorts. After observing for a few minutes we took deep breaths and crossed the threshold. The artist interrupted his work long enough to tell us to pick out a design and that he'd be with us in a minute. My nose wrinkled involuntarily when it detected the rancid fumes from urine, feces, and vomit spilling out of the door-less toilet in the rear of the parlor.

Ignoring our seedy surroundings we studied the scores of designs hanging on the greasy display boards as though we were picking out wallpaper. Stump chose a skunk that resembled Flower from the Disney movie, *Bambi.* A girl in Dallas often called him a polecat, he explained. Dufo selected the stars and stripes, and I picked out an anchor with USN underneath. I figured that a real US Navy tattoo might be a way to bond with my enigmatic father. An hour later we walked out of the parlor with our new tattoos protected by paper dinner napkins Scotch taped to our skin. The Spearman's Ale was beginning to wear off, but not the pride we held for our badges of manhood. After all, we were now . . . men of the sea.

The next morning I awoke to dull pain in my left biceps. I peeked under the napkin and stared at an ugly mass of red and blue ink mixed with congealed blood.

"Dear God," I whispered, "why'd you let me do this?" Stump and Dufo were asleep, blue and blood red polka dots covering the white sheets around their shoulders.

Vince was sitting at a table, polishing his brass. "How's it feel?" he asked while peering at his belt buckle in the sunlight.

"Terrible," I moaned. "Why didn't you stop me?"

He blew on the buckle, gave it a couple of quick buffs, and looked up, flashing the gap between his two front teeth. "What?" he chortled. "And hold you back from becoming a 'real man of the sea'?"

I looked at the mess oozing from under the dinner napkin and remembered Vince's caveat back at the San Carlos Hotel. "That's one of those forever-type things."

* * *

During the last week of Pre-Flight our class was to report to the Aviation Medicine Laboratory. Pete Zarek marched us to a small structure near the academics building and we filed into a soundproof room. A mirror covered the entire wall facing our desks. Ron Warden and I grabbed two seats together and dropped our book bags. A headset, two pencils, and a form resembling a test answer sheet lay on each desk.

"I don't like this, Fitz. I think we're gonna be guinea pigs for a secret experiment."

"Where'd you ever get that idea?" I asked. Ron was suspicious of everything.

He tilted his head at the mirror in front of us, then leaned closer. "When we came in," he whispered, "I heard a sailor tell a buddy that when we get through with this test we won't be able to hear for a week." He pulled out his pack of Luckys. "Can we smoke in here?"

I noted most desks were equipped with an engine piston turned upside down to serve as an ashtray. "I guess we can," I answered. Navy airplane engines must really chew up pistons, I decided weeks earlier, since the heavy, steel receptacles served as ashtrays in every classroom on the air station. A little nervous, I pulled a Chesterfield out of my sock and used Ron's match to light up. Ron flicked his Lucky several times and by the time he took his first drag, the ash was missing. While I held up my cigarette for him to gain a relight I figured he had to be mistaken about the oncoming impairment to our hearing. Surely the Navy wouldn't do anything to hurt their future Naval Aviators.

"*May I have your attention, Gentlemen?*"

I assumed the face that went with the voice on the loudspeaker was somewhere behind the mirror. I was beginning to think Ron was right.

"*We appreciate your volunteering to participate in this test of aviation audio and visual adaptability.*"

"Volunteered? Who the hell volunteered," whispered Ron. "And what is 'aviation audio and vision adaptability', anyway?"

"Shhhhh," I said, "maybe we'll find out."

"*On each desk you will find a form with columns of empty squares,*" the voice continued. "*Listen to the instructions on your headset and write the numbers in the squares as directed. Are there any questions?*" There was a murmur as heads leaned toward one another, but no questions. We adjusted our headsets and waited.

Suddenly the lights dimmed and the room exploded with a hundred aircraft engines running at full throttle. We picked up our pencils from the vibrating desks and a low, sexy, female voice crackled through our earphones.

"*Place the numbers that you hear in the first column.*"

I wrote each number, but it was no easy task. If I could determine the number over the engine noise I had trouble placing it in the tiny square on the answer sheet under the 25-watt, red light bulbs provided for illumination. When we finished the first column the engine volume increased a notch, as though another flight of B-29's joined the formation. As the noise increased, the voice on our headsets became softer and the light dimmer.

"*Now place the numbers that you hear in the second column.*"

Again we did as instructed, or tried to. When we completed the second column we put our pencils down and waited. The engine volume increased a few hundred more decibels. My mouth was cotton-dry and my ears throbbed.

"*Now place the numbers that you hear in the third column.*"

I placed my head six inches above the quivering answer sheet and began to write. Thirty minutes later we were on the tenth column and my head felt like I had warbling kazoos stuck in both ears. After another 15 minutes I could no longer differentiate between engine noise, residual ringing, and the woman's voice. Suddenly it was over. Although the engine's stopped, their echo continued to pound on my eardrums unmercifully.

"Amen to that," Ron moaned as he slouched in his seat and pulled a cigarette from his pocket. When he held up the match his trembling hand fanned out the flame. Eventually he lit up, nervously flicked his Lucky into oblivion and jammed it in his piston ashtray without enjoying one gram of soothing nicotine.

When dismissed we staggered outside and shielded our eyes from the blazing sunlight. The airplanes zooming overhead seemed to be flying without engines and automobiles paraded silently by our building. Not even the blast of their horns could penetrate the incessant ringing in my ears.

"Say again? Would you repeat that?" I said to Pete Zarek seemingly mouthing his orders as we gathered in front of the building.

He repeated his command to fall in three times before we finally got the idea and lined up in some semblance of a formation. A few minutes later we marched away, looking like a company of zombies en route to the netherworld. We were never told why we were subjected to such torture.

* * *

On a chilly Friday in November we donned our swords and marched to the parade ground behind the chapel. At the end of the graduation ceremony we stood with our diplomas in hand and listened to our company commander give the long-awaited command: "UN-furl . . . TIES!" We reached between the second and third buttons of our shirts and smartly pulled out what Marines called field scarves. We were no longer Pre-Flight cadets required to keep our ties stuffed in our shirts; we were student pilots appropriately allowing them to fly proudly in the Florida breeze.

Our ranks, however, had already diminished by 10. Of the 42 NavCads in our Pre-Flight class, five washed out for academics, two could not learn to swim, and three asked to DOR (drop on request) for reasons ranging from a pregnant girlfriend—you couldn't be married and remain in the NavCad program—to lack of motivation. The remaining 32 of us loaded our gear on the shuttle bus and departed for primary flight training. Ron Warden, along with a dozen of our classmates, was assigned to Naval Air Auxiliary Station (NAAS) Corry Field, a primary flight training base located across Bayou Grande from NAS Pensacola. Stump, Dufo, Vince, and I headed for NAAS Whiting Field six miles north of Milton, Florida.

Well, I thought, looking out the window at the SNJ Texans parked at Chevalier Field, I've survived Pre-Flight. Now comes the real test—learning to fly those babies. I slouched in my seat to take a nap, but when I closed my eyes I saw Ryan's Aeronca spinning round and round toward the rolling Kentucky farmlands. My eyes popped open and I spent the rest of the drive to Whiting Field fighting off chills and nausea.

Chapter 6

The first day at Whiting I tagged along with Stump, Dufo, and Vince on a tour of the flight line. They wanted to look over the WWII vintage aircraft in which they hoped to spend the next nine months. As for me, I hoped I would last nine days. When we climbed up on the wing of the first Texan we noted a name painted under the canopy rail.

"Don T. Stalb," mumbled Dufo while running his hand along the letters. "Do you suppose we'll get our names painted on an airplane, too?"

"I don't know, Dufo," I said, "seems odd they'd paint all the cadets' names on all these SNJ's."

"Maybe Stalb's an instructor or the squadron CO," said Vince. "Surely no lowly cadet could have his name painted on an airplane."

On our way to the hangar we met a first class petty officer. He appeared knowledgeable enough to answer our question about the names.

"Do you know if we can get our names painted on an airplane like Donald Stalb did?" I asked pointing at the SNJ on the line.

The sailor glanced at the airplane, then eyed the three of us suspiciously. "You're kidding, right?"

"Nope. We saw Don Stalb's name on that one over there and figured we might get ours on one, too."

He looked down at the tarmac and shook his head. Then he looked up and grinned. "I hate to disappoint you, but that's supposed to read, 'Don't Stall.' It's a reminder for you guys to avoid getting low and slow on your solo flights." He nodded at the words under the canopy rail and then pointed at two other Texans on the flight line. Both had "Don't Stall" painted under the canopy.

"Someone got cute and doctored the letters," said the sailor. "Nobody gets his name on an airplane around here, not even the skipper. That only happens in the movies." He walked away chuckling.

After shaking off our embarrassment we entered the hangar. The place was overflowing with activity. Instructors and student pilots sat opposite each other at cafeteria tables lining the far wall, instructors doing the talking, students listening intently. A large schedules board dominated the middle of the hangar. Sailors holding chalk in one hand and an eraser in the other, periodically added or made name changes to the list of students, instructors, and airplane numbers. In one corner a snack bar served hamburgers, hotdogs, French fries, coffee and soft drinks.

Dufo pointed at a cadet wearing a Mae West life vest with "BUAER," printed across the back. "Maybe we don't get our names on our airplanes, but it looks like we get them on our life preservers. At least Cadet Buaer does."

"I once knew a guy named Bauer," I said, "but I never saw it spelled with the 'u' in front of the 'a'. Maybe it's a foreign spelling or something."

While Stump was busy writing on his notepad, Dufo tapped him on the shoulder. "Stump, do you figure we better check out our Mae Wests now so we can get our names painted on the back like Cadet Buaer over there." He pointed to the NavCad sitting at a briefing table.

"I doubt if BUAER's his name, Dufo. That word was all over my dad's flight gear. It's short for Bureau of Aeronautics."

"Yeah," I said, glancing at Dufo with a shrug, "that's what I figured, too." Duped again by my ignorance and Dufo's power of suggestion.

As we headed for the hangar door, my face as red as when we came in, two NavCads talking by the schedules board caught my attention. One was another face in the crowd, but the other guy looked like he'd been whittled out of number one pine. His khaki flight suit was cinched around a narrow waist that angled up to wide shoulders and his trunk-like neck supported a chiseled head capped with a crew cut. He was the cadet I saw marching to the swim tank and sneering at me at the boxing smoker. I moved closer. That high pitched, bluegrass vernacular had matured to a deep, articulate drawl, but there was no doubt as to whom it belonged.

Their conversation ended, Willy Rumford put his hands on his hips and walked toward me, eyes as cold as ice cubes. "If it isn't Tommy the Twerp from the big city. I'd know that skinny frame anywhere."

"Willy Rumford," I said extending my arm. "I can't believe it."

"It's Will," he said gripping my hand like it was an ax handle. He shook it once and let go abruptly. My knuckles hurt like hell, but I held my smile.

"How'd you end up down here?" I asked.

"Well, Fitz-*gerald* . . . or should I call you nose wart?"

I forced a smile. "Tom or Fitz will do."

"Well, Fitz-*gerald*," he said, as though he were spitting a rotten peanut, "after two years studying agriculture at the University of Louisville, I found out I hated farming even more than I thought, so I took the NavCad pledge. The question is, how did *you* end up here?" He pointed at my jaw. "The last time I saw you near an airplane you were wiping puke from that protruding chin."

Other than his speech and size, nothing about Will had changed. "That was a long time ago. Sorry about your dad, by the way. How's your ma doing?"

Will snorted. "Best you worry about how you're gonna achieve the impossible and not about my Ma's welfare. As I recall, Ryan told you to do yourself a favor and stay away from airplanes. You get on the wrong bus or something?" Will folded his arms across his thick chest, biceps straining against the sleeves of his flight suit.

"No bus," I said coldly. "I arrived in an old Mercury convertible. Only time will tell whether I belong here or not. You started flying yet?" I wanted to turn the conversation to a friendlier note.

"Yep, and it's going fine—as I expected. But I doubt it'll go as well for you, Fitz-*gerald*. The way you treated Ryan's Aeronca should have been a good indicator this is the *last* place you ought to be. When you need help filling out a DOR form, let me know. Don't wait to be filtered out like moldy chaff from good wheat." Without waiting for a response he walked away, melting into the field of khaki flight suits.

"Good to see you, too," I muttered. I turned around and joined Stump, Dufo, and Vince sitting at the snack bar. While they devoured their hamburgers and cokes I toyed with my French fries and stared into space.

"What's up, Fitz?" asked Vince between gulps. "You upset about something?"

"Ran into an old friend, that's all. He was the last guy in the world I expected to see down here. The jerk hasn't changed one iota."

"Must have been a wonderful friendship," said Stump with a chuckle.

"Did I say 'friend'? Poor choice of words." I dipped a fry in ketchup and wrote WR on my napkin. Stump and Duffo glanced at each other and shrugged. We resumed eating in silence. Reflecting on the unlikely meeting with my childhood adversary, I shouldn't have been surprised to see him. Although we were only 10 at the time, both of us did vow to become pilots.

Later we visited the training office and were chagrined to learn 165 more hours of ground school awaited us over the next few months. The remaining hours were reserved for flying, drill, and physical fitness, in that order of priority. While in the office we checked the flight instructor assignments. Mine was Navy Lieutenant (Lt.) Hobart Axton. Hope he's more forgiving than my cousin, Ryan, I mused.

Lt. Axton was short, stocky, and a chain smoker. Using all of his leisure time to restore vintage foreign cars, he had permanently

804-UPCH

blackened fingernails, a nose full of blackheads, unkempt oily hair he combed with his stubby fingers, brown teeth, and breath that would shrivel a clove of garlic. The few times I saw him out of his flight suit, his uniform looked as though he kept it wadded up in the trunk of his VW Beetle, to be used only in emergencies. Nevertheless, he turned out to be one of those unforgettable teachers who make a difference.

While briefing me for the first lesson in the pre-solo "A" stage, Lt. Axton was interrupted by a loud racket followed by the crash truck's horn and siren. He mashed his cigarette in the piston ashtray and hurried toward the hangar door with me close on his heels. When we arrived on the flight line we saw an SNJ collapsed on its belly, the landing gear folded neatly under its wing roots. The propeller, now bent like a jack handle, had dug a pothole in the asphalt under the still smoking engine. The instructor stood next to the aircraft shaking his head while the student leaned against the fire truck, head bowed in embarrassment. Lo and behold, it was my impetuous classmate, Dufo Hartwood. Lt. Axton talked to the instructor for a few minutes, then motioned for me to come with him back to the hangar.

"First time I've seen that," he chuckled.

"The student's a buddy of mine, sir. What happened?"

"Your friend started the engine with no problems. After going over the pre-taxi checklist, Lt. Ross told him to unlock the tail wheel and pull out of the parking area." He paused to dig out a Life Saver. After popping it in his mouth, he offered me one. I shook my head, hoping he would take two, maybe three more.

"Remember this, Fitzgerald," said Axton reaching for a cigarette. "The knob to lock and unlock the tail wheel is round and behind the flap handle. The knob to raise and lower the gear is much bigger, shaped like a wheel, and forward of the flap handle. Your friend pulled the wrong knob. When the landing gear came up, down came the SNJ, the prop ripping the tarmac like a two-bladed buzz saw. The yellow bird will need a new engine, propeller, and some sheet metal work, but it'll fly again."

"I didn't think the gear would come up without the power push." I said. The power push was the lever that actuated the hydraulic system prior to raising the landing gear.

"It won't. Unfortunately he remembered it went with the big knob. Don't worry about your friend, Fitzgerald. If he's lucky it'll be the worst mistake he ever makes."

I doubt it, I said to myself. After we finished our brief we checked out our parachutes. Lt. Axton showed me how to lift the inspection tab and ensure the chute had been packed within the last 90 days.

"If it's been squashed in there for four or five months, it'll be slow to blossom when you pull the ripcord," he said. "Might even decide not to come out at all," he added, flashing a brown, toothy smile.

Not funny, I thought, while checking my card. I noted the chute had been re-packed within the last two weeks. I watched Axton thread his arms through the harness straps, lift the dangling seat pack off his rear end, and hold it to one side with his left arm. When I duplicated his actions he nodded approval and we walked toward the flight line. It was easy to find our assigned aircraft. Its bright, canary yellow paint stood out among the surrounding Texans.

"Just out of overhaul," Axton said, rubbing his hand over the wing. "With this new paint job and rebuilt engine it should fly like a new airplane."

I climbed on the left wing and watched Axton drop his chute in the rear bucket seat, draping the harness straps over the corners of the backrest. I did the same in the front cockpit. Then he followed me around the airplane while I did my first preflight inspection. While checking over the aircraft I recalled the two-item preflight checklist I saw in an aviation-training manual published circa 1913.

Rule #1. No pilot will take a machine in the air unless it looks like it will fly. Rule #2. If the machine's propeller is bent or splintered, the wings are sagging at a peculiar angle, or the motor is spewing fluids, consider rejecting the machine for flight.

After finishing the preflight I climbed in the cockpit. On the third attempt I managed to get the SNJ's engine started. Lt. Axton told me to commence taxiing. I carefully placed my hand behind the flap handle, felt for the small knob that unlocked the tail wheel, and pulled, half expecting the aircraft to collapse on the tarmac. But it did not and we eased out of our parking spot and onto the taxiway.

Even in the front seat I found it impossible to see over the nose while taxiing. Lt. Axton talked me through S-turns, which allowed me to peek around the engine for anything that might be in my way. S-turning required considerable coordination of throttle, rudder, and brakes. The least amount of inattention resulted in an embarrassing side trip onto the grass or a 360-degree twirl in the middle of the concrete. I avoided the grass, but before reaching the runway managed to perform one tight circle on the taxiway.

Stopping was tricky. To apply the brakes we pressed the tops of the rudder pedals, alternating left and right. Jamming the brakes simultaneously caused the Texan to flip on its nose and dig the prop into the concrete. While alternating brakes I held the bottoms of the pedals firmly with both heels to keep the rudder amidships and avoid swerving all over the taxiway.

Like too many lessons in my life, I learned the danger of simultaneous braking the hard way. While S-turning I misjudged distance and was about to climb up the tail of another airplane. Instinctively I popped both brakes. Up came the tail and I waited for the inevitable clacking of the prop against concrete. Fortunately, the momentum wasn't quite enough to carry us over and the tail plopped back on the taxiway, hitting hard enough to rattle our eyeballs. Lt. Axton laughed and told me I learned a valuable lesson at a cut-rate price.

When we took the runway I prayed that Axton, like most of the other instructors, would make the first takeoff. Nope, I was to learn this cold turkey. My ride in the Aeronca flashed through my mind. When we were in the air would the control stick bite me like it did then? I locked the tail wheel, being careful to have my hand on the small knob and not the big one, pushed the throttle all the way to the stop, and eased the right rudder pedal forward to counter the torque. The Texan's engine roared to full power and we accelerated down the runway. When I sensed the airframe becoming light on the wheels I eased the stick forward, allowing the tail to lift off the runway. The airspeed passed 70 knots and I pulled back gently. The SNJ rose gracefully from the runway, still accelerating toward its climb speed of 90 knots.

"Damn, that was easy," I mumbled.

"Gear," crackled a voice through my headset. I pulled up the handle, but nothing happened.

"Power push," crackled my headset once more. I placed my left hand on the hydraulic power control lever and pushed it firmly to activate the system. The gear unlocked and nested in the wing roots. So far, so good. To make sure I was flying and not motoring along US Highway 90, I allowed myself one peek at the Florida countryside. From then on I looked at nothing except an empty horizon. I saw neither the earth nor the sky, only a fuzzy line that separated the two. My fear wouldn't allow me to look at anything else.

Most former cadets can recite something profound about that first ride in an SNJ, but all I remember is the smell. Fresh paint, fear induced sweat, and exhaust fumes combined to create a unique odor that is permanently stuck in my nostrils. For months I had imagined this flight to be an awe-inspiring, momentous entry into a brave new world; but once I was airborne, all I wanted was to get through the hour without doing something stupid or barfing up my breakfast.

Ryan had said that a monkey could fly an airplane. Well, maybe a monkey could fly it straight and level, but landing the temperamental Texan is a challenge to even the most aeronautically adept aviators. With conventional landing gear—two main wheels and a tail wheel—the Texan landed in a full stall, with the tail slightly low in what is called a three-point attitude. Although Air Force pilots preferred to land the SNJ on the main wheels first, the NavCad was trained to land tail down, an attitude that allowed the tail hook to engage the arresting cable on a carrier deck.

The book said we were to make a coordinated descent, gradually bleeding off the airspeed to arrive four or five feet over the runway, tail down, slightly above the stall. When the airplane lost flying speed it dropped the final few feet, simultaneously kissing the runway with all three wheels. Voila! A perfect landing. Oh, how I wish it had been that easy.

My first attempts were as coordinated as the Three Stooges in a tap dance recital. I wobbled down the final approach too fast, then too slow, then too high, then too low. When I made contact with the runway the landing turned into the dreaded porpoise maneuver. Instead of making a three point landing, I hit flat, the main gear slamming on the runway and bouncing back into the air, banging the tail wheel against the concrete on the way up. To avoid a stall I pushed the nose over causing my tail to raise high behind me. Down I went, hitting the main gear once more, bouncing back in the air and thumping the tail wheel against the concrete on the way up, followed by another bounce, and so on. Lt. Axton would grab the controls before these partially controlled crashes deteriorated beyond anything salvageable. While debriefing my third disastrous period of practice landings, Axton tried to reinforce what little confidence I had left.

"Fitzgerald, the SNJ is probably more difficult to land than any other airplane. Learn to land this feisty, yellow bird and you can land anything in the US Navy inventory. By God, I'm gonna teach you to fly this machine and get it on the ground or we're both gonna die trying."

I was afraid his dying prediction might come true before the flying part. I decided that for Axton's sake, if I couldn't land safely on my flight the next morning, it was time to follow Ryan's advice and quit. That night I roughed up a letter to DOR from the flight program. It was either do it the next day, or out I went.

On my flight the next morning, Axton had to take over the controls on the first five tries. Lining up on runway for my last landing attempt of the period—and of my flying career—I set up my descent, adjusted power, and prayed for a miracle. Four feet over the end of the runway I eased the stick back slightly to get my three point attitude, felt the stall, the drop and . . . squeak-squeak-squeak . . . made a landing Charles Lindbergh would have envied. Before Axton allowed himself to get excited he asked me to do it one more time to prove the last one wasn't a fluke. I did it again, not quite as smoothly, but certainly acceptable. "If you can do three in a row," said Axton over the intercom, "we'll celebrate."

I did and we did, by performing a series of slow rolls on the way back to Whiting. I think Axton was more excited than I was. I was one landing from dropping out and ending my misery, yet I made it. "Not meant to fly, eh, Ryan?" I mumbled. "We'll just see about that." Buoyed by success I tackled the remainder of A Stage including spins, crosswind landings, and emergencies with fervor.

* * *

Toward the end of A Stage, I stood in the snack bar line talking with Vince. His roommate at Whiting was Phil Castle, a former right end for Purdue. Phil was barreling through primary like a box turtle. First, he couldn't land the airplane. When he got over that hurdle he couldn't learn how to recover from a spin. Then he had an appendectomy and after three weeks of recuperation, started the syllabus all over again. Already at Whiting two months longer than his classmates, Phil knew all the flight instructors and their peculiarities like his own name. Through Phil, Vince had learned which instructors to avoid.

Burgers and fries in hand we found an empty table and sat down. Vince nodded his head at a cadet with a dark stain on his back. "See that guy by the schedule board with the wet flight suit?"

I looked in the direction of his nod. It was a chilly day and I was wearing a sweatshirt under my flight suit to keep warm. I knew that the wet spot on the cadet's back couldn't be from perspiration. "Yeah, what about him?" I said holding up a French fry. They were soggy and I had to hold my head back to get one in my mouth.

"He's one of 'Pistol Pete' Peterson's students. Must'a had a bad flight, but it doesn't look like he got a down." A down was an unsatisfactory flight grade.

"How do you know?" I asked.

"Pistol Pete uses a squirt gun on his students. The pattern on his back isn't big enough for him to have gotten an unsat." The moist spot was the size and shape of a football.

"His instructor uses a squirt gun? You must be kidding," I said.

"Nope," insisted Vince, shaking his head. "Peterson packs a squirt gun in his flight bag. Every time his student screws up he squirts him in the back." Vince wiggled his right forefinger like he was pulling a trigger. Then he paused to take a bite of his hamburger, chewed slowly, and after swallowing, continued. "Pistol Pete doesn't run a tab on his kneeboard like most flight instructors. He figures if his squirt gun goes dry you made too many errors. So he gives you a down."

"Unbelievable! How do they let instructors do things like that?"

"Fitz, in primary the guy in the rear cockpit is king. He can do any damn thing he wants, short of murder." He lowered his voice. "Hell, that's one of the few benefits they get from being flight instructors—to play God. When they get back in the fleet they're just another squadron pilot or a staff puke." He leaned closer and whispered. "And you know what?" I shook my head. "Some of these instructors are a hair this side of psychotic." He backed away. "You're lucky you have Axton. He's no poster boy, but Phil says the little squirt's a damn good flight instructor." I nodded agreement and we finished our grease burgers.

That afternoon I was at the scheduling board waiting for Axton when I felt a tap on my shoulder. I turned around, expecting to see my instructor. It was Vince and he was motioning toward the hangar door.

"Here comes Pistol Pete with another water baby," he said grinning.

Lt. Peterson walked into the hangar with his student following properly to his left and one step behind. When they walked past I noticed the student's entire back was soaking wet. He tossed his helmet on the briefing table, plopped down on a chair, and faced the wall, arms folded across his chest in disgust.

"Now, that's what a down pattern looks like," said Vince nodding toward the cadet. When he finished debriefing his demoralized student, Pistol Pete went to the water fountain, stuck his pistol in the stream, and pulled back the plunger. "He's reloading for his next flight," said Vince, showing the gap between his teeth. We watched Pistol Pete put his squirt gun in his flight bag and walk over to the schedule board to pick up his next student. I don't know if I was glad or sympathetic when I discovered his next student was Will Rumford.

"Vince, that NavCad with Peterson. Know him?"

"Yeah, it's Will Rumford. Why?"

"He's the boyhood chum I told you about who turned into a real jerk."

"Rumford's the only guy who comes back from Pistol Pete's flights with a dry flight suit," Vince said with a shrug. "He may be jerk, but he's gotta be pretty good with the stick and rudder."

"Wonderful," I said.

* * *

Part of A Stage was learning the emergency procedures for engine failures at low and high altitude. Low altitude was easy: maintain flying speed, open the canopy, raise the landing gear and drop flaps, turn off fuel and electrical switches, and land straight ahead. The important thing was to maintain a proper glide speed and avoid the temptation to turn back to the airfield, which could cause a stall at low altitude, a quick way to buy the farm.

A high altitude emergency required more planning. Vince gave me Phil's mnemonic aide for the high altitude emergency checklist: Glide, gas, gear, grass, prop, top, talk, chalk. Phil's poetic ditty held clues for all the items on the checklist: adjust trim to keep the best *glide* speed; switch to fullest *gas* tank; raise the landing *gear*; look for a suitable *grass* field for the forced landing; put the *prop*eller in high pitch to reduce drag; open the *top* (canopy); *talk* (make the Mayday call); and *chalk* off the items on the emergency checklist to ensure they have all been covered. Seemed simple enough.

The first low altitude emergency Axton gave me was a walk in the park. We departed from one of the outlying airfields and when I passed through 400 feet with the landing gear already on the way up, he pulled the throttle back to simulate an engine failure. Since my canopy was still open and the landing gear were up, I simply called that I was simulating turning off my switches, adjusted the trim for a 95-knot glide, and while gliding straight ahead toward a recently plowed field I made my Mayday call on the intercom.

"Good job," he said, after taking the controls and adding power. "Looks like you've been studying."

Later in the flight he gave me my first high altitude emergency. While flying over Cantonment, a small town north of Pensacola, he pulled the throttle back to idle and announced that I had lost my engine. No sweat, I thought. I have 6000 feet, that's plenty of altitude and there's all kinds of good landing fields within gliding distance. This is gonna be a snap. I trimmed the Texan for a 95-knot glide and reached back in my brain for Phil's little ditty. Let me see, I have my glide, now what was next, grass or gas? Grass, I think. I looked for a field and spotted a pasture about two miles north. That'll do, I thought, and banked in its direction. Now what's next? Was it the landing gear? The aircraft shuddered. Whoops! I let her drop to 70 knots. Gotta watch my airspeed. I dipped my nose to gain a few knots. Back to my memory aide. OK, landing gear. Remembering that I raised them after take-off, I jumped to the next item. Ok, now, the propeller. But do I put it in high or low pitch? Hmmm. Low pitch will give me more RPMs, so I guess I better put it in low pitch. I pushed the propeller control all the way forward. OK, now what? Oh yeah, top. I pulled the latch and slammed the canopy all the way back on its rails. "Damn!" I mumbled as I watched my checklist fly away in the wind stream. Oh, well, I have Phil's ditty. Let's see . . . glide. I readjusted trim for 95 knots—check; OK, prop and top are done.

The SNJ shuddered again. Watch it Fitz! Almost another stall. I have to watch that airspeed more closely. There now, back to 95 knots, but I seem to be going down very fast. Hmmmm. Oh, well, my pasture is right over . . . where'd that pasture go? Oh-oh, I'm below 3000 feet. Geez, we're descending so damn fast. What's goin . . . ? Oh, great, the gear's down. I know I raised it back at . . . ! Axton. That sneaky SOB dropped it when he pulled the throttle back. No wonder the aircraft tried to stall on me twice. I should have eyeballed the gear handle to make sure it was up. I hit the power push to regain hydraulic pressure and yanked up the gear handle. There, the gear's up. OK, back to grass. Aha! There's a golf course over there and it has a couple of long fairways where I can set her down. Whoops, not that one—got a sharp dogleg to the right. I'll take the straight fairway to the ninth hole over there by the clubhouse. Let's see, glide, grass, gear, gas . . . or was it gas first and then grass. There, gas is . . . Whoops! I put the gas on the empty tank. Stupid, stupid, STUPID! You're supposed to switch to the fullest tank, not an empty tank, dummy. Oh, noooooo, my altitude's 1000 feet. I'm descending like a rock. Fitz, you jerk! The prop is supposed to be in high pitch, not low pitch. All that extra drag pulled us down like we were trailing an anchor. And now I've lost the golf course. Where the devil did it go? Oh, man, I'm in big trouble! We're at 500 feet and I haven't even made a Mayday call. My *high* altitude emergency is a now a *low* altitude emergency. I'd better land straight ahead in those woods. Oh, wow! Look at all those oak trees. They'd shred this plane like it was made of tissue paper and me along with it. Well, looks like my proverbial plot on the old farm is dead ahead.

"I have it." Lt. Axton took the controls and pushed the throttle forward. I raised my hands to signal I had given him the airplane.

"What happened, Fitzgerald? I gave you over a mile of altitude to find a suitable landing field and go over your checklist. How in the hell did you turn an easy high altitude emergency into a low altitude calamity where you were gonna crash into the worst landing site in northwest Florida?"

Once more self-doubt enveloped me like a black shroud. That night I went over my emergency procedures like my life depended on them, which it did of course.

On our next flight I knew my procedures cold and Axton took me on to the next lesson—spin recovery. With the exception of when I crossed my controls in the stall and flipped us inverted—a dangerous maneuver in any aircraft—I handled spins fairly well, surprising both Axton and myself. Although I seemed to start each phase of A Stage with a near disaster, I was doing great compared to my roommate, the amiable, but mischievous French Midshipman, Raoul Toussaint. Whenever I was feeling down, a conversation with Raoul perked me up.

Raoul, with his granite jaw, sparkling blue eyes, and athletic build, should have been a model for a French fashion magazine. When he arrived in the US, however, his insufficient command of the English language hindered his progress. Even after several remedial English classes, Raoul continued to have problems communicating.

We Americans use "up" as an adverb as well as a direction away from the center of the earth. We mess *up* the garage, fix *up* the room, and back *up* the car. The term, "clean it *up*," in aviation talk means to raise the landing gear, flaps, speed brakes, or tail hook, whatever is hanging out "dirtying *up*" the airplane. As far as Raoul was concerned, however, "up" meant a direction and nothing else.

After Raoul's first take-off his instructor, LCDR Bailey, noted he had neglected to raise the landing gear. He gave him a few more minutes then said, "OK, Raoul, clean 'er up." Raoul yanked on the stick and put the Texan in a steep climb resulting in an immediate stall. Bailey grabbed the controls and recovered only a few feet over the terrain, all the while, he declared later, trying to figure out what he had said to cause his student to do such a crazy maneuver. After that the flight went well, until Bailey was ready to head back to Whiting Field.

"OK, Raoul, time's up. Let's go. . . . " Before he could finish they went into a zoom climb and another stall. Bailey recovered again. After handling the controls for a few minutes he gave the aircraft to Raoul and told him, "I don't understand, Raoul, what the hell's up, any. . . . " Once more, up and away they went. Although reluctant to concede failure, Bailey was compelled to recommend Raoul for a disposition board.

The Student Pilot Disposition (SPEEDY) Board recommended that Raoul take more remedial English lessons and return to flight training. The Admiral concurred. "Some American expressions are confusing to foreigners," he said after hearing Raoul's side of the story. "Midshipman Toussaint deserves another chance." Raoul told me in confidence that after a while he figured out what Bailey meant when he said, "up." By that time, however, he couldn't resist the temptation to "play a joke."

Raoul had been at Whiting twice the normal time, thanks to the initial language problems, one unintentional wheels up landing, and his capricious nature. And there was also Camilla, his lady friend in Milton. She loved Frenchmen in general, and the attractive and amorous Raoul Toussaint in particular. Raoul often reflected on Camilla's attributes.

Showing his devilish smile he cupped his hands on his chest. "She has teets thirty-seex and waist tweenty-two." Then he paused, gripped an imaginary steering wheel, and raised his eyebrows. " . . . and she has Plee-mooth, feefty-four. That is good, too, no?" Raoul couldn't shake the French custom of putting the adjectives behind the nouns.

Raoul's taste for mischief was contagious and it eventually rubbed off on his instructor. While returning from one of their dual flights, he asked Bailey if he would like to play a trick on the control tower. By now accustomed to Raoul's penchant for practical jokes, Bailey listened to his proposal and couldn't resist going along.

Raoul ducked down in the front cockpit and called the tower, asking them in his strong French accent if he could fly by so they could check to see if his landing gear were down and locked. Wanting to help out a foreign cadet in trouble, the tower controllers readily approved his request. When the Texan flew by, the tower controllers noted that the landing gear appeared down and locked, but they were alarmed when they saw him—actually, Bailey—flying the aircraft solo from the rear cockpit. That was a major safety violation.

"SNJ four-one-bravo, your landing gear appears down, but, uh, you shouldn't be soloing the plane from the rear cockpit. That's against regulations."

"*Sacre' bleu*!" said Raoul, bent over and out of sight in the front cockpit, "I feex." Bailey flew outside the pattern and when he brought the SNJ by the tower the second time he hunched down out of sight and Raoul sat upright in the front cockpit.

"Is OK, now?" asked Raoul, waving at the tower. The operators stared at the Texan, at each other, again at the airplane, wondering how that Frenchman managed to get out of the back cockpit and strap in the front cockpit, to say nothing of the airplane flying by itself while he was doing it.

"SNJ four-one-bravo, we don't know how you did that, but you better come back and land right away."

"Do not understand. You say geet back in rear cockpeet?"

"No, no!" they yelled. "Land *now*!" The tower operators panicked and called the crash crew, safety office, and the training officer.

Bailey made one more wide circuit. As he made a third pass by the tower, Raoul hunched down once again and Bailey waved from the back cockpit.

"Is OK, now?" Raoul inquired in his microphone while out of sight. While the operators stared dumbstruck, the safety and training officers stuck their heads together, discussing ways to get this crazy Frenchman back on the deck in one piece.

Bailey made a tight 360-degree turn, widely circling the tower. At the completion of the circle Raoul popped upright and they both waved. The tower operators' faces turned several shades of red. Laughing, the safety and training officers threw Bailey extended middle fingers. While the tower operators cursed the horseplay, the officers descended the ladder mumbling about how they would get even with their fellow flight instructor.

Chapter 7

On my A-12, Axton asked me to make a few landings at the Milton 'T' (T-shaped) Airport. After three or four, three-point squeakers in a row, he told me to proceed to NOLF (Navy Outlying Field) Pace, a square mile of smooth grass a few miles west of Whiting. After our first landing he told me to taxi near the crash crew and stop. Realizing what was coming, my heart accelerated like a stock car at Daytona.

While unstrapping he yelled, "It's all yours, Fitzgerald. Make six touch-and-go landings then pull over and pick me up." Before I could object, he jumped out of the rear cockpit, took a copy of *Hotrod Magazine* out of his flight suit pocket, and walked to the radio cart near the crash vehicle.

Without any apparent concern about my ability to fly the SNJ on my own, Axton lay down on the grass, rested his head on his helmet, and began enriching his knowledge of overhead cams in V-8 engines. I looked over my shoulder at the empty rear cockpit, then faced to the front and stared at the grassy airstrip as though it was the road to Armageddon. My hand was on the throttle but I was unable to push it forward.

When Axton didn't hear the engine revving up, he waved me on, yelling, "Go on, Fitzgerald, you'll do fine."

I swallowed and nodded my head. With a quivering hand, I eased the throttle forward and began rolling over the bumpy grass field. The lightened Texan leaped in the air and I adjusted the trim to compensate for the empty rear cockpit. Although I was flying alone for the first time in my life I concentrated on the landing pattern so intensely that I had little time to enjoy this important milestone in my fledgling aviation career. When I had one landing under my belt I was able to relax slightly, enough to discover a world I had never known before.

From its deep rainbow hues to its soft pastels, I never knew the earth was so colorful. Railroad tracks and power lines stitched the quilted landscape. Varicolored cars, buses, and pickup trucks sped from one town to another like the inhabitants of bustling anthills. I marveled at how the Gulf of Mexico transitioned from a royal blue to a brilliant turquoise as the water approached the snow-white beaches of the Florida panhandle. Only the fall colors in my home state could compare to the beauty I saw before me that day. I leaned into the wind stream and let a blast of cool air massage my face. I had never before felt so glad to be alive.

On my sixth approach I looked down at Axton's prostrate form. His arms were folded across his chest and his magazine spread across his face. After landing, I back-taxied to the radio cart. Awakened when I added throttle to turn into the wind, he threw off his eyeshade and tossed me a thumbs up. Grinning broadly, he climbed on the wing and shouted, "Good job, Fitzgerald. Let's go home." Was he really sleeping? I wondered.

When we landed at Whiting, Axton opened his jackknife, yanked out my tie, and cut it off a couple of inches below the knot, traditionally known as severing one's bonds to mother earth. Later that day I followed another tradition. I bought a bottle of his favorite whiskey, wrote his name across the label with the note, "Thanks for not giving up on me," and left it at the O Club bar. With that important task accomplished, I went to the PX and purchased the gold bar with an anchor in the center. I proudly attached it over my left breast pocket. Now everyone would know that I was a solo student pilot. When back at the barracks I sat down and wrote Ryan a letter telling him about my first solo flight.

> Dear Ryan, I think this was the most important day of my life. I flew my first solo today! I can't begin to tell you what it felt like to take up that Texan all by myself. It's like I stepped into a whole new world. What am I saying? You

> already know what it feels like. After today I have a feeling I'm going to make it all the way. I've decided I want to be a fighter pilot like you were. Who knows, maybe I'll carry on your legacy after all. Your soloed cousin, Tommy

This time Ryan answered within a week.

> Dear Tommy, OK, you've soloed . . . so what? That elementary feat in no way means you'll earn your wings. Most washouts occur well beyond the first solo. Cousin, you're barely getting started. Ahead there's a long, bumpy road full of chuckholes, most too deep and too wide for a guy with your meager talents to negotiate. I have a bad feeling you're gonna fall in one of those holes real soon and break your neck. My plea still goes. Come home now, on your own, rather than be kicked out—or worse, carried out. You said you wanted to become a fighter pilot? You have to be kidding. Your unimpressed cousin, Ryan.

I was over six feet tall and weighed 185 pounds. I could take a beating without being knocked down or out, run five miles without stopping, swim a mile fully clothed, display a macho tattoo on my left arm, and solo an SNJ Texan, supposedly the most difficult airplane to learn how to land. But to Ryan, I was still a 10-year-old kid puking my guts out in a tailspin over Kentucky. I asked myself why I kept writing to this guy. Good or bad, I answered, you have nobody else with whom you can share your feelings. Live with it. After wiping my eyes, I folded his letter and placed it with the others.

* * *

Later that day I was walking back from the mess hall and bumped into Will Rumford. Up to now we had only grunted an unpleasant greeting or two in the hangar. He stopped and pointed at my solo bar.

"Finally did it, eh, Fitzgerald. I thought it was too early for Santa Claus to be handing out presents."

Will had been wearing his solo bar for two weeks. Patting my shoulder he repeated his advice about quitting. I pulled my shoulder back and scowled. "Back off, Will. I'm in no mood for this."

"Look," he said condescendingly, "I have to admire you for struggling through your first solo, but from here on it gets a lot tougher. Now's a good time to get out with your head held high."

He sounded so much like my cousin Ryan it was frightening. Were they teaming up against me? "I'm touched by your concern, but I think I'll stick around."

"Suit yourself. I'd sure hate to see you wash out and embarrass your whole family. They deserve better, Fitz-*gerald*." Will gave me a patronizing pat on the back, and continued on his way.

As we headed in opposite directions I decided boyhood chum or not, Will Rumford was the biggest jerk I'd ever met.

"Hey, Fitzgerald!"

I turned. Will was standing 15 yards down the sidewalk, his hands resting on his hips.

"Yeah?" I said. "What's the problem, now?"

"No problem. I'm heading for the gym. Care to join me?"

Warning bells sounded.

"Well, how about it?" he asked.

"Sure, why not." Allowing foolish pride to shove aside good judgment, I followed him to the base gymnasium. After all, my day couldn't be any worse than it already was.

When we entered the gym several NavCads and sailors working on punching bags and free weights greeted Will like family. In the locker room I jiggled my brain trying to remember the combination to my still shiny lock. Should have used this gear more, I thought, watching Will proudly uncover the rippling muscles across his chest and abdomen.

"How about working out on the mats?" he said as we left the

locker room. "We can practice the moves they taught us in Pre-Flight."

More warning bells. Will was built like a piano mover and I had heard he wrestled at the University of Louisville. This was an invitation to absorb pain and humiliation, but being the proud soul that I was . . . "All right," I mumbled. "Just remember I'm no wrestler."

"I'm not crazy about it, myself—too many rules. But it's a good conditioner." Will carried his toned-up frame to the center of the mat and turned around. "Let's get started," he said glancing up at the wall clock. "I got a flight in an hour." We leaned into each other assuming the position for competition.

Will pinned me five times while I didn't have one takedown to my credit. The guy was a pile of slippery muscle and sinew driven by unlimited power and energy. Each time he released my crumpled body he used me for a springboard to leap in the air, grunting in triumph. As in the Pre-Flight smoker, I was too stubborn to quit. The closest I came to a takedown was when Will slipped and fell in a pool of my own sweat. He hadn't worked hard enough to produce any of his own. After 30 minutes toying with me he pressed my shoulders on the mat in a hold that threatened to pull my arms out of their sockets. When my groans became embarrassing he eased off, slapped me on the chest and pulled me from the mat like I was a bag of dirty laundry.

"Let's lift some weights," he said while wiping my sweat off his hands. "You look like you've had enough wrestling for one day." Rubbing my aching ligaments and muscles, I followed behind the victor like I usually did when we were kids. While he puffed his way through a series of curls and bench presses using anywhere from 150 to 200-pound weights, I did a few exercises with 15-pound dumbbells. Thirty minutes later Will left to make his flight and I sat alone in the locker room, massaging my ravaged body while pondering how much I detested Will Rumford.

* * *

After a few of us from the same Pre-Flight Class flew our first solo we went to Pensacola for a weekend of celebration. Pete Zarek, our former class leader, drove his car. Stump Fowler, Derrick Gardner, and I rode along. We pooled our assets and took two rooms in the San Carlos Hotel. Before going upstairs to dress for the beach we went to the bar for some liquid refreshment. While nursing our third Spearman's Ale, Stump set his bottle on the table and said, "I have a suggestion."

"We're listening," said Pete.

"Let's get a hooker," said Stump with a grin.

"A what?" I said, holding my mug next to my lips.

"A hooker. I heard my dad tell a friend that a liaison with a honey in the San Carlos is a must-do for Navy pilots. Kinda like tossing down a few at Trader Jon's."

"A hooker ain't exactly the kind of honey your dad was probably talking about," said Derrick. "The San Carlos has class. This ain't some dive in the Bronx. Why don't we find some girls on the beach, take 'em to dinner and a movie, and if we're any good they'll let us bring 'em here to fulfill our fantasies." He took a swallow from his mug and wiped his mouth. "Whatta ya say?"

Stump shook his head. "Romance is too complicated, too expensive, takes too long, and relies too much on luck. My way it'll probably cost less and we have a sure thing. In fact, if we go in together the way we did on the rooms, we can get a hooker for about ten bucks apiece." He leaned forward and lowered his voice. "And Derrick, no hotel is too classy to provide a hooker. I know the bell captain. He'll take care of us." He scooted back in his chair. "Well?"

I mulled this over for a moment. I had never been with a prostitute and I was nervous about this venture into the unknown. Yet, I supposed it was one of those rites of passage I would have to experience sooner or later. Undecided, I sipped my Spearman's Ale and listened to the discussion.

"There's mental health considerations, too," said Pete. "A corpsman once told me that a guy's hormones build up tremendous pressure and his willy is . . . well, sort of a relief valve. When the pressure gets near the red line, one way or another you're supposed to relieve it. I, for one, am nearing the red line. I'm with Stump."

After a moment of silence two heads nodded in agreement. Who could argue with a former staff sergeant in the Marine Corps? My bobbing head joined the other two making it unanimous, but I was already trembling like an adolescent in his first round of foreplay.

"Great!" said Stump. He looked at his watch. "It's eleven hundred. Kinda early, but I'll go talk to the bell captain. He'll know if one's available." He stood up. "If he can help us out I'll ask him to send her up to the room I signed for. We'll use one room for the ramp," he said grinning, "and the other room for the active runway." He turned on his heel and was gone. Five minutes later Stump came back and gave us a thumbs up. "Fifteen minutes and we're in business."

Actually, what he meant was, she was in business. We followed Stump upstairs and made ourselves comfortable. I'd never been inside one of the rooms in the San Carlos. It was five times the size of our room at the barracks. Below the the12-foot ceiling rimmed with a triple row of crown molding, a large fan rotated so slowly I could count the blades. The four-poster bed had a solid mahogany headboard that easily weighed 100 pounds. The room was furnished with a sofa and easy chairs, ornate floor lamps, hand-carved end tables, and an antique secretary with a matching straight back chair. When I used the bathroom I was impressed with the ceramic tile floors and walls, hand carved mahogany cabinets, pedestal marble sink with shiny brass fixtures, raised bathtub that could easily accommodate two people, and a porcelain commode on a platform large enough to be the proverbial throne. I walked back in the room and considered my classy surroundings. It was an honor to bed a lady amidst such elegance, I decided, even if she was a hooker.

At precisely 1135 we heard a knock on the door. Pete opened it and stood aside. Standing in the threshold was an attractive woman about 30 years old, smartly dressed in a business suit and high heels, and carrying a briefcase. She had shoulder-length brown hair, artfully applied makeup, and a figure that was shapely, but not voluptuous. I immediately thought of the Avon Lady.

"Did you gentlemen call for travel assistance?" she asked with a smile that curled my toes. "Perhaps I can satisfy your needs."

"Why thank you, Miss," said Pete. "I'm sure you can." He looked her over approvingly as he closed the door behind her. She eyed each of us, I suppose to mentally figure the amount of effort needed to complete the engagement.

"Fifty dollars for all four and only one at a time," she said curtly. "The rest of you will have to leave until it's your turn. I won't work in front of an audience." Then she sat on the bed and asked who was going to be first.

So it cost us another couple of bucks, I thought. She's probably worth it.

"No problem about privacy," said Stump. "We have the room next door for the, uh, action."

"Fine," she said, looking at her watch. "I'm afraid I don't have a lot of time, gentlemen. I have another appointment in less than an hour. Like I said, who's first?"

Stump looked around. "My idea, guys. I should get the honors."

Pete looked at the rest of us, we nodded, and he pointed to the door. "Be our guest, Stump, but don't take all day."

Stump led the lady to the door. She followed him out, briefcase in hand, as if they were on their way to a sales meeting. Derrick and I sat on the bed. I tried to hide my anxiety by thumbing through magazines like I did at the dentist's office. Pete, who had been with a hooker or two, dropped in an easy chair and closed his eyes.

Twenty minutes later Stump walked in rubbing his lips with his handkerchief. "She's terrific!" he said grinning from ear-to-ear.

Pete was next. We expected a long wait, but in no more than 10 minutes, he was back in the room. "I told you I was near the redline," he said frowning. "I might as well have been in the back seat of my Ford on prom night. I hardly started and it was over." He dropped on the bed like a rag doll, his pressurized system apparently relieved.

I motioned for Derrick to go ahead. I guess I wanted to put this off as long as possible. Trouble was, the longer I put it off the more anxious I became.

Derrick took a lot of time, and time was running out. When he returned his face expressed pure delight. "She's all yours, Fitz." He plopped on the bed next to Pete. As I opened the door Derrick sat up on one elbow and added, "You're gonna like her. She reminds me of a girl in my old neighborhood in the Bronx." He fell back on the bed, still smiling.

Walking out the door I thought briefly about the girls in my old neighborhood. Two houses down were the six nuns from the new Catholic Church—enough said about them. A Hispanic family lived across the street and their well-endowed daughter cracked me with her geography book every time I peeked at her cleavage. Then there was the Polish girl who would nuzzle up close and blow in my ear. When I tried to touch her breasts she smacked me on the side of the head and told me I was behaving like an animal. A school chum who was a self-proclaimed expert on sex said he read about girls like her. "When girls tease you, then turn mean-spirited like that, their system's overdeveloped and they're going through puberty and menopause at the same time."

As far as I was concerned, the girl servicing my fellow NavCads didn't resemble any of my neighbors. I stopped at the door, knocked, and walked in. She was leaning against the headboard wearing a sheer negligee. Rhino reacted immediately and I shoved my hands in my pockets to camouflage my condition.

"Better hurry up, honey. Times a wast'n," she said, patting the bed.

I fumbled with the buttons on my shirt and unzipped my pants.

"My, my," she cooed. "You are ready, aren't you." I felt my face redden. Considering the activity in my loins I wondered how there could be enough blood above my waist to make me blush.

Sitting on the edge of the bed I kicked off my shoes and lowered my trousers over my ankles. While I finished undressing she eased her negligee from her shoulders. When it rested teasingly on the tips of her breasts I leaned forward thinking, San Carlos fantasy, here I come!

RRRRRRRRINNNNGGG. My eyeballs focused on the small alarm clock hopping across the nightstand. Pushing me back with one hand, she reached over and pushed the "off" button.

"I'm so sorry, honey, but we've run out of time. This is my lunch hour and I only have a few minutes to make my other appointment before I have to be back at work." She glanced at her watch. "I really have to hurry."

She pulled her negligee straps over her shoulders and swung her legs onto the carpet. I felt like I'd been awakened before I could consummate a wet dream.

I tried begging. "Please, lady, this isn't fair!"

She turned away to step into her panties and garter belt. "I have standards," she said over her shoulder. "If I can't do it right I don't do it at all."

"That's OK," I pleaded. "Standards aren't a problem. I really don't mind a rush job. Five minutes, two minutes—I need your services real bad."

She grabbed her hose. "Like I said, I have another appointment before the end of my lunch hour. And he's a regular, so I can't disappoint him."

"Lunch hour? What do you do, anyway? I mean, I thought this is what you do." She laughed while she snapped her nylons to her garter belt.

"I only do this part-time to pay for school. I'm a business trainee." She stepped into her skirt and pulled it up her slender legs.

"Can I call you sometime, maybe later this afternoon?"

"Are you kidding? I'm not about to give you the number where

I work. All I need is for my boss to take the call. If you need my travel services, just tell Chilton, the bell captain," she said straightening her seams, her skirt hunched up around her hips.

Watching her dress was torture. "Can't you call this guy, or maybe the office and tell them you're sick or something."

She stepped forward and gently touched my cheek. "I'm sorry, really I am. Maybe some other time. Here's your twelve-fifty back."

When she laid the money on the bed and backed away I grabbed my trousers and slid them up over my ankles.

"Try me next weekend," she said, opening her briefcase. "I should be free on Sunday." She grabbed make up and a comb, and walked to the bathroom.

"But who should I ask for?" I yelled through the door.

"Tell Chilton you want Joy. It's my working name."

Well, I wanted Joy today and I didn't get it or her, I said to myself. But acknowledging defeat I finished dressing, picked up my $12.50 from the bed, and left. Walking to the next room with my chin on my chest, I was convinced that when I left Pensacola I would be the only NavCad who hadn't been laid in the San Carlos Hotel. "This is what you get," I mumbled, "for being fourth in line for a business trainee moonlighting as a hooker on her lunch hour."

When I told the guys what happened Pete tried to console me by revealing how he once had a performance problem. "Don't worry," he said, patting my shoulder, "you'll get it up next time."

I started to argue, but figured what's the use. First, the hooker left me in total frustration, then I lost the respect of my peers. What a lousy afternoon.

As we started down the stairs toward the lobby I caught a glimpse of our moonlighter in her neat business suit, briefcase in hand, knocking on the door of a room across the mezzanine. When the door opened my disappointment turned to anger. Will Rumford stepped aside to let her through the threshold.

"Dammit!" I mumbled. "Of all the people, he has to be her regular."

"What's the problem?" asked Pete.

"Just cursing my luck," I said watching the door close. Someday, somehow, I promised myself, I will realize my fantasy in the San Carlos Hotel, but it definitely would not be with Miss Joy, the two-faced, moonlighting hooker. Her body had been forever tainted by Will Rumford.

* * *

A few days later I was in the hangar nibbling French fries at the snack bar when I spotted Charles Haley loaded down with two hamburgers and a milk shake. Charles and I had exchanged pleasantries now and then and I pointed to an empty seat at my table.

"How's the flying going?" I asked when he sat down.

"Your instructor cut you much slack, Fitz?"

"Not a lot. He's patient and a good teacher, but if you mean does Axton go easy on me, the answer's, no."

"I got a flight instructor who treats me like a kid in elementary school, except he can't bring himself to call me by my name. 'OK, son,' he says. 'Now this control stick is like a lever. A lever gives you mechanical advantage. Y'all know what that means, don't you, son?'

"Fitz, I spent two years at Indiana State studying engineering and I do know a little about simple machines. 'Well, this lever is connected to the aile-rons,' he says, pointing to the wings, 'and the ele-va-tor,' he says while pointing to the tail. 'Now the stick is what y'all use to fly the airplane. Y'all understand that, son? Now, I know this all sounds difficult, but I have faith you'll overcome your upbringing and learn all this.' By the time we get airborne I feel like I'm gonna explode."

Lt. Miller was either ridiculously thorough or so ingrained with prejudice he was convinced Haley had the brains of a five year old. I bet on the latter.

"Do you think he's *trying* to humiliate you?" I asked.

"Did he humiliate me? Hell, yes, he did. On purpose? Probably not. He's a typical southern liberal. Unlike bayou rednecks who reek with malice, southern gentlemen like Miller ooze patronizing Christian tolerance." Haley dropped his burger, leaned back, and sighed. "I really do love flying, once he lets me have the controls. But I don't think I've ever made a landing without him riding the stick and the rudder pedals to touchdown. I guess he believes if he gives the controls to a colored boy he'll never make it home alive, sure as if it's an unwritten law of motion."

"Try to hang on, OK? I know you've got a thick skin," I said with a half smile. "I never made a mark on you in that Pre-Flight smoker."

Haley frowned. "Believe me, this black skin is no thicker than yours." But his frown quickly faded. "In fact, my nose still smarts from when you tagged it in that smoker in Pre-Flight." We both laughed and finished our lunch talking about what airplanes we'd like to fly in the fleet.

* * *

On one of my dual B Stage (precision) flights Axton told me to enter the landing pattern at NOLF Baghdad for some practice crosswind landings. I made a standard entry and when we completed our second touch and go, I recognized Dufo's voice on the radio. Because he was flying solo, the crash crew felt obligated to warn him about the stiff crosswind on the duty runway.

"No problem," answered Dufo.

While proceeding downwind I watched his approach. The touchdown went well, but after a few feet of roll the crosswind caught his left wing and he swerved onto the grass along the right side of the runway. He regained directional control, swerved back to the runway, and became airborne. No harm would have been done if his wing tip had not clipped the crash crew's outhouse and knocked it over—with it occupied. Lt. Axton told me to orbit overhead until they cleaned up the mess along side the runway. We watched the crash crew roll the outhouse over so they could open the door and let the sailor out, pants still bunched around his ankles. Poor Dufo, I thought. What is he gonna pull next?

On the way home Axton took the controls and without warning, rolled the SNJ upside down and pulled it through an inverted half loop called the split-S. Up to that point I had never been in any high-g maneuvers. The result of the unexpected 4-g pullout was inevitable. Blood pooled in my lower extremities and I blacked out.

When g forces subsided, allowing blood to return to my oxygen-starved brain, I was in a semi-conscious state of disorientation. Thinking I was tumbling end-over-end through space, I clawed at the canopy in an uncoordinated effort to bail out. Recognizing the symptoms, Axton spoke calmly on the intercom, assuring me everything was OK. Within seconds I regained my senses and was left with a horrendous headache and acute nausea. All the way back to Whiting Field I fought to hold in my lunch. Still feeling queasy when I killed the engine it took me a little longer than usual to crawl out of my cockpit. Lt. Axton waited on the tarmac, a naughty twist in the corner of his mouth. I didn't smile back. I felt so bad that if he had held up a DOR form I would have signed it on the spot.

"Sorry you blacked out on that split-S," he said. "Feeling better?"

His breath attacked my nose and I drew back, my nausea returning in full force. Although I wanted to puke my guts all over his squatty little body, I fought off the urge and managed a weak smile.

"Better," I lied. After we tucked our parachutes under our left arms he patted me on the shoulder and we walked back to the hangar.

"Look, Fitzgerald," he said in a fatherly tone. "Forget about your stomach for a minute. We start aerobatics next week and I wanted to teach you an important lesson. You may think that was a lousy trick back there, but sometimes the lousier the trick, the better the lesson's learned."

I figured I'd remember this one for a hell of a long time.

"When you're gonna pull g's, tighten your gut, scrunch down in your seat, and grunt like you're passing a watermelon. That helps stop your blood from pooling below your torso." He stopped, squatted over the tarmac, and in a strained, staccato voice said, "If . . . you grunt . . . like this . . . you'll be fine."

Two cadets on their way out to their airplanes stopped to watch what looked like a flight instructor trying to take a crap on the parking ramp. Red-faced, Axton straightened up and waved. The gawkers looked at each other and continued toward their aircraft.

"Remember," he said, "if you don't tighten up you'll do what you did today—go out like a blown fuse. Worse, you might not recover in time to pull out of your maneuver." He patted me on the back again and we quickly walked to the hangar for our formal debrief.

Lt. Axton's lesson helped me enjoy aerobatics, not that I found all of the maneuvers easy or comfortable. The slow roll was a case in point. Coordinating rudder and elevator while slowly rolling along the aircraft's longitudinal axis was a challenge. I had a habit of scooping out of the roll, allowing the nose to drop 300-500 feet during a maneuver that was supposed to be performed without losing altitude. After Axton coached me through 10 or 15 slow rolls my scoop diminished to less than 50 feet, certainly not perfect, but for me a major accomplishment.

The Immelmann turn was another tough one. It's a dogfighting maneuver developed by Max Immelmann, a German ace in WWI. It begins as a loop, but the aircraft rolls upright on top resulting in a 180-degree turn in a vertical plane. On top the airspeed diminishes to near stall. When I tried to roll the aircraft, my long legs got in the way of the stick causing such a sloppy rollout we often fell off the top, occasionally in a spin. Lt. Axton kept after me, coaching, prodding, and encouraging, while praising the least improvement. Finally I learned to coordinate stick and rudder for an acceptable rollout in spite of my gangly legs.

While debriefing after a bad aerobatics flight I grumbled about how difficult the maneuvers were. Axton reminded me that loops, Immelmann turns, barrel rolls, wingovers, chandelles, split-S's, and even slow rolls, either in whole or in part, were used during air-to-air combat.

"For God's sake, Fitzgerald, will you grow up and stop your whining? This is kid's stuff. If you want to be a fighter pilot, you have to be better at aerobatics than your enemy or he'll blow you out of the sky like he was shootin' skeet at the county fair. Now, either learn how to do these maneuvers well or set your sights on flying blimps, seaplanes, or helicopters."

From that time on whenever I did a maneuver I imagined myself engaged with a Russian MiG-15, my aerobatic skills determining whether I would win or lose the dogfight. It helped me get thorough C Stage, but at night I lay awake, hoping my life would never depend on how well I performed an Immelmann turn.

* * *

While coasting through the last flight of C Stage, Axton told me to land at Pace Field. He wanted me to see an airplane that crashed the day before. Entering the landing pattern I saw the mangled remains of a large aircraft on the east end of the field. Several men in white coveralls were taking measurements as others poked around the wreckage. We landed and taxied near the accident site, remaining well clear of the red tape surrounding the blackened hulk that was once a formidable weapons system of the US Navy.

"What is that, sir, some kind of WWII airplane?"

"That used to be an AD Skyraider, the best close air support aircraft ever invented. I'll take the controls so you can get a better look."

When I felt him grab the stick I moved my hands to the canopy rails. The name, Skyraider, was familiar. Ah, yes, I remembered. The fatal crash at NAS Grosse Ile the day I took my tests to enter the NavCad program.

"That's the biggest prop plane I've ever seen," I said staring at the huge, twisted propeller. All four of its seven-foot blades were curled around the engine cowling. Each wing pushed back against the fuselage was bigger than both of ours put together.

"She can carry over 12,000 pounds of ordnance, twice the load the four engine B-17 Flying Fortress carried on her legendary missions to Berlin," said Axton while maneuvering the SNJ around the wreckage. "I saw them work in Korea. There wasn't a soldier or Marine who didn't cheer when he saw a flight of AD's arrive to give him air support."

While he talked I peered at the cockpit. The mangled seat was exposed, its torn, sponge rubber padding covered with dark, crusty stains. A lump rose in my throat. "How about the pilot, sir, did he make it?"

"Nope. When he ran his tanks dry over Brewton he tried a dead stick landing here at Pace, stalled, spun in, and bought the farm. He misjudged badly all the way around. The AD's a powerful machine, but she won't run on empty and she doesn't forgive mistakes at low altitude."

"So I've heard," I said.

"I wanted you to see the consequences of poor fuel management, Fitzgerald. Avgas isn't made out of elastic. It just-plain-won't-stretch! Get an eyeful and don't ever forget it. OK, she's yours. Let's go home." I grasped the stick, shook it, and taxied to the takeoff spot.

While climbing out of Pace Field I glanced over my shoulder for one more look. The once proud Skyraider was now a pile of rubble in a shallow crater. The image of the blood-soaked backrest remained with me well after we landed back at Whiting Field, as did Axton's comment about the possible consequences if I was ever tempted to "stretch" my fuel.

* * *

My confidence soaring, I was convinced I would pass my aerobatics check with ease and be on my way to Saufley Field in a few days. Feeling good about my progress, I sat down and wrote another letter to Ryan. I hoped that with primary flight training behind me, Ryan would finally admit that my skills were probably good enough to get me my gold wings.

> Dear Ryan, Your twerpy relative has finished primary and will soon be on his way to formation and night flying. Oh, I forgot to tell you that Will Rumford's here. The guy's turned into a real pain in the butt. He's always slinging insults and telling me to drop out—much like you do. Last week I saw what was left of a dive-bomber after the pilot tried to stretch 500 gallons of avgas into 525 gallons. He bought the farm trying to dead stick his aircraft into a grass field. Pretty ugly mess. I know better than to ask you if you ever ran out of gas. I just can't see you making a mistake like that. Hope all is well at the radio station. Get ready to eat crow. I'm moving on up with the big boys and I see gold wings in my future. In fact, as I write this letter I'm massaging the wings on the old squadron patch you gave me 10 years ago. So far it's been a great good luck charm. Bye for now. Your aerobatic cousin, Tommy

Chapter 8

On March 9th, I passed my aerobatics check, packed my bags, and boarded the shuttle bus for NAAS Saufley Field, a few miles north of Pensacola. At Saufley we would learn formation and night flying, plus cross country navigation. So far I had been instructed never to fly within 2000 feet horizontally or 1000 feet vertically from any other aircraft. I must now learn to fly in groups of two, four, even six airplanes. The confidence I brought with me from Primary was waning fast.

When our bus arrived at the gate I looked up at a six-plane echelon approaching the runway for landing. They appeared close enough for the pilots to reach out and touch fingertips. How, I wondered, can they fly that close without running into each other? I tried to tell myself that like my first landing and first solo, this indomitable hurdle would soon be behind me. But it didn't work. I was scared to death.

The command was divided into flights of six students and one instructor. The training office assigned me to the flight led by LCDR Tony Herbert, a stocky, red faced fighter pilot with a cigar stub protruding through a roguish grin. His bulbous nose had more squiggly red and blue lines than a road map. A Corsair pilot who left active duty after WWII and flew in the ready reserves, Herbert was recalled for the Korean War. When the stalemate halted in a truce three years later he decided to stay in the Navy for a 20-year retirement. He had a ribald sense of humor and a relaxed way of instructing. It appeared I had lucked out with another Lt. Axton. I was starting to feel better. It didn't last long.

When Herbert introduced me to the other students in his flight I was dismayed to discover that Will Rumford was one of them. I massaged my shoulders remembering the pain and humiliation I endured on the wrestling mats at Whiting Field. When we shook hands my knuckles cracked under his anaconda squeeze.

"I must admit I'm surprised you're here, Fitz-*gerald.* Never thought you'd make it this far."

"With you as my inspiration, how could I fail?" I said smiling.

"Cute. Well, let me know when you want another wrestling lesson." He turned his massive back and resumed his conversation with another NavCad. Two days later Herbert sat in my back seat and taught me how to fly two-plane formation. The NavCad in the other SNJ was my Pre-Flight roommate, Vince Fabrizio. When airborne I watched carefully as Herbert demonstrated how to use reference points on the lead aircraft to get the proper angle for a tight parade position. Flying slightly stepped down, Herbert lined up the lead aircraft's tail wheel with the left wing tip, then inched closer and closer—while I held onto my seat, convinced we would collide—until we were 25 feet canopy-to-canopy. While maneuvering a few feet back and forth and in and out, Herbert explained relative motion—action between two moving bodies—and how to control it with coordinated adjustments of the stick, rudder pedals, and throttle. Then he backed off a few feet and let me have the controls. At first I felt his hands lightly on the stick following my every move. After he was assured I would not chop off half of Vince's wing with my prop, the stick and rudder pedals were all mine.

When I proved I could fly a loose parade position we tried cross-unders, moving from Vince's right wing to his left wing while flying in close formation. Then it was Vince's turn, his instructor waving his hands in the back seat like he was directing an orchestra. While he struggled to stay on my wobbly wing Herbert reminded me the importance of flying a good lead.

"Fitzgerald, it's like pulling a trailer. You always have to be aware that you're not alone. Every movement of your controls, every power change or change in configuration, impacts your wingman."

The next day we practiced free cruise where the wingman uses maneuvering instead of throttle adjustments to stay with the leader. When Vince banked left I moved to the inside of his turn to keep my proper nose-to-tail distance. If I started to ease too far forward I moved to the outside of his turn until I drifted back to my proper position. When Herbert was satisfied that I had the idea we switched leads and Vince gave it a try.

That same day we learned formation rendezvous. The rendezvous was a little tricky since it required us to control relative motion from long distances, mostly by varying our bank angle as we approached on the inside of the leader's rendezvous turn. On my first attempt I zoomed in so fast I was forced to duck under Vince's aircraft to avoid a collision. I came in much slower on the next try and learned new meaning to the saying, "slow and steady wins the race."

That afternoon the mail included an answer from Ryan. Expecting praise for finishing primary, my heart sank as I read his letter.

> Dear Tommy, So you got through primary. Don't get too excited. That's merely the crawling part. Formation is where you stand up and learn to walk, trot; then run like hell. When you fall down, you get hurt real bad. Ask an instructor how many cadets were killed in aircraft accidents so far this year. I bet most of them bought it in formation flying. It's definitely not for guys who freeze on the controls. Remember the Aeronca? Like you said, kid, you're in with the big boys now. Don't tempt fate. Toss in the towel and come home. As far as Will goes, the two of us talked about the Air Force and Navy cadet programs a while back so I'm not surprised he's there. He's a good stick and should do fine. Now there's a guy who really could become a fighter pilot. I haven't seen him for a year so if he's a pain in the butt like you say, I have no idea what brought it on. Knowing how you goaded him when you were kids, I suspect you're the problem, not him. For

> the umpteenth time, come home. Your frustrated cousin, Ryan P.S. You might as well toss my old patch in the trash barrel. You're gonna need more than a good luck charm to get you through flight training.

I read the letter over a dozen times, frustrated with his stubborn lack of respect for my accomplishments. OK, so he respects Will's ability a lot more than mine. Well, screw them both. I placed the letter in the file with the others. Ryan was going to eat a lot of paper if God saw fit to get me through this adventure in one piece. As for Ryan's patch? I reached in my pocket and rubbed it gently. "Go to hell, Ryan," I mumbled. "My faded cloth talisman isn't going anywhere."

* * *

After three flights Herbert put Will, Vince, Stump, and me up for our two-plane formation check rides. Because second opinions were required for phase evaluations, another instructor rode in our back seats and decided whether we were ready, or not ready, to fly solo in formation. Vince flew with Stump and I flew with Will. Lucky me, I thought, when I saw his name on the schedule along side mine.

Will's check pilot was Lt. Barlow, the Saufley Safety Officer, and I drew Captain Eberhardt, a macho Marine from another flight. He had a reputation as a "screamer," an instructor who considers shock and humiliation the ultimate teaching tools. After hearing all the horror stories about Eberhardt, I was surprised to see things start out well. His briefing was routine and as we walked out to our assigned aircraft he told me this was a milk run and I shouldn't be the least bit nervous. Relieved, I wondered how all those nasty rumors about this amiable instructor ever got started.

Everything was going smoothly until we joined up with Will and his instructor over the Cantonment paper mill. As I closed on our initial rendezvous the milk run turned into a nightmare. My

304-UPCH

headset exploded as Eberhardt screamed I was too fast, too slow, too close, too far, too everything, punctuating each complaint with an obscenity and a smack on the control stick. While crossing under Will's tail to switch wing positions Eberhardt smacked the stick so hard it flew out of my hand, causing my left wing to miss Will's horizontal stabilizer by mere inches.

"What a shitty—*smack*—cross under," he screamed. "If this is a safe for solo formation check I'll kiss your ass—*smack*! Hell, you can't even hold onto the friggin' stick—*smack*! You're the worst friggin'—*smack*—pilot I ever flew with, Fitzgerald. Who in the hell taught you to fly, anyway, the friggin' Keystone Kops? *smack-smack*."

My ears throbbed from the verbal thunder crashing through my headset. In 15 minutes my hands shook, sweat stung my eyes, and my cramping bowels threatened to disgorge my last three meals all in one gut-wrenching spasm. The only respite was when it was Will's turn to fly on my wing. But then I had to listen to Eberhardt laud Will's performance as though he were another Chuck Yeager.

"Now, why can't you fly like Rumford, Fitzgerald? See how smooth he is? He's not jerking around like a friggin' Mexican jumping bean the way you did. Hell, if you flew half as good as your wingman you'd be a friggin' ace." When I started one of the required turns he went ballistic, even though I made a shallow and smooth entry.

"Hold this damn aircraft steady, you idiot!"

He grabbed the stick and took control while Will moved in and out of our radius of turn using free cruise to maneuver. I had to admit Will was flying a good wing position. Eberhardt continued to berate my performance.

"See how nice he uses free cruise and does those cross-unders? Why in the hell did I have to get stuck with the only spastic retard at Saufley?"

Being accustomed to the relaxed teaching styles of Axton and Herbert, the shock of this madman's methods about did me under. Ryan was right. I was flying with the big boys and was failing miserably. Whatever confidence I had built up over the last few weeks melted away in one hour.

On the way back to Saufley, Eberhardt's raving tapered off to a few sarcastic remarks and an occasional kick of a rudder pedal. Mercifully, when we broke over the runway for landing it ceased all together. From the tongue thrashing I took throughout the flight I was positive he was writing up my first down chit as we taxied into the parking area. When I lowered my drained body onto the tarmac I was stunned to see Eberhardt smiling broadly, his left fist motioning a thumbs up, and his right arm extended for a congratulatory handshake.

"Damn good job, Fitzgerald. The air was rough today, but you hung in there in fine shape." I cautiously accepted his hand and shook it weakly.

"No need to debrief," he said with the wave of his arm. "I'll tell Herb you got a solid 'up.' See ya around, kid." He strutted toward the other instructor who was debriefing Will on the way in to the hangar.

I coldly stared at Eberhardt. He probably hadn't the slightest idea how much I detested him, not that he would have cared. Did he think he was obligated to give us some sort of stress test? Or did the guy have some kind of split personality? To cap off my day, when we returned to our cubicle Will rode me about my performance on his wing.

"You almost clipped my tail on one of your shaky cross-unders, Fitz-*gerald*, and your rendezvous would have been mid-airs if I hadn't been on my toes." Will leaned forward and punched my chest with his index finger. "You're really dangerous, you know that? It's not just *your* neck hanging out there anymore; you could take one of us to the farm with you. Why don't you DOR before you kill somebody?"

I was in no mood for his insults. "Will, what in the hell's your problem? Every time I turn around you're crawling on my back."

"I told you long ago, Fitzgerald, you *don't* belong here. Get out before you kill yourself—not that it would be any loss."

That night self-doubt invaded my soul and I figured it was time for another letter to my doubting cousin. He might like this one.

> Dear Ryan, Maybe you were right. I had my first formation check ride today. My check pilot screamed the entire flight, claiming I was a Dilbert—you know, a klutz. Will, who was my wingman, said I almost rammed him on my cross-unders and rendezvous, but he always says I stink. Funny thing was, when we landed the check pilot said I did fine and gave me an "up." Now I don't know what to think. I may not be Jimmy Doolittle, but I don't need to be treated like a punching bag, I know that much. If I have another flight like that one I think I'll follow your advice and give it all up. At least you and Will would be happy. Your dejected cousin, Tomm

* * *

When we began to fly solo in sections (two airplanes) and divisions (four airplanes) Herbert prodded us to fly tighter wing positions by calling us pussies, the ultimate insult to any aviator. When we were told to pick a name for our flight it was only fitting that we chose "Herb's Perverted Pussies."

Dufo Hartwood was a pretty fair artist and painted a logo to hang above our briefing table. It was the rear view of a scrawny, bat-winged tomcat leering over his shoulder while exposing a red and very bald rear end. We thought it was an appropriate piece of work by the guy whose vapors from his own rectal aperture had become notorious within the corps of NavCads.

The logo lasted only one day before the training officer, LCDR Percy Hathaway—called Percy the Pussy by Herbert and many NavCads—paid us a visit. He looked at Dufo's artwork and told Herbert to get rid of the poster. "You're gonna have to choose another name," he ordered. "Get one that's more acceptable to mixed company."

"What mixed company?" argued Herbert. "There's never a female within a hundred yards of this hangar."

"Captains and admirals are the same as mixed company," responded LCDR Hathaway with a deep sigh. "Sorry, Tony, your sign has to come down."

After much pleading, Hathaway reluctantly allowed us to keep the name, as long as we didn't display the unregenerate cartoon above our briefing table. Herbert waved his hand mockingly at the Flight Training Officer. "Percy, only a pussy wouldn't allow these guys to display what you know damn well is the cleverest logo in this entire command." The straight-laced LCDR Percy Hathaway, USN, shook his head in disgust and walked away.

On my first solo formation flight Herbert paired me with an officer student pilot, Ensign Blake Hampton. He was a "ring knocker," a member of a select group of inflexible careerists fresh from the Naval Academy. Although most Academy graduates were decent guys, we heard that the most pretentious knocked on an underclassman's door with their huge, blue-crowned Academy rings instead of rapping with their knuckles like normal human beings. In fact, Hampton was so proud of his ring he rolled the crown underneath when he went palms up and rolled it to the outside when he went palms down. I surmised that he did this to ensure we would never forget the enshrined, nautical womb from whence he came.

While Herbert briefed us for our formation flight, Hampton repeatedly turned to me as if he were my interpreter—or I were a simpleton—and explained Herbert's remarks in minute detail.

"OK, Fitz," said Herbert while moving both hands through the air, "you'll move into free cruise like this and. . . . "

"What the Lieutenant Commander means," interrupted Hampton while turning in my direction, "is that you take a thirty-degree bearing on me, your leader, adjust to a distance of twenty-five feet, nose to tail. . . . " and blah, blah, blah.

After several interruptions Herbert had enough. He stood up, put one foot on his chair and leaned forward on his knee. "Ensign Hampton," he said chomping on his cigar so hard that juice ran out the corner of his mouth, "even though Fitzgerald and I are not Academy graduates, believe it or not, I can speak the King's English and he can understand it. Now shut the hell up!"

While I silently cheered, Hampton stared at Herbert considering, no doubt, whether he should accept this rebuke from a drooling, cigar chomping, non-Academy, reserve officer, or set him straight. Discretion won out and he was silent for the remainder of the briefing.

During the flight Herbert had us switch leads several times so we could both practice rendezvous, tight parade, and free cruise positions. Hampton had the lead when the period ended. Herbert took up a position a few plane lengths behind us and told Hampton to head back to Saufley. He instructed Hampton to fly to the initial point for the traffic pattern, call the tower, and take us to the active runway for landing. Then he said something he regretted.

"Hampton, just ignore me back here and lead us home as if you were on your own. And Fitzgerald, don't be a pussy. Hang in there nice and tight and show the tower what Herb's students are made of."

On the way home I was lagging a little, struggling to keep the relative motion between our two aircraft at a minimum. Herb told me I was flying parade like a three-legged, pregnant pussy chasing a yo-yo, and to close it up. I lined up Hampton's tail wheel on his left wing tip, cautiously inched forward, and hugged his fuselage like an extra coat of paint. Wanting to look good over the airfield, I ignored everything in my peripheral vision, keeping my eyes glued on Ensign Hampton as though he were leading me to Valhalla. He almost did.

Ensign Hampton, who was as tense leading as I was flying his wing, hit the initial point fine and while peering straight ahead, signaled with his hand to switch to the tower frequency. Afraid of losing my tight position while switching hands on the control stick, I figured I could wait and make the frequency change after we separated over the active runway.

Somehow Hampton became confused. After the tower gave him the active runway—the one being used for take-offs and landings—he flew right on past and lined up on an inactive runway running 90 degrees to airfield traffic. That put us dangerously out of phase with the landing and departing aircraft.

Meanwhile the control tower and Herbert frantically radioed Hampton to abort his approach and reenter the pattern. Hampton, with his academy-trained, mission-oriented brain, was concentrating on leading us down the center of the runway—albeit the wrong one—and failed to heed the urgent calls on the radio. Herbert flew along side and waved at Hampton to get his attention. Following his original instructions to the letter, Hampton kept his eyes straight ahead, ignoring Herbert's signals as well as the mayhem we were causing over the airfield.

Hampton broke off over the off-duty runway and I took a trail position behind him. Busy dodging all the aircraft seemingly flying erratically around us, I still had not changed my radio to tower frequency. When I finally switched to the tower after touchdown, I heard the operators screaming for everyone to stay clear of some screwed-up student pilots messing up the landing pattern. "Wow, are those guys in trouble," I mumbled.

When I narrowly missed an aircraft lifting off the runway to my right and had to jam throttle to avoid one landing to my left I called the tower and told them that I nearly collided with the two airplanes using the wrong landing pattern. When they heard my identification they told me stay off the air and proceed to my parking spot immediately. "I was only trying to help," I mumbled.

I followed my stalwart leader onto the ramp and was surprised to see Lt. Barlow pacing back and forth in our parking area. Two spaces down the line, Herbert climbed out of his aircraft and slammed his kneeboard on the concrete, sending cards, maps, and pencils scattering in all directions. He stormed over to Ensign

Hampton and gave the Naval Academy graduate such a butt chewing he probably thought he was back in his plebe year at Annapolis. The ensign, being such a proud, rigid, and polished kind of guy, was devastated.

While we waited for Herbert to finish with Hampton, Barlow explained how we had caused three or four near midair collisions plus two near misses on the runway. "You guys are in a heap of trouble."

I hoped I was considered the lesser offender since I was the wingman. On the other hand, I had to admit I was culpable since I had not changed to the tower frequency at the initial point. Then again, I rationalized, even if I heard the tower's call, I don't know how I could have convinced the hard nose Ensign to change runways, when he wasn't even paying attention to his instructor. Regardless, I was convinced that this would be where my flying ends and the paint chipping begins. Ryan and Will were right after all.

Lt. Barlow waited for Herbert and Hampton to join us and then we all walked to the Training Office. Waiting at the door was Percy the Pussy Hathaway, only he was now Percy the Tiger with flared nostrils snorting unrestrained fury. The five of us climbed the stairs to the privacy of the safety office where I figured we would be canned from the program. I had grown to love flying and wanted more than anything to be a naval aviator. Now it was all over except for being stripped of my solo bar, drummed down the flight line, and shoved out the main gate.

Herbert ordered us to sit at a table while they conferred in the opposite corner of the room to decide our fate. Whatever was going on, it was Herbert and Barlow against Percy the Pussy. Hathaway kept shaking his head while Barlow and Herbert argued their point with animated passion. Suddenly Hathaway tired of their consolidated attack, threw up his hands, and yelled, "All right, all right, do it!" and stomped out of the office.

Do what, I wondered? SPEEDY board? Firing squad? Court martial? Come on and get this over with. I watched Herbert shake

Barlow's hand, like they were proud of ending our flying careers. Then Herbert stared at each of us, shook his head sadly and departed, quietly closing the door behind him. "Here it comes," I mumbled.

Lt. Barlow took two notepads from his cabinet. I began to mentally formulate my official statement, the first step toward a dismissal from the flight program. He dropped the pads and two pencils on the table in front of us.

"Start writing," he said coldly.

Hampton and I looked at each other. "Our official statements?" we asked.

"No. You will write a one thousand word essay on why it's dangerous to land on the wrong runway of a busy airfield and how you're going to assure us that you will never do something so stupid again!"

Ensign Hampton narrowed his eyes. "Then what happens?" he said, probably expecting as I did, that this was merely the first phase of our punishment.

"Then Herb and I read them to determine whether you've learned your lesson," said Barlow with a half smile. "If you write a hell of a lot better than you fly, you're home free . . . this time. You better thank your lucky stars, guardian angels, or whatever, that you have Herbert for your instructor. Anyone else and you guys would be on your way out to the front gate, bags in hand." Silently, I thanked my guardian angel for Lt. Barlow as well. It had obviously been a team effort to save our hides.

Although obviously relieved, the pompous Ensign's face turned deep red. The reserve officer he had shown so little respect earlier had just saved his career. On the other hand, here he was an honor graduate of the US Naval Academy, writing a punishment essay like a fourth grader caught shooting spitballs. Hampton blew out a sigh, slumped in his chair, and started writing. I lowered my pencil and began composing my opus on aviation safety. "It is unwise to land on the wrong runway because. . . . "

When I returned to our cubicle an hour later, a gloating Will

Rumford was munching on an apple. On the blackboard was a cartoon depicting two Texans flying opposite to the Saufley Field landing pattern oblivious to airplanes falling out of the sky around them. Hangar scuttlebutt travels fast.

"You're back?" Will said while wiping apple juice off his grinning lips. "This time I thought you were a goner for sure. Must be luck of the Irish, eh, Fitz-*gerald*? Sure as hell couldn't be your skill. Anybody so dumb he lets a ring knocker lead him around by the nose should be cleaning out heads on garbage scows, don't you think?" Will took another bite of his apple.

"Rumford, your mouth resembles an overflowing commode more every day, you know that?"

"Just trying to speed along the inevitable," he said, spitting an apple seed at my feet. "After all, what are old friends for?"

"Go to hell," I said pushing past his bulky frame.

A letter from Ryan topped off my lousy day.

> Dear Tommy, So you had a check pilot who's on an ego trip. Grow up, kid. Guys like that are in every flight school and every squadron. Next time you see him, take a look at his wristwatch. I'll bet you it's big and showy. It's a common oddity among boastful fighter pilots and screaming flight instructors—the size of their wristwatch is inversely proportional to the size of their genitals. In other words, big mouth and big watch—little wiener. Aside from that, if you can't take a little stress now, what would you do in combat? It all proves what I've said all along. You're in way over your head. The next time Will tries to get you to DOR, do it. He's only acting in your best interests. Drop out now and come home sitting upright in a Pullman instead of lying prone in a casket crammed in a dark corner of the baggage car. Your Aunt Connie wrings her hands every time I mention one of your goof-ups. Pa just shakes his head. I haven't talked to your folks lately, but Ma says they're as scared for your

welfare as we are. Please come home, Tommy. Your
pleading cousin, Ryan

Now Ryan, Aunt Connie, Uncle Trevor, and maybe even my own mom and dad were convinced I was going to kill myself. They were worried, so what? That didn't excuse their pleas for me to quit. None of them were quitters. Why did they think I should be one? "Oh, God," I prayed out loud, "please let me succeed at just this one thing, so I can prove them all wrong."

* * *

Friday afternoon Herbert invited all the Pussies to join him at the O Club for happy hour. With the exception of Hampton, who was still sulking about our screw-up over the airfield, our entire flight sat at a long table near the bar and shared several pitchers of beer. A group of flight instructors we knew to be former fighter pilots gathered around a piano and sang a serenade to their less aggressive colleagues.

Oh, there are no fighter pilots down in hell,
The devil couldn't catch them when they fell,
He caught all Three Musketeers, transport pilots, bombardiers,
But there are no fighter pilots down in hell.

After the first verse Herbert invited us to join in. We were in the middle of a rousing chorus when an ensign jumped on the bar and reached for the ship's bell hanging above the cash register. When he grabbed the lanyard an ear shattering CLANG stopped the singing in mid-verse. Every head turned toward the door and stared at a red-faced, Marine second lieutenant standing in the threshold, sweeping his cap from his head as if he were pawing at a pesky fly. Everyone cheered.

"Too late, jarhead, pay up!" yelled the ensign holding the lanyard. He leaped off the bar and received pats on the back for spotting the covered officer who forgot the platinum rule observed by every US Navy and Marine Corps Officers' Club around the world. Herbert got our attention and pointed to the engraved plaque under the ship's bell. Vince Fabrizio went to the bar and read the two sacred lines for the benefit of his fellow cadets:

HE WHO ENTERS COVERED HERE;
BUYS FOR ALL, A ROUND OF CHEER.

I took a quick head count. There had to be at least 50 officers and cadets present. Wow! That's a tab over $20, I thought. I pitied that hapless second lieutenant emptying his wallet on the bar, but welcomed the free beer anyway. The alert ensign who rang the bell was a tall, thin New Yorker named Ted MacKenzie.

* * *

I soon discovered that Eberhardt was not the only instructor cadets hated to see in their rear cockpit or chasing their flight. There was "Lead Thumb" Howland, so named because he gave a thumbs down to more cadets than all the other instructors combined. Howland verbally chewed up his students and spit them out before pinning the down chit on their chest. I made it my mission to never be in the same air or hangar space with Lead Thumb Howland.

Conversely, there was Nervous Nellie Baxter. Basically a decent guy, LCDR Nelson Baxter kept his cool until something happened to make him think he might not return to Saufley in one piece. An example was when he had to dodge his two solo students during a practice rendezvous to avoid getting wing tips rammed into his fuselage. Shaking like a leaf, he stopped the flight and brought his students home for a very long lecture on aviation safety. He didn't give them downs, but made them repeat the flight, calling it an incomplete. Neither student made that mistake again.

When a cadet in his front seat almost hit his leader during a cross-under, Nellie grabbed the stick, moved out a safe distance, and radioed the other instructor to stand by for a few minutes. After his nerves settled down, Nellie broke away and put the cadet through continuous loops, rolls, and Cuban eights until he puked all over the front cockpit. "Be more careful up there . . . and I won't do this back here," he said while rejoining with the other Texan. The rest of the flight was uneventful.

The instructors loved to ride Nervous Nellie about his short fuse and he retaliated with practical jokes whenever he had the opportunity. One day Herbert—Nellie's greatest antagonist—was helping a cadet perform his preflight. Nellie snuck up and put a huge pile of dog crap in Herbert's cockpit. LCDR Herbert was furious, but had to admire Nervous Nellie's audacity. At one time or another LCDR Nelson Baxter had caught half the instructors in similar pranks around the hangar or in the O Club.

One morning as I sat down for my brief, Herbert told me my hop with him had been canceled. He had volunteered me to fly as a last minute replacement in another flight. The instructor was Nervous Nellie Baxter.

"I don't understand, sir, why me?" I asked.

Herbert nodded toward a table across the hangar. "Seems one of Nellie's students got the screaming runs this morning. Rumford reminded me you were up for your six-plane check, so you're it. Now get going."

I was fuming. Will Rumford was one block ahead of me in the syllabus, yet he fixed it so I'd fly with Nervous Nellie Baxter instead of him. Oh, well, I thought. LCDR Baxter's OK, as long as I don't do anything really stupid.

"You'll do fine," said Herbert, noting my apprehension. "You'll like flying with Baxter. Go have a good time and don't ask any more questions."

I hurried across the hangar toward Baxter's cubicle to join the other five students in the flight.

"Are you Fitzgerald?" he asked when I arrived.

"Yes, sir," I replied.

"Herbert says you're pretty good. I noticed you bounce when you walk, though. Bouncing makes me nervous . . . can be dangerous in the air," he said, shaking his head. "You don't do that in the air, do you, Fitzgerald?"

"No, sir. That is, I don't bounce, sir." That was Dufo's habit, not mine.

"We'll see. OK, let's get started." After a detailed brief including the exact order of our maneuvers, he told us he ran overtime, so we had to hurry and get to our airplanes. He'd meet us at our rendezvous point, the Styx River Bridge, in fifteen minutes.

We ran to the loft and with our parachutes slung under our arms, hustled lopsided to the flight line. I spotted Nervous Nellie near the hangar door already climbing into his SNJ. By the time I reached my assigned aircraft he was starting his engine. Damn, I said to myself. I'll be late getting to the rendezvous point. I hope that doesn't set him off.

As I climbed on the wing, a hand grabbed my shoulder. I jerked around angrily. I didn't have time for fun and games.

"What in the—Commander Herbert! What's going on, sir?"

"Go back to the hangar, Fitzgerald. I'm taking your aircraft." As he climbed in the cockpit he kept his eyes on Baxter taxiing toward the take-off spot.

"But, sir, what aircraft do I take?"

"Go check in the hangar," he said, waving me away from the aircraft. "See ya later." He hit the starter and as I jumped on the tarmac the Texan's engine roared to life.

Now that I had to switch airplanes, there was no question I wouldn't make it to the rendezvous point on time. Then I noticed the same thing had happened to all of the cadets in Baxter's flight. Angry at being hijacked, we joined up and hurried back to the hangar for new aircraft assignments. Something crazy had to be going on, but we hadn't any idea what it was.

As we walked through the hangar doors Will pulled us aside and revealed how LCDR Herbert had organized the greatest aviation prank of all time. "Come on, we can listen to the whole thing," he said pointing to the crowd gathered around the base radio near the training office.

"I can hardly wait," said Dufo leaning over the radio, rubbing his hands. "He's finally gonna get his just desserts."

On a check flight, Baxter told Dufo he was getting a down because he didn't know how to perform a formation criss-cross. It was a joke, of course, but Dufo took him seriously and he pulled out all the books, trying to find out how to do the criss-cross maneuver. Another time he told Dufo to get some prop wash in the maintenance office and clean his propeller during his preflight. Dufo spent all morning looking for a bucket of prop wash—actually the wind created by a rotating propeller, not a cleaning solution. A sailor tuned the radio to Baxter's assigned frequency and we waited for the games to begin.

The six flight instructors flew to the rendezvous point, all arriving late on purpose. Baxter castigated his six "cadets" about the importance of punctuality before beginning the sequence covered in the briefing.

Then it started. For an hour the six instructors treated Baxter like the runt of the litter. They closed him in the center of a seven-plane formation, squeezed him in what Herbert later called a "turd sandwich"; then broke away in opposite directions leaving him temporarily without students. When he was able to round them up he told them to form a right echelon and try some carrier break-ups and rendezvous. Airplanes scattered in five directions. Eventually they rejoined in a left echelon and when Baxter told the leader to make his breakaway to the right, the leader broke left into his wingmen.

When he finally formed them in a column behind him, he broke off left and told the "students" to join on him in a carrier rendezvous. The join-up resembled a string of linebackers blitzing a quarterback. Baxter had to bounce up, down, and sideways to avoid being rammed by each seemingly out of control aircraft. When he had them together they argued over the air as to who should be in front.

"Ah got it," said Herbert in a phony, low-pitched drawl. He left his number six position and leap-frogged over the formation to the number one spot. The frolicking instructors screamed their objections in confused, cadet-like voices.

"No, lemme have it. You had it last time," cried Barlow, diving under Herbert and assuming the lead.

"No, no, it's my turn," shrieked Major Slocum. "You guys never let me be first." He rolled up and over the group to the lead position.

Enough was enough. LCDR Nelson Baxter turned into Nervous Nellie.

"You demented Dilberts are gonna get me killed! We're going home, end this chaotic nightmare, and have a long session on aviation safety."

Having more fun than they anticipated, his "students" ignored his order to join-up and continued to work over the frustrated flight instructor. When they gathered in some semblance of a formation, the leader, Major Pop Slocum, slowly reduced throttle. One at a time, all six SNJ's stalled and spun out of the flight.

For the entire hour the hysterical Nervous Nellie Baxter flew in the middle of his rampaging "students" trying to herd them home. He finally gave up and headed toward Saufley by himself, hoping his covey of hellions would follow like Mary's little lambs. Instead, they dived and rolled around him, like a swarm of Sopwith Camels chasing a lonely Fokker back to its Prussian aerodrome. When Baxter had his gaggle in the vicinity of Saufley Field he begged the control tower to help him get his "demented Dilberts" on the ground. The tower operators, in on the caper, told him he was on his own.

The mischievous instructors turned the landing phase into culminating chaos. When they made their approaches the runway watch, another of Herbert's confederates, fired warning flares at Baxter who had his wheels down, instead of at the instructors who had their wheels up, while making low passes over the wrong runways. On their final pass his "demented Dilberts" put their wheels down at the last instant, all landing on separate runways. Meeting at the runways' intersection, they weaved around each other like Dodgem Cars in an amusement park.

When they met at the flight line LCDR Baxter, still unaware of what had transpired, radioed his "Dilberts" to park their aircraft and report to the training office. "You will be lined up at attention when I arrive," he yelled, "and unless you are all suffering from carbon monoxide poisoning, you are in great danger of being dropped from flight training." Then he parked his aircraft at the end of the flight line and stomped into the hangar to wreak havoc among his six maniacal cadets.

The six instructors, still giddy from their hour of frolic, were lined up at attention as ordered when Baxter arrived. When he discovered the identity of his "Dilberts" and saw the guffawing sailors, NavCads, and instructors gathering around him, he knew he'd been had. His face changed from turnip purple to cherry red and while laughing raucously, shook the hand of each instructor. When he got to Herbert, he punched him playfully. "You got me this time, Tony, but you better keep checking your six o'clock because one of these days. . . . "

To my knowledge Nellie Baxter was never able to pull anything on Herbert equal to his nerve-racking flight with the "demented Dilberts." Later, I heard that Nervous Nellie Baxter soon became known as Calm and Cool Baxter, the instructor who could have the wackiest cadet in flight training and not get the least bit flustered. After all, no cadet could begin to scare him like the six "demented Dilberts." Herbert, on the other hand, was so busy watching his behind for Nellie's reprisal, he became a nervous wreck, himself.

* * *

Following a string of accidents throughout the training command, two of them fatal, the Perverted Pussies sat around a table at the Saufley ACRAC and talked about what we would do if we faced an airborne crisis such as an imminent midair collision or a raging fire in the cockpit. Stump Fowler, a devout Roman Catholic, had no doubts about how he would react.

"If I had even the slightest warning," he said soberly, "I would spend those precious seconds reciting a Hail Mary and asking for absolution."

"You have to be kidding," scoffed Will. "How could you have the time or the presence of mind to say a prayer while you're frantically working in the cockpit to save your tail."

"Well, I believe a prayer is what would save my tail, as you put it," he said, setting his jaw firmly. "I have no doubts about my faith—or my priorities."

"We're not questioning your faith," Vince chimed in, "but remember the old saying: 'God helps those who help themselves.' I'd rethink those priorities."

The following Friday we walked into happy hour threading our way through a maze of hands maneuvering over tables, their owners acting out their past week's harrowing experiences. Credibility of the stories varied with the number of beers consumed. We found a table and after the waitress brought us a frothy pitcher of Spearman's Ale, we began sharing our successes and failures over the past five days. Stump leaned forward and raised his voice to be heard over the hum of conversations, the jukebox, and the clink of beer mugs.

"Guys, I have a confession to make."

"About what?" I said. We lowered our mugs, expecting to hear he lost his virginity or caught VD.

"Remember last week when I talked about what I would do if I was about to buy the farm?"

Will wiped his mouth with his fist. "Yeah, you'd whip out the beads and do a Hail Mary," he said with a chuckle. "So what?"

"Last night I had my first night solo. After my second takeoff I was marveling how Pensacola's lighted streets were like strands of a dew covered spider web. You know what I mean?"

I nodded impatiently, wishing he would dispense with the

poetry and get back to the subject. "We get the picture," I said. "So what happened?"

"Suddenly out of this twinkling kaleidoscope comes the flashing wing lights of another SNJ. He's heading right at me. I mean, I could've reached out and touched his cockpit. Man, I thought for sure I was about to have my first midair collision."

"What do you mean, 'first midair'?" gibed Vince. "With midairs there's only one to a customer. You're too dead to enjoy a second." We nodded agreement.

"Did you crank off a Hail Mary?" Will asked with a smirk.

Stump looked at us sheepishly. "Truthfully, all I could think to say was. . . . " he stared at his beer mug. "Well, the first thing that came out of my mouth was . . . well, it was. . . . "

"C'mon, out with it," snapped Will.

Stump looked down at his beer shamefully and mumbled, "Oh, shit!"

Eyes narrowing, we looked at each other then back at Stump. "Say again?" I asked, not sure I caught him right.

He looked up, scanned our doubting faces and said, "I hardly ever swear, but all I could think of was, 'Oh shit!' Then I rammed the stick forward and closed my eyes. When I opened them the other SNJ was gone and I was still flying." He stared at the table and lowered his voice. "It's amazing. I didn't pray, recite a Hail Mary, or anything. All I said was, 'Oh, shit,' yet, I'm still alive." His face was contorted with agonizing guilt, but I was confident the Almighty wouldn't hold this against him. Looking up he said quietly, "Guys, I think maybe I've got a guardian angel. I'm not sure, but it could be my father."

"Oh, come on," said Will waving away Stump's assertion.

"Pilot's do have them, you know," I said.

"Not you, too," said Will.

"Yep. Remember what Ryan said about deceased pilots becoming sort of guardians of us mortal pilots? I think one saved Ryan and me from getting killed that day he took us up in his Aeronca."

Will shook his head. "Took *you* up, you mean. You screwed up his airplane so bad I didn't get my ride, remember?"

"OK, but you got your ride later and a lot more after that. The point is that Ryan acted as though he believed they existed."

"That was only talk," said Will. "He was trying to ease your fear so you wouldn't chicken out."

"Will's the duty cynic," I said. "I like my cousin's idea, that they could be former pilots flying around the sky trying to keep guys like us from killing ourselves." I scooted my chair forward. "Think about it. We fly . . . they fly. They have wings . . . we're earning our wings. When we're up there we enter their domain where those guys can keep an eye on us. It makes sense."

"Guys? My priest said there's no girl or guy angels—just angels," said Stump.

"Not if they're former pilots, like your father," said Dufo, shaking his head. "They definitely have to be guys."

"But there's girl pilots, too," I said. "Amelia Earhart, for example."

"Well, she can look after the females," said Dufo, "I want mine to be a guy. Besides, we're talking about military pilots, not civilians."

Will grabbed his beer. "I can't believe what I'm hearing. If you guys need protectors, fine, but I'll do OK on my own." He took a long swallow and belched.

Stump raised his finger. "Word of caution. My priest said that guardian angels—wherever they come from—have something called a region of influence, sort of a safety zone. If you end up outside that zone by doing something reckless or stupid, they can't help you."

"Well, I'm not ashamed to say I need one," I said. "Like you found out last night, Stump, sometimes things happen you can't control."

"I'm in," said Dufo. "I need all the help I can get."

Will stared at Stump. "What I don't understand, Fowler, is

where in the hell was God's little messenger when your old man bought the farm in Korea?"

"My dad flew into a barrage of anti-aircraft fire. His wingman told my mom that it was like flying through a fireworks finale on the fourth of July. A whole army of angels couldn't have saved him." Stump took a swig of his beer. "But I remember Dad telling me how he escaped lots of close calls during training flights, as though someone had been looking out for him. I like to believe my dad's watching over me, now."

"Let's hope he does a better job with you than the one did watching over him," grunted Will.

"I respect your beliefs, Stump," said Vince with a shrug. "It's just that I'm not much on religion."

"You may respect those beliefs a lot more after your first MiG engagement," I said. "Remember the old saying: 'You don't find many atheists in foxholes.'"

We did agree on one thing. We were willing to accept help from anywhere we could get it. All except Will, of course. He didn't need anybody.

"Here's to our guardian angels," said Dufo, waving his mug around the table. "May they be with us when it counts the most."

"Here, here!" we toasted in unison. "To the angels!"

Surprised to hear Vince's voice chiming in with the rest of us, I leaned over and whispered. "I thought you were a skeptic."

"Just in case I'm wrong," he said flashing the gap between his teeth. "Besides, I like the part about when we buy the farm we get to fly around like a bird for eternity. Now, that's what I call paradise."

Will drained his mug and banged it on the table. "You guys are all nuts. I got better things to do." He wiped his mouth and left.

Whether we had guardian angels protecting us or not, Stump found out something we would all learn sooner or later. When you are beating off the snakes in the cockpit, nothing else has a higher priority, even a Hail Mary. By the time we left the ACRAC everyone except Vince had come up with a name for his angel. Vince said if he needed one he would borrow mine.

That night I decided to bring Ryan up to date.

> Dear Ryan, Things are going better so I've decided not to DOR—at least not yet. You were right about the accidents in formation flying, but so far (knock on wood) not yours truly. By the way, were you serious when you mentioned that pilots have guardian angels? And that maybe they're former pilots that bought the farm? A bunch of us were talking about it the other day after one of the guys had a close call. Following your lead, I declared my belief in a heavenly protector. I've called him Gabriel. I hope mine will watch after me as well as yours has watched over you. I have a six-plane formation check and basic night flying remaining at Saufley. Barin is next. There we get gunnery, bombing, and the big C-Q! That's carrier qualifications. Wish me luck. Still hanging on with all ten fingers . . . Your formation-flying cousin, Tommy.

* * *

LCDR Herbert needed an extra guardian angel just to protect him from Dufo. While Herbert was briefing a six-plane formation flight, Dufo began tapping one foot and rubbing his hands together. When sweat poured from his forehead and he began tapping on the table with his pencil, we all knew what was coming—except Herbert, that is. Until now, Herbert had been spared Dufo's problem with flatulence.

Annoyed at Dufo's fidgeting, Herbert told him to knock it off. Dufo stopped tapping, but his stomach gurgled like a Maytag washer with a light load. We shuddered, knowing this was going to be the greatest challenge our intrepid instructor's nose had ever encountered. When the gurgling in Dufo's lower bowel changed to a loud rumble, Herbert looked at him sympathetically and said he should not have skipped lunch. Knowing lunch was not the problem, we clenched our nostrils and braced for the inevitable.

Herbert was explaining how a six-plane formation is composed of three, two-plane sections when he was interrupted by what sounded like a rupture in the Goodyear Blimp. While Dufo's face turned a vivid shade of scarlet, a putrescent cloud crept from under the table and crawled up Herbert's torso. When it reached his face he grabbed his nose and gagged.

"G-good Lord," stammered Herbert while holding his nose in a futile attempt to salvage his sinuses. He closed his eyes trying to protect them from toxic rot, then opened them slightly and rested them on Dufo sitting by himself on one side of the table.

"Hartwood, you stay here," wheezed Herbert. "The rest of you guys, save yourselves!" We jumped up as one and raced out the nearest hangar door, never coming close to catching our fleet-footed instructor.

The same week we briefed for our first night flight. The lights in the hangar were dim and we wore red goggles to preserve our night vision. After the brief, Herbert picked up his helmet and said he was going to the head. Dufo decided he would also take the opportunity to relieve his nervous bladder. The head was dark, but with dim, red lighting so we could take off our goggles while using the facilities.

When Dufo walked in he started to remove his goggles then decided to leave them on and be doubly protected. Barely able to make out the shadows of two people using urinals on the far wall, he made his way to what looked like a vacant urinal to their left. Unbeknownst to Dufo, the shadow on his right was Herbert, chatting with another instructor about the rain clouds building up over the Gulf of Mexico. Towering over his shorter instructor who had his left hand on his waist and his helmet dangling from his elbow, Dufo commenced to relieve himself.

When Herbert heard splattering, he looked to his left and saw a stream of urine pouring into his flight helmet. Peering through the dim light he recognized Dufo, who assumed, of course, that his penis was pointed at a vacant urinal, not at a critical piece of his instructor's flight equipment.

"Hartwood! What in the hell are you doing?"

"Oh, hello, sir. Just taking a nervous pee. Do you really think we're in for a downpour?"

LCDR Herbert didn't answer. He just stared at his dripping, foul smelling flight helmet.

* * *

A few days later I received a call from Raoul, my French roommate at Whiting Field. He was on his way back to his native country. It seemed that Raoul had crashed his last Texan. This time he stalled on a landing approach. He was in the process of recovering when he ran out of airspace and plowed into a field a quarter-mile short of the runway. When the crash crew arrived Raoul was sitting on the squashed nose of the Texan reading a sex novel and smoking a cigarette while pools of aviation gasoline poured from the wings of the stricken aircraft.

"Enough," cried the Admiral, after noting that this was Raoul's fifth SPEEDY Board. Raoul said he was very sorry to leave his lady friend with the "teets thirty-seex and the Pleemooth-feefty four." On the other hand, he was looking forward to returning home to Marseilles, France. He planned to team up with another French cadet who had washed out and start a charter flying service.

* * *

Naval aviators flew all kinds of machines, from jet fighter and prop attack aircraft off carriers, to seaplanes, multi-engine transports and patrol aircraft, even helicopters and dirigibles. If I was a Marine Corps aviator, however, I would be limited to jet fighter/attack or propeller attack, with a remote possibility of multi-engine transports or helicopters. According to the latest scuttlebutt, at the time I expected to finish training the Navy would have a shortage of pilots to fly the large seaplanes and maybe—God forbid—dirigibles. I knew NavCads could request a commission in the Marine Corps rather than the Navy. One reason I had not taken this option earlier, however, was that Will Rumford had been accepted for the Marine program when he was back at Whiting. I wanted as much distance between us as possible.

My last week at Saufley I read a summary of assignments for the new pilots graduating from the Advanced Training Command and broke out in a cold sweat. The rumor was true. If I didn't act soon I could easily end up in lumbering seaplanes or dirigibles where the closest thing to aerobatics was a little turbulence on a four-day flight over the Atlantic Ocean. Will Rumford, or no Will Rumford; it was time to apply for a commission in the Marine Corps.

A week after submitting my application I reported to the Marine Corps Selection Board composed of five Marine flight instructors. I was intimidated the moment I walked in the room. The senior member began the questioning.

"Cadet Fitzgerald, the Marine Corps is not for everyone. You will always be expected to put the Corps first—certainly above yourself and often before your family. Are you prepared to do that?"

"Yes, sir," I said sitting ramrod in my chair. "The Corps will be my life."

A corporal entered the room and dropped a note in front of the major. He read it, frowned, and passed it to the other four members. After reading the note their faces scowled at me like I was Satan, himself.

"Cadet Fitzgerald," said the major, "we've been informed that back at Whiting you had a questionable record."

"Sir?" I asked, puzzled. "I completed Primary right on schedule and without any downs."

"According to our information," he said holding up the note, "you almost washed out at Whiting—couldn't land the SNJ. And here at Saufley you landed on the wrong runway resulting in several near misses over the airfield. It almost got your wingman, a respected Naval Academy graduate, busted from the program."

I wondered who could have been feeding them this information. Surely not Axton or Herbert. They wouldn't stoop so low as to pass on such garbage.

"One more thing, Cadet," he continued. "We understand a Marine candidate suggested a wrestling match to help get you in shape. You accepted, but instead of using all of your resources to pursue victory, you offered no resistance, allowing your body to be used as a dummy for relentless pummeling. That's hardly the Marine Corps way."

Now I understood. It was that rat, Will Rumford. I denied the first two charges, respectfully asking the Board to contact my flight instructors if they doubted my word. "As far as the wrestling match," I said, "my opponent was an experienced wrestler and built like a gorilla. I fought to the best of my ability even though I was hopelessly outclassed. I don't deny losing, but I strongly object to the charge that I didn't try to win."

"Very well, Cadet. We'll postpone our judgment about your flying ability until we can check out these anonymous allegations." After a short consultation with his fellow Board members he added, "We'll accept your version of the wrestling match since there's no way this charge can be substantiated."

Axton and Herbert must have backed me up because the next afternoon I found a note on the schedules board informing me that my application had been approved. While showering that night my USN tattoo stood out like the scarlet letter on Hester Prynne's breast. No more tank tops during workouts, I decided. From now on this aberration on my upper arm is my own business. As far as Will's attempt to torpedo my chances to go Marine, I decided to let it pass. He failed and that was all that mattered.

Because the OIC's of the cadet barracks were Marine Corps captains, a disproportionate share of Marine candidates were promoted to cadet officers. Less than a week after being approved by the Board I mysteriously gained leadership ability and instead of small anchors on my collar tips, I now sported two gold bars, the insignia of a cadet lieutenant. My perks for taking muster at company formations and keeping a few records were better liberty hours and admittance to the officers' dining area with real silver and cloth napkins. This was my first experience with RHIP—rank has its privileges.

After passing my six-plane formation check flight I was packing my belongings for the bus trip to Barin Field when my roommate tossed me a letter that arrived in the afternoon mail. It was from Ryan.

> Dear Tommy, I'm surprised you've made it through formation and night flying unscathed. But as you said in your letter, the next hurdle is the biggest and most dangerous of all—aircraft carrier landings. I'm scared for you, Tommy. You're blood kin. I can't bear the thought of seeing your mom and dad weeping over your mangled body, or whatever's left after the sharks get done feasting off your remains. In regards to guardian angels, a squadron of dead fighter pilots or even the mighty Gabriel won't be able to save you from crashing into the back end of one those boats while it's bouncing around like a cork in a baby's bath water. Anyway, you may be out of luck. I have it on the best authority that any guardian angels worth their salt turn down assignments to protect Navy pilots. Too much work trying to keep those crazy bastards out of harm's way. It's not too late to save yourself, Tommy. Come home NOW! Your early "mourning" cousin, Ryan

Chapter 9

NAAS Barin Field was 20 miles west of Pensacola near the sleepy little farming town of Foley, Alabama. I was excited about the prospect of using the SNJ for a weapons platform and accomplishing the feat that separated us from Air Force pilots: landing on and taking off from an aircraft carrier. Before starting gunnery, the training office assigned us to a week on the skeet range. The Navy considered skeet shooting an excellent method for teaching us how to lead a target. Thanks to some rifle competition in college ROTC, I learned the knack of picking off clay pigeons quickly and found it great fun.

The day I finished the skeet range I ran into Will Rumford in the Barin ACRAC. Being a Marine candidate he was also a cadet officer, but instead of two bars on each collar tip, he wore three—cadet captain. He was nursing a beer while playing the pinball machine. Tired of avoiding confrontations with the egotistical blockhead I approached the pinball machine and braced for his usual barrage of insults. After he pulled the plunger to shoot the third steel missile up the slot he squeezed in a few push-ups against the machine before taking his first swat with the flippers.

"Geez, Will, should you be doing all that exercising? You might use up all your allotted heartbeats."

"I'm really touched by that concern, Fitz-*gerald*," he said after puffing out a long exhale, "but more concerned that you've been accepted as a Marine candidate. When I heard the news, frankly, I almost had heart stroke." He shoved the machine so hard I checked the scoreboard to see if the TILT sign had illuminated.

"I'm sure you were surprised," I said bitterly, "after you tried to sabotage my chances with the board."

"What are you babbling about now, Fitz-*gerald*?"

"Don't play the innocent lamb. Someone called the board and passed along a bunch of crap about my flying and how you pulverized me on the mats back at Whiting. Funny how your name was the first to enter my mind."

"You're nuts," he said calmly. "I'm not the only guy who wants you out of here." Will interrupted his play long enough to turn and give me his hateful stare. "What are you complaining about, anyway? They took you in, didn't they? Quit whining and grow up, for God's sake." He punctuated his command with a snap of the plunger sending another steel sphere up the chute. Will exaggerated working the flippers as though each press was a 50-pound twist on a torque wrench.

"You know, Fitzgerald, if you're gonna be a Marine, you have to tone up or you'll embarrass the rest of us." He glanced down at his chest and grinned. "My girl back at the University of Louisville's gonna melt when she pins those gold wings on these steely pecs."

"I know you're really tough, Will, but that might hurt. Better let her pin them on your uniform, instead," I said tapping his chest. He was right. Even through his shirt, it felt like I was tapping a bowling ball.

He pulled away as if my hand were contaminated. "Very funny." As I turned to depart, he said, "You manage to hit anything on the skeet range? Seems you couldn't hit a barn door when we were kids . . . " he paused to chuckle, " . . . except with the tractor, that is." Will pulled the plunger and guided the fourth ball through the maze of bumpers, gates, and buttons. The pinball machine clunked and chimed like he had hit the jackpot.

"Little Willy Rumford has an excellent memory," I said over the din, "but I've done a little shooting since then. I dinged every one of my clay pigeons. They told me I wouldn't have any problem leading the target sleeve."

When the ball dropped through the final gate he looked at me and sneered. "Get serious, city boy. When you shoot at the sleeve you won't be using a twelve gauge shotgun with a three-foot pattern of buckshot." He held his thumb and forefinger in front of my nose. "That thirty caliber machine gun fires one little bullet behind the other, and from a hell of a lot farther away." He pulled the plunger on the final ball and shifted his concentration to his game.

At the mess hall that evening I loaded my tray with chicken legs, milk, and turnip greens and looked for a place to sit. The only empty space was at a table with three other cadet officers, one of whom was Will. I nodded a greeting, sat down, and pulling a vial from the condiment tray, dumped a generous amount of vinegar on my greens. Realizing I had forgotten my dinner rolls, I excused myself. When I returned I detected a few snickers, but figured Will had been busy entertaining our dinner partners with tales of our childhood. I grabbed my milk and took a healthy slug.

"*Ugh*!" I cried, banging my half empty glass on the table. The milk was disgustingly sour.

Will looked up straight-faced and innocent. "Gee, what's wrong, Fitzgerald? Milk a little tainted? Funny, mine's OK. How about you guys?" The two cadet officers sported nervous smiles and nodded their heads in agreement.

"It's not tainted, it's full of vinegar and it's obvious where it came from, you stupid jerk." Waves of quiet spread over the cadet mess hall like ripples on a pond.

Will froze and stared at me coldly. "Better watch your mouth, Fitzgerald. I outrank you and I don't take very well to insults."

"Then knock off the cheap tricks," I replied, "and act your age as well as your cheesy rank."

"Maybe we better forget the 'cheesy rank' and step outside where we can settle this like men," he said laying his napkin on the table. He scooted his chair back and stood up.

Well, I thought, the showdown has finally arrived. I pushed my chair backward, but as I stood I felt a hand grip my shoulder like a vise. Captain Brannigan, our Marine Corps OIC, once the leading heavyweight boxer at the Naval Academy, stood between us, his other hand clamped on Will's neck. He was the only guy I'd met who made Will look puny.

"Seems we have a disagreement here," he said calmly. "I don't like to see Marine candidates having disagreements. Sets a bad example." I fought off a moan as his finger tips dug around my collarbone. He pulled us closer and spoke slowly.

"I like them (*squeeze*) . . . to save their energy (*squeeze*) . . . for the gunnery range, CQ, and especially for killing commies. Am I clear?" (one more, big *squeeeeeze*) When Will nodded through a grimace, the captain turned his head toward me.

"Y-yes, sir," I grunted, trying not to betray my agony. "Clear . . . as a bell."

"Fine." Captain Brannigan released us, gave each of us an affectionate pat on the back, and walked back to his table.

As he sat down, Will rubbed the back of his neck and whispered, "Count your blessings, nose wart."

The hum of conversation slowly returned to the mess hall, but Will and I finished our meals in silence. That night I lay awake in my bunk wondering how long it would be before we settled this rivalry, or whatever it was, behind some darkened hangar.

* * *

Captain Brannigan was right. Gunnery took a lot of energy. But it was much more exciting than anything we had done so far. Once over the Gulf we lined up in a right echelon 1000 feet abeam and above the tow aircraft flown by our instructor, LCDR Davis. The sleeve trailed 100 feet behind and, because of the cable's weight, 25 feet below his aircraft. We rolled off our perch in a tight, descending left turn, reversed, and closed on the sleeve, taking an appropriate lead through the glowing web of our gun sights. Within a prescribed range and dive angle we fired a short burst of tracer ammunition—made visible by its fiery trail—from our 30-caliber machine gun, synchronized to shoot harmlessly through the propeller—most of the time. It was important to release the trigger before our angle off the sleeve closed to the point where the bullets endangered the tow plane, or more specifically, Davis's unprotected backside.

We were cautioned about target fixation, a phenomenon where the pilot is so intent on getting good hits that he flies into the sleeve, a potentially fatal collision for the cadet and the pilot in the tow plane. After breaking off our run we dove under the sleeve and climbed up and over the tow plane, sliding in the rear of the echelon to wait our turn for another go. When we flew 50 miles over the Gulf, Davis reversed course and we resumed our firing runs from the opposite side of the tow plane.

The Navy used a simple method to determine gunnery scores. The SNJ's in each flight were loaded with different colored ammunition. When a bullet passed through the sleeve, a little of the paint stayed behind. After the flight the tow plane dropped the sleeve on the airfield. The ordnance department tallied the red holes, blue holes, etc., and checked the number of rounds fired from the SNJ loaded with that color ammunition. Then they placed the percentage on a scorecard. Twenty hits out of 200 rounds fired equaled 10 percent.

Instructors encouraged us to share our results, the idea being that competition was a good motivator. I was never proud of my tally but managed to meet the percentage milestones. Bombing, however, was another story. I enjoyed tossing a miniature bomb at a target at a prescribed speed, release altitude, and dive angle and finished with decent scores. The same with strafing. One of the NavCads in our flight was Beau Thomason. Beau had the best gunnery scores at Barin, shooting well over 40 percent on every flight. Considering his limited experience and the antiquated equipment, that was an impressive accomplishment.

Not all gunnery went smoothly. On one very hazy day we waited patiently in the hangar while the Training Officer agonized over whether he should cancel the gunnery flights, launch later when the haze cleared, or launch now, hoping it would clear by the time the flights reached the Gulf. After some deliberation he decided the weather was marginal, but not bad enough to get behind in the training cycle. "Launch Aircraft!" blared from the hangar's loudspeakers. We hurried to the flight line and climbed into our cockpits, anxious to get our gun sight on the sleeve.

While strapping into our aircraft we were not aware that another flight a few minutes ahead of us mistakenly took the same track as ours. To make matters worse, the other instructor elected to take his flight far out in the Gulf where he thought visibility might improve. About the time LCDR Davis told us to commence firing on our southbound track, the other flight had reversed course to the north and begun their inbound firing runs. As a result, two planes towing target sleeves and twelve trigger-happy cadets converged on the same milky airspace over the Gulf of Mexico at a closing rate of close to 300 miles an hour.

Unaware another flight was boring in toward us I lined up on the sleeve with the best angle and range I had all morning. For a frozen moment I imagined Will Rumford in my gunfight. As I increased the pressure on the trigger orange tracers streaked by my canopy and a yellow SNJ coming from the opposite direction filled my windscreen. Under eyes as big as dinner plates, a NavCad's pale lips flapped the message, "Please, d-don't shoot!"

"CEASE FIRE, CEASE FIRE, EVERYBODY CEASE FIRE!" Both instructors screamed frantically over the radio, trying to prevent a tragedy.

Jolted back to reality, I relaxed my trigger finger and the horror stricken cadet disappeared under my port wing. Seconds later his flight's tow plane, cable, and sleeve swept under my starboard wing. It was over. The instructors terminated gunnery practice and took a quick head count. Miraculously, no one was missing.

Walking from my Texan to the hangar I began trembling when I reflected on how perilously close I had come to being shot down—as well as shooting down my first aircraft. That frightening moment gave me a preview of what it was like to be a fighter pilot in combat, a vision that kept me in a cold sweat that entire night.

Later that week we were in the code room trying to learn sending and receiving Morse code by key and blinker. The petty officer in charge announced that Captain Brannigan wanted to see all Marine candidates at 1600 for an important announcement.

"The Corps is starting a new program to man its influx of rotary winged aircraft," said the captain while passing out a bulletin. "If you opt for helicopters right now, advanced fixed wing training will not be required. Instead, after completing CQ you will go directly to NAAS Ellyson Field and start helicopter training."

The offer had two significant advantages. We would be exempt from the dreaded instrument syllabus known to wash out scores of cadets in advanced training. In addition, we would earn our wings and commission two or three months earlier than if we continued fixed wing training. Both were strong inducements to go helicopter. Several accepted, but I was not one of them. If I was going to finish this endeavor it would be as a jet fighter pilot, not driving a clattering mass of moving parts through space. After this announcement, however, I began to worry about where my career as a Marine Corps aviator would take me. I might be assigned to helicopters after graduation, whether I wanted them or not. Maybe I should reconsider this thing about a Marine commission, I thought. I put off the decision until after qualifying aboard the aircraft carrier.

The CQ phase commenced with a demonstration flight at an outlying airfield. The landing pattern altitude for field carrier landing practice (FCLP) was only 200 feet and our airspeed a few knots above the stall. Within those parameters there was no room for mistakes. Therefore, at least one flight with an instructor pilot was in order before we were allowed to begin FCLP on our own.

On a muggy day in June, six of us climbed into the front cockpit of our airplanes with our instructors sitting in the rear cockpit, a presence we hadn't experienced for several weeks. We flew to NOLF Bronson Field, about a half-mile east of Perdido Bay, the body of water separating Florida and Alabama. Although students were always required to wear life vests, many instructors wore a Mae West only on gunnery flights. After the instructors demonstrated how to fly the pattern and follow the signals of the Landing Signal Officer they gave us the controls and watched us make a few FCLP's. If all went well they declared us safe and the next day we flew our practice sessions solo with our instructor LSO using fluorescent paddles to wave signals from the end of the runway.

On our first FCLP the Texan ahead of us coughed twice and spit a trail of black smoke. The instructor, LCDR Ferris, calmly announced he had an engine failure and that he would ditch in Perdido Bay. All eyes followed the struggling Texan as Ferris made a perfect water landing from the back seat. While he and his student pilot evacuated the sinking aircraft, the LSO alerted air sea rescue and within 10 minutes an ASR helicopter and seaplane were orbiting the crash site.

The HO3S, a single engine Korean War vintage helicopter, hovered over the two airmen and lowered the horse collar for the pick up. A large wooden ball secured to the cable above the collar provided stabilization and helped keep it afloat. Although Ferris did not have a life preserver, he was a strong swimmer and motioned for the cadet to go up first. The cadet slipped into the collar and was quickly hoisted into the helicopter. The hot, humid air and extra weight placed a heavy load on the underpowered HO3S and it struggled to maintain its hover. The pilot, however, was confident it could handle one more passenger and directed his crew chief to lower the cable for Ferris.

With the soaking wet, 230-pound flight instructor dangling 40 feet above the Bay the old chopper faltered. Afraid he was about to lose control, the pilot ordered the crew chief to cut the cable. The petty officer grabbed the bolt cutters and snipped the cable, sending Ferris plummeting into Perdido Bay. As he entered the water, the wooden ball smacked him squarely on the head. Stunned, but not unconscious, he surfaced, rubbed the bloody knot on his scalp and signaled the helicopter pilot with his extended middle finger that, among other things, he was OK.

The seaplane pilot saw the instructor get clobbered and realizing he had no life preserver, landed his aircraft in Perdido Bay hoping to reach Ferris before he drowned. Unfortunately, as the aircraft water-taxied toward Ferris its outboard wing float ran squarely over his head. The crew watched in horror as, once more, the luckless flight instructor disappeared below the bay's choppy waves. A crewman leaped from the rescue aircraft and swam toward the spot where the struggling Ferris was last seen. Ferris bobbed to the surface, rubbing a second bump on his bleeding scalp.

"Are you all right, sir?" called his would-be rescuer.

Ferris motioned for the sailor to keep his distance. "You guys just go on and I'll swim to the beach on my own."

"But sir, that's almost a mile away. Why don't you come with us?"

Ferris shook his head and again waved his hand for the sailor to stay back. "Son, three Navy aircraft have tried to drown me in the last thirty minutes. I'll take my chances with the sharks and jelly fish."

Ferris started swimming toward the Florida side of Perdido Bay. Twenty-five minutes later he walked up on the beach holding his throbbing head with one hand and massaging jellyfish stings with the other. He climbed into the front of the awaiting ambulance, smiled at the driver, and said, "Corpsman, all I need is a couple of aspirins—one for each lump your buddies gave me back there."

* * *

When we began CQ training Dufo Hartman confided in me that more than anything, he wanted to be a Marine pilot. He submitted his application and reported to the Selection Board for his interview. After the first two questions, sweat rolled down Dufo's forehead and a growl rolled noisily down his lower GI tract. He excused himself and walked out of the building to allow the pocket of flatus to diffuse harmlessly into the atmosphere. The Board members waited patiently and when Dufo returned they resumed the interview. After only a few moments another bubble tickled his colon and again he excused himself, but this one was a little more persistent and a thin trail of vapor followed him out the door. Though only a few cc's escaped, they were enough to singe the nostrils of the Board members. When Dufo returned, a note from the senior officer was on his chair suggesting that Dufo come back in a couple of weeks when he felt better. "In the meantime," wrote the Major, "read over this manual on Marine Corps leadership."

Dufo thumbed through the pages and noted that part of a Marine's creed was to be aggressive. "When confusion or conflicting orders occur," he read, "a good rule to follow is to act in accordance with the last order received. Above all, act. Do not sit and do nothing."

"Hmmm, food for thought," muttered Dufo, walking out the door.

Our instructor LSO for carrier qualification was Major Robert Arnet, an even-tempered, veteran Marine pilot. For carrier landing operations the LSO stood on the stern of the ship; and during FCLPs he stood on the end of the runway where he guided our landings by waving his paddles. It was a very stressful job and we felt fortunate to be under the tutelage of a man as patient as Major Arnet. Patient, yes, but then he never had a student pilot like Dufo Hartwood. It wasn't long before another tale of Dufo's escapades was making its way through the barracks.

We were practicing FCLPs on the east-west runway at NOLF Magnolia, between Foley and Mobile Bay. After making our touch-and-go landings on the simulated flight deck we looked ahead for the last Texan coming downwind, took an appropriate interval, and turned to follow behind for our next approach. To prove his aggressiveness to Major Arnet, Dufo turned downwind too quickly, cutting out Will Rumford and causing him to swerve out of the pattern to avoid a midair collision. Will had his faults, but bad radio discipline wasn't one of them. As I expected, he held his tongue and did a 360-degree turn to regain interval. In the meantime Dufo ended up too close to the aircraft ahead of him. He had to extend his downwind leg beyond the field boundary before turning back toward the runway. Thanks to Dufo, what should have been a tight oval traffic pattern became a line of aircraft scattered from Foley almost to Mobile Bay. His patience on the brink of exhaustion, Major Arnet grabbed his microphone and told Dufo that after his next FCLP he was to continue flying west until he heard the Major's call to start his downwind turn. Dufo acknowledged the order with an appropriate, "Aye, aye, sir."

Following his next FCLP, Dufo continued flying west as ordered. When Major Arnet saw Dufo at a good position to make his turn back to the east he keyed his microphone only to discover that his transmitter had failed. Proceeding with his "last order received," Dufo continued westward skimming over the treetops of southern Alabama at 200 feet, well below the minimum 500 feet above any person or structure and 1000 feet above the highest obstacle in a populated area. Major Arnet, confident that Dufo would soon suspect a radio failure, waited for him to turn around and return to the pattern. But when he disappeared into the afternoon sun Arnet raced to his airplane and radioed us to return to Barin while he flew off in pursuit of Dufo.

Major Arnet frantically chased after his wayward cadet, calling him on all of the channels on his radio. Since he never got the call to turn, Dufo assumed the flight had switched frequencies. He flipped through the radio channels, not staying on one frequency long enough to get a clear message from anyone, let alone the instructor. Without further orders to countermand his last one, Dufo continued westward on his legendary sortie, but couldn't resist taking a few side trips when he saw something interesting.

Skimming the tall pines and magnolias, Dufo curiously watched scores of vacationers scatter in panic from the golf course, pool, and marina at the elegant Grand Hotel on Mobile Bay's eastern shore. While flying over Mobile Bay he buzzed a regatta and his prop wash forced the leading sloop to make an unplanned tack, knocking it out of the race. He triggered the air defense alarm at Brookley Air Force Base south of Mobile and veering southwest, traumatized the floral and avian treasures of the world famous Bellingrath Gardens.

Continuing westward he buzzed the control tower at Keesler Air Force Base near Biloxi, Mississippi, then waved at the cheering maidens and snarling matrons at the exclusive girls' school in Gulfport. When Major Arnet finally caught up to Dufo he found him sitting on the wing of his aircraft at the New Orleans Lakefront Airport. Major Arnet pulled along side Dufo's Texan and shut down his engine. Dufo jumped off his wing, strutted over to his instructor's airplane, and gave the major a snappy salute. Major Arnet saluted back and before he could ask him what he thought he was doing in New Orleans when he was supposed to be practicing carrier landings in Alabama, Dufo made a request.

"Sir, I carried out my last order until I was about to run out of fuel and I would be most grateful if you would mention that fact to the Marine Candidate Selection Board when it meets in July."

"Rest assured," said the incredulous Major Arnet.

* * *

Ten days and 50 FCLPs later our instructor declared us ready to try our luck on the aircraft carrier. On the morning of May 31, 1955 our flight of six nervous cadets took off, rendezvoused on Major Arnet, and turned south toward the Gulf of Mexico. Fred Engle, a hard-nosed Prussian from Illinois, was on the major's wing and would be first in the landing pattern. Dufo Hartwood was next. Then came Bobby "Buff" Brewster, Dufo's bosom buddy from Memphis, Tennessee.

Buff got his nickname from the Brewster Buffalo, a Navy and Marine Corps fighter used in the beginning of WWII. Like the aircraft, Buff was chunky, underpowered, and not much good in a fight. While Dufo was tall and lanky, Buff was short and squatty, sort of like Laurel and Hardy. During the brief Dufo and Buff lay on the deck with their heads resting on their helmets. They were totally relaxed, as if this was no different than a FCLP at Bronson.

Jerry Sipko, a high-strung guy from Peoria, Illinois, was fourth. During the entire briefing he quivered like a bow string and his complexion blended with the milky sky visible through the open hangar doors. I figured Jerry would probably lose his breakfast before he climbed in his cockpit. Will Rumford was fifth. I had to admit that he was the best performer during FCLPs and I expected him to make six landings in six passes. I was last in the formation—tail end Charlie.

Climbing to 3000 feet, we crossed Alabama's white sandy beaches, went "feet wet" over the Gulf, and searched the blue horizon for the telltale wake of the USS *Monterey*. Remembering how I was so impressed with the *Monterey*'s size when I visited her during Indoctrination, I expected to see a huge ship out there somewhere with a flight deck a mile long. Surely this is not the big deal everyone makes it out to be, I rationalized.

When Arnet called the *Monterey* at 12 o'clock low I saw a foamy wake leading up to what appeared to be a small river barge. My glazed donut and black coffee breakfast inched up my gullet. This can't be the ship Tech Sergeant Flanagan showed us that morning, I told myself. She looks Lilliputian compared to the one I saw at the NAS Pensacola pier. My hand tightened on the control stick. Sweat seeped through my leather glove, ran down my forearm, and dribbled in my lap. Feeling the moisture in my crotch, I thought, so what? Before this is over I'll probably wet my pants, anyway.

Major Arnet called the ship's Air Boss for signal Charlie—clearance to enter the landing pattern. When cleared to come in he passed the lead to his wingman, Fred Engle, peeled off the formation, and dove on the ship's stern. Fred made a gentle bank to the right as the *Monterey* turned into the prevailing westerly winds. The Major landed on his first pass and taxied to the elevator. " God," I prayed, "he made it look so simple; please make it that way for me." While the forward elevator lowered the major's

SNJ to the hangar deck, he took his position on the LSO platform. He then radioed Engle to lead our six-plane formation over the ship, make a carrier break up, descend to 200 feet, and take interval for the landing pattern. We did everything fine up to that point.

As tail end Charlie, I was too far back to see what was happening on the ship's stern, but I could hear Arnet calmly talk Fred in for his first approach. Fred had trouble with his line up and was too steep in the groove—final 50 yards of his approach. Major Arnet signaled a wave-off—add power and abort the approach. As Fred flew over the ship the major told him he must avoid the overshoot. The resulting steep angle of bank to get back on centerline could easily induce a stall. There would be no recovery at a mere 200 feet.

When Dufo made his approach the major gave him a wave-off for being too slow in the groove. After he added power, however, Dufo lost sight of the aircraft in front of him, Jerry Sipko. He turned down wind too soon cutting Jerry out of the pattern. Jerry had to swing far outside to avoid a midair collision which, from the squealing protest we heard on the radio, only increased the anxiety flooding his cockpit. The rest of us did a 360-degree turn to keep our interval somewhere near acceptable. It was de'ja' vu Magnolia Field.

Major Arnet radioed us to keep our interval and above all, try to relax. When Buff came around for his first try the major had to wave him off half way through his approach. Buff forgot to lower his tail hook. That mistake would cost him a case of beer for the LSO crew. Jerry Sipko took a wave-off for being too high and fast, then climbed and left the pattern, heading north toward Barin Field.

"Where are you going, Sipko?" radioed Arnet.

"I-I can't do this," Sipko stuttered apologetically. "I'm gonna DOR. I'll see you back at the airfield, sir." Instead of answering, Arnet told us to close up the pattern and keep coming, as though Jerry's announcement were expected.

On Dufo's second pass he took another wave-off, this time for being too slow and too low in the groove. So low, in fact, that Arnet and his assistant had to dive in the safety net to avoid being clubbed by Dufo's port wing. For that, he got a stern warning to shape up or head back to Barin with Sipko.

Will took several LSO corrections throughout the approach, but got a cut—the signal to chop power and land—and made his first arrested landing. I allowed my interval on Will to get a little tight and Arnet had to wave me off.

After Fred overshot the centerline again he straightened out, but was very slow in the groove forcing Arnet to signal a cut, so Fred would lower his nose toward the flight deck and avoid a stall. Fred made a wobbly touchdown, his tail hook missing the stern's round-down by inches and snagging the number one cable.

"Dash one, that was too close for comfort," scolded the major. "Watch your line up and airspeed. If I hadn't given you a cut, you would have stalled in the ship's wake. OK, let's everyone settle down and get aboard." It was Buff's turn and although he lowered his tail hook this time, he forgot to lower his flaps. That cost him a second case of beer. I grimaced as the normally calm Major Arnet shattered the airwaves with a barrage of expletives.

Dufo finally got a cut, snagged the number three cable, and in the excitement of making his carrier arrestment, locked his brakes and blew both main tires. The deck crew pushed his Texan to the elevator where he descended to the hangar deck, switched to Major Arnet's aircraft, and was back in the pattern in minutes.

With Jerry on his way back to Barin, Will moved up a slot and started his approach. His pattern was Roger—OK—all the way and he made his second arrestment. After he was airborne the deck crew had trouble resetting the cable forcing me to take another wave-off, this time for a fouled deck. Angrily I added power. I had a Roger pass and doubted I would do that well the next time around. When I passed over the stern I glanced at the fearsome cavern in the aft end of the ship referred to the "spud locker" by fleet pilots. It was there, a few feet below the flight deck, where many a carrier pilot terminated his approach, career, and his life.

It was Fred's turn. He overshot for the third time, but only slightly. The major was able to talk him in for his second arrestment. Although I had yet to get aboard, at least I had one Roger pass under my belt. The delays were beginning to wear on my nerves. The Aeronca's cockpit flashed across my eyes and I thought of the spud locker as the gaping mouth of another dragon waiting to devour me. Working my sticky tongue around my dry gums, I told myself this was the most important thing I'd ever done in my entire life. I had to get my yellow peril on that flight deck or it was all over.

On my next pass I took a little extra interval and when abeam of the island, started my turn. At the 90-degree position I spotted Arnet on the LSO platform. His paddles were slightly low. I added an inch of manifold pressure and pulled gently on my stick until I saw his paddles straighten to form a crucifix, the signal that my approach was right on the money. Reducing power slightly, I continued my descent, my eyes darting back and forth between the LSO and the flight deck's centerline. Major Arnet tilted his arms left and I eased out some bank, adjusting my line up. He brought his paddles level but moved them slowly forward and then back—a little slow, add more power. I added another inch of manifold pressure. When I started to float upward I lowered my nose, increasing my speed slightly. His correction worked perfectly and I entered the groove on speed, on centerline, on glide slope. Finally, the cut.

When his right paddle sliced across his throat I yanked the throttle back to idle, popped the stick slightly forward to avoid a premature stall, pulled it back to regain my three-point attitude—and waited. My teeth jarred when all three landing gear slammed against the flight deck. A split second later the tail hook engaged the number four cable and my body flew forward against my shoulder straps. The Texan abruptly decelerated and stopped 75 feet down the flight deck. I stepped on the brakes and congratulated myself. Thomas Quinton Fitzgerald just landed his airplane on an aircraft carrier. He had slain the dragon!

"Wake up, Fitzgerald!"

Major Arnet was yelling on the radio for me to watch the deck crew so they could get me out of the arresting gear and back in the air. Fred was at the 90-degree position and would be landing in a few seconds. I snapped out of my euphoria and looked to my right to see the impatient deck handler opening his fists repeatedly while pushing his hands back. He was signaling to release my brakes and allow the Texan to roll backward, removing the tension from the arresting cable. I dropped my feet from the tops of the rudder pedals and began to move backward. When he closed his fists above his head I held the brakes while the deck crew disengaged the cable and secured the tail hook in the clasp under the tail. Signaling that my hook was in place he turned me over to the flight deck officer who immediately gave me the turn-up signal. I pushed my throttle all the way forward and when he pointed down the flight deck I released the brakes. Engine power, the stiff sea breeze, and the *Monterey*'s 22-knot speed boosted me into the air in less than 300 feet of roll. I flew straight ahead, looking over my shoulder in time to see Fred take his cut and grab the number two cable.

Bathed in elation, I stuck my head in the air stream and yelled, "YOWEEE!" loud enough to be heard back at Barin Field. Then I reminded myself I had five more traps before I was qualified. I made them on my next six passes, waving off once because the preceding aircraft had not yet cleared the arresting gear. After my final trap I joined my five wingmen orbiting the ship. Major Arnet launched minutes behind me and took his place at the head of our six-plane formation. Five jubilant, carrier qualified NavCads and one exhausted instructor LSO were on their way home.

That first landing aboard the *Monterey* was more thrilling than my first solo, first night and formation hops, and the first time I fired on the sleeve all combined. One thing I learned early about naval aviation was that regardless of how exciting one day would be there were bigger thrills over the horizon. I knew I would never voluntarily exit that road of unparalleled excitement. I was going for the gold.

When we returned to Barin we hurried to the PX and replaced our single solo bars with double bars and anchors, the emblems signifying that we were aircraft carrier qualified. The next emblem we pinned over our left breast pockets would be a pair of gold wings—we hoped.

That afternoon Captain Brannigan walked up to my table in the mess hall and told me to call LCDR Herbert at Saufley Field. Must be a records problem, I thought. Maybe I forgot to sign off one of my evaluations or something. After waiting on the line for a couple of minutes I heard his familiar voice.

"Fitz, I got bad news. Stump bought it today."

My body tensed, as though I'd been jabbed with a jolt of electricity. Stump had been held back at Saufley because he broke his arm in a game of touch football. "What? How did. . . . "

"He was flying lead on his six-plane formation check," explained Herbert, "when the cadet rendezvousing on him lost control and rammed his wing into the rear of Stump's fuselage."

"Oh, God, no," I moaned.

"It gets worse. He might have made it, but his canopy was jammed and he couldn't get out. He went down with the airplane. I'm afraid there wasn't much left. At least the other cadet was able to bail out. He's OK."

"His poor mom," I said ignoring his report on the other cadet. "She lost both her husband and son to naval aviation. She'll never make it."

"I know Helen," said Herbert reassuringly. "She'll make it, all right." After telling me about the plans for Stump's funeral Herbert wished me well and hung up.

I tried to block out the image of Stump struggling to free himself from his cockpit as his Texan spun into the swamps of northwest Florida. Not his father or a battalion of guardian angels could help him out of a mess like that. I remembered the time I blacked out during Axton's split-S back in Primary and the terrifying sensation that I was going to crash and couldn't escape from the cockpit. That nightmare had become reality, but for a friend instead of me. No longer having an appetite, I left my dinner sitting in the mess hall and went to the barracks.

Most of our Pre-Flight class attended Stump's funeral at the Barrancas National Cemetery. I was deeply moved by the honor guard escorting the flag-draped casket, the seven-man rifle squad, and the lone bugler hidden among the trees—all the elements that provide a military funeral with its unparalleled dignity. I flinched when the riflemen fired each of their three volleys, then listened to the bugler send the mournful call of *Taps* across the sea of white markers rooted in the manicured landscape. When the honor guard folded the flag and the officer presented it to Stump's mother—the second one she had been presented in three years—I couldn't hold back the tears. Stump wanted so much to be a Navy pilot and fight for his country. He never made it, but his ultimate sacrifice was no less real than that of his father who died in combat.

Only two days ago I was savoring the thrill of being carrier qualified; now I was deeply saddened by the tragic loss of a comrade. How could something capable of making me feel so much alive, at the same time make me feel so miserable? The warnings in Ryan's letters hit home. Flying's exciting, all right, but it's also a scary business. If I was going to hang around for the long haul I knew that survival would require my full attention, not only to my own performance, but also to that of my wingmen. If I needed proof, all I had to do was think about Stump's gray casket being lowered into that cold, dark pit in Barrancas National Cemetery.

After I returned to Barin Field I met Fred Engle and Will at the ACRAC and we talked about Stump. When I mentioned that Stump was buried near his father, Fred shook his head and flashed a grin. I frowned at his insensitivity.

"I mean no disrespect, Fitz. It's just that we were so different. He was here to please his father's ghost and I'm here because my old man fought like a lion to keep me back in Illinois. Hell, I wasn't serious about joining the NavCad program until I saw how angry my old man was when I told him. It was an opportunity to get back at him I couldn't pass up, so here I am."

"Back at him for what?" I asked.

"For being such a damned dictator," he replied.

"But why would he be against your being in the military?"

"I know it sounds crazy—militaristic Germans and all that—but my old man's the exception. From what I've read in our family history, the most promising men and women of the Engle clan were killed off in the Franco-Prussian War, WWI, and WWII—especially WWII. Combat gobbled up five of my uncles and several aunts were killed in bombing raids. So my old man hates the military almost as much as he hates me." Fred picked up his beer and walked to the pinball machine.

From what I saw at the ship, Fred's determination to defy his father might have placed him in a business where he was ill-suited. Then again, I shouldn't be critical. Was I any better suited for this business than he was? Ryan sure didn't think so.

Will signaled for another beer and faced me. "Why are *you* here, Fitz-*gerald*? To prove to your cousin you're not a twerp, to commit suicide, to get some of us killed, to embarrass your family—what?" He grabbed the neck of his beer bottle and joined Fred at the pinball machine.

I grasped the edge of the bar and told myself to stay calm. As much as I was growing to hate my childhood chum, I also hated the thought of fighting him. Aside from Brannigan crucifying both of us, Will probably would pulverize me like he'd squash a bug. Yet I knew if he continued with his vendetta, eventually he would wear me down and I would have to take him on, regardless of the consequences.

Excited about my CQ, yet saddened by Stump's death, I wanted to share my feelings with someone I hoped would understand. I fired off a letter to Ryan.

> Dear Ryan, Hold on to your hat. I am now a carrier pilot. So is Will. Last week we qualified on the USS *Monterey*.

> We will soon be on our way to the last phase of Basic Flight Training. There's too much to tell about CQ in a letter, so I'll save it for when I see you in person. Surely by now you have to admit that you might be wrong about me. You were right, however, about the dangers of formation training. The other day I lost a good friend when his wingman rammed him during a practice rendezvous. It was doubly tragic since Stump's father was a Navy pilot and was killed in Korea. Stump's death is the ugly flip side of a business that can make a person feel more alive than any other thing he does in his lifetime. This was an up and down week, but I think I'm going to make it, Ryan. Your CQ'd cousin, Tommy.

Ryan answered this one quickly.

> Dear Tommy, I admit you're one up on me now. I've never even seen an aircraft carrier up close and now you've landed on one. But don't get cocky. You still have a long way to go before they pin on those gold wings. Pretty soon you'll be flying bigger and faster airplanes. Remember, the faster you go the harder you hit the ground. By the way, if you see Will, tell him I said, "Way to go, pal!" Sorry about your friend, Stump, but at least now you can see what could be awaiting you in the wings, so to speak. There may be guardian angels, Tommy, but there's also the Grim Reaper waiting for his chance to pounce when your angel is looking the other way. As you said, that's the ugly side. Best you not forget it. Believe me, the worst is yet to come. Your truth-telling cousin, Ryan

After I read his letter I started to throw it in the GI can, but I changed my mind. Instead, I read it one more time and placed it in the drawer with all the rest. But if Ryan wanted Will to get his, "Way to go, pal," message he could send him a telegram.

* * *

My worries about what aircraft I would fly after getting my wings were justified. While packing to leave for our next phase of training at NAAS Corry Field, I heard more scuttlebutt. Newly designated Navy pilots were going to jet squadrons while Marines were getting orders to propeller attack bombers or the most unglamorous transport airplane ever built, the bulky R4Q Flying Boxcar. Its lascivious sounding designation, Aw fork U, was most appropriate. I couldn't take a chance on missing jets. I had to make my move.

Knowing I might be stepping into a barrage of retribution I sheepishly went to Captain Brannigan and submitted a letter to withdraw my application for a Marine Corps commission.

He read my letter and slowly raised his head. "Do you know what 'Semper Fidelis' means, Fitzgerald?"

Although I'd heard the Marine Corps motto, I was ashamed that I didn't know what it meant. "No, sir," I said softly. "I'm afraid not."

He shook his head. "Why am I not surprised? It means 'Always Faithful.' That's loyalty, Fitzgerald, real loyalty. Hell, Benedict Arnold had more loyalty than you do," he snarled. As he pulled a pen from his desk drawer he said, "While I'm endorsing this chickenshit letter remove your cadet officer's bars and lay them on my desk. I'll give them to somebody who's got some guts."

Reluctantly I complied, regretting the loss of my mess privileges and longer liberty hours more than my sudden, inexplicable loss in leadership ability. "Oh well," I muttered while walking down the passageway, "at least Will and I will be headed in opposite directions. And once again my tattoo and service will be compatible."

Chapter 10

On June 10, 1955, I checked into NAAS Corry Field for introductory instruments and night cross country, the last flying requirements before going on to advanced training. We sat through a few boring lectures on instrument flying and reported to the facility housing the Link simulators, affectionately known as the "blue coffins." The Link was an SNJ cockpit on a pedestal, capable of 360-degree directional movement and a bank angle up to 45 degrees. "WARNING," read the placard in the cockpit. "BANK ANGLES STEEPER THAN 45 DEGREES MAY CAUSE STRUCTURAL DAMAGE OR SYSTEMS FAILURE."

A sliding, opaque canopy over the cockpit prevented the student from using outside references when operating the simulator. My civilian instructor sat adjacent to the trainer and monitored the flight's progress by watching a stylus trace my route over the prescribed diagram on his desk.

The blue coffin "flew" nothing like an airplane. We were warned to expect a one or two-second delay between input to the controls and a response by the trainer. That idiosyncrasy made it difficult to time or coordinate turns. During my first Link hop I scanned the various flight instruments trying to remember what was said in the lectures about developing a scan.

"Let me see," I mumbled. "Check the gyro horizon, then the altitude, now the airspeed, back to the gyro horizon, altitude again, gyro horizon, airspeed, over to the turn and bank indicator—keep that ball in the center, back to the gyro. . . . " and on and on.

When I felt I had my scan right and the Link under control I pushed the stick and nudged the rudder for a left turn, forgetting about the sluggish response. Being the impatient sort, I pushed the stick harder to the left and kicked full left rudder. *SSSHHHHHH*, the trainer sounded like an 18-wheeler hitting its air brakes. It abruptly banked 60 degrees where it hit the stops with a loud *CLUNK*. Leaning far to the left, it spun on its pedestal trying to produce a turn equal to the excessive amount of bank and yaw I put in the controls. Hearing the noise behind him, my instructor backed out of his chair, but before he could turn around, *WHAM*! The coffin caught him from behind and down he went. He jumped up and ran around the trainer slapping at its disabling button trying to shut it off before it ground itself into sawdust. He finally made contact and it slowly came to a stop.

Anxious to get out of my blue tilt-a-whirl, I opened the canopy, rose from the seat, and facing the cockpit, groped for the first step on the boarding ladder. Still a little woozy from my wild ride in the blue coffin, I missed the step and fell backwards on the deck. The instructor helped me up and eased me into his chair. While wiping his face with his handkerchief, he gave me his counsel as calmly as the occasion allowed.

"Damn it, Fitzgerald, ease up! Save your aerobatics for your tour with the Blue Angels. These machines can't take that kind of abuse."

* * *

After a week of Link training we flew five basic instrument flights under a hood in the back seat of a Texan. Next, we flew four local night flights and finished with a night, round robin—a circuitous route and return to home base. The 175-mile round robin went from Corry Field, northwest to Bay Minette, Alabama; northeast to Brewton, Alabama; southeast to Milton, Florida; and west back to Corry. During our briefing I noticed on the schedule that Dufo was flying in the airplane ahead of me. I made a mental note to give him plenty of room.

At Bay Minette, Brewton, and Milton, an instructor circled at 4000 feet, 1000 feet above our assigned altitude. We were briefed to turn on our landing light and call out our number on the radio as we passed over all three towns, so the instructor could check us off. As I approached Bay Minette I listened for Dufo's call. It never came. Should I circle my present position in case he was off course so he would have plenty of room to get around Bay Minette? No, the guy behind me might fly up my rear end. I continued on course, hoping to hear his call at any moment. Dufo never checked in.

I turned over Bay Minette, flashed my landing light and made my call. The instructor had me verify my number twice, then called Dufo's number, trying to determine where he was. No answer. I got a sinking feeling. First Stump and now Dufo. Had he crashed in the marshes between Corry and Bay Minette? Was he lost over the Gulf? When the aircraft behind me made its call over Bay Minette Dufo still had not called in. As the instructor continued to call Dufo's number, the concern in his voice caused me to assume the worst. Dufo went down somewhere northwest of Pensacola.

While on my approach back at Corry the tower announced on the emergency channel that the search for Hartwood's aircraft had been terminated. They'd discovered the crash site, I concluded. I pictured my classmate's broken body lying inside the twisted hulk of his SNJ Texan somewhere in the Florida or Alabama swamps.

I should have known better than to worry about the indestructible Danny Hartwood. After I landed I found him in the ready room, reading a paperback. He looked in pretty good health for surviving an airplane crash.

"Where have you been, Dufo? I thought you bought a slice of the old farm."

He looked up with his carefree grin. "Oh, hi, Fitz. I made a little screw-up, but I came out OK." He went back to his reading.

I couldn't let it drop there. "Well, what the hell happened?" I snapped. "Half the instructor staff plus the Coast Guard were looking for you out there!" I lowered my voice. "I was worried sick, you jerk. What gives?"

"Sorry, Fitz," he said, lowering his paperback. "I was concentrating so hard picking out landmarks in the dark that I forgot to make my call over Bay Minette. I knew I'd blown it and might get a down, so when they called I faked a radio failure."

"What about the landing light?" I said. "You could have at least signaled and let them know where you were."

"The landing light. Nuts! I forgot about that. Anyway, when I landed I went to the Training Officer and told him I had a radio failure, hoping he wouldn't check my airplane. Lucky for me, he didn't. He just said I'd have to fly a repeat Thursday night." He shrugged and went back to his novel.

I stared at Dufo as he sat there engrossed in his reading. He must have a squadron of guardian angels following him around, I concluded. Looking out for Dufo Hartwood is definitely not a one-angel job.

* * *

Eighteen days from the day I checked into Corry I packed my bags, boarded the shuttle bus, and reported to the Navigation Training building at NAS Pensacola. While waiting to check in I heard more scuttlebutt. New Marine Corps pilots were being assigned to jet fighter or attack squadrons while a large percentage of new Navy pilots were going to multi-engine sea and land based patrol squadrons. I'd die if I had to fly huge, lumbering seaplanes. I wondered if I dare put in another application to be a Marine Candidate. They might laugh me out of the boardroom. Besides that, if I was reinstated I could end up at the same air station as Will Rumford. And there was my Navy tattoo. If the Marine Corps discovered my traitorous body art, would they let me have my commission? The hell with it all, I decided. If I wanted to fly jets it was worth a shot.

The next day I submitted my letter to the Marine Corps Selection Board and said a prayer to my guardian angel. I reported to the Board with a white sidewall haircut, wearing a freshly laundered and starched uniform with my brass sparkling and shoes shining like lacquered walnut. The senior member of the Selection Board was Colonel Sanford Stone, the CO of the Marine Aviation Training Support Group at NAS Pensacola. A decorated pilot who was wounded twice in Korea, he was as hard as his name implied. He led off with the obvious question.

"NavCad Fitzgerald, you've applied once, been accepted, withdrew your application, and now you're reapplying. Can't you make up your mind?" He leaned forward, his ruddy complexion blending with the scarlet Marine Corps flag behind him. The other four officers were slightly less frightening, but definitely not impressed with the indecisive NavCad sitting before them. All five Marines glared at me coldly, waiting for my answer. Remembering Lt. Axton's explanation of why Marines loved to be supported by the AD Skyraider, I began.

"Sir, in the last few weeks I've learned that a Marine pilot's most important mission is to support ground troops. If you'll give me a second chance I'll support them with every bomb, every rocket, every round of my twenty millimeter cannons, and if necessary, with my external fuel tanks, bomb racks—anything I can drop from my aircraft, sirs. I'll use my Skyraider's propeller as a whirling machete, strewing the enemy's guts over the battlefield until it looks like a field full of macaroni, if that's what it takes to protect my Marines."

Stone's hardened expression turned to putty. His fellow Board members leaned forward, aching to join in the battle I conjured up before them. With clamped jaws I moved my head from left to right locking on to each face briefly before moving to the next. I saw excitement but not concession, so I called up the reserves.

"Sirs, every time I see a set of dress blues adorned with the globe and anchor I want to be a Marine pilot so bad I can taste it. I may be just the son of a WWI vet, an old gunner's mate who still breaks his back every day in one of Detroit's auto plants, but if you'll give me another chance you'll never be sorry. I guarantee that those Marines on the ground needing air support won't be sorry either." All was quiet, and then . . .

"Accepted!" blurted Colonel Stone, slamming his fist on the table. He whipped open my application and quickly jotted his signature.

"Concur!" shouted the others, pulling out their pens.

"Semper Fidelis!" I yelled. I bit my lip watching four heads pop up, eyes narrowing. Had I gone too far? Then a grin spread across each face.

"Semper Fi!" they echoed, fists in the air.

That afternoon with my $200 uniform allowance in hand, I walked into the Rice Uniform Company in the basement of the San Carlos Hotel and placed a down payment on over $600 worth of custom fit, service tropical and green gabardine uniforms, dress blues, and all their accessories. My new uniforms would be available at Rice's shop in Corpus Christi, Texas in mid December, the time the salesman predicted I would finish my last phase of training. My payments would begin after I was commissioned. I was committed.

Chapter 11

After finishing a series of radio navigation problems in an enclosed cubicle called the "broom closet," I reported to the Chief of Naval Training for my orders to the Advanced Training Command. I was surprised to find Charles Haley, my Pre-Flight boxing opponent, sitting in the waiting area dressed in civilian clothes. He had passed me up at Saufley and I assumed he had finished Corry at least a couple of weeks ahead of me. I sat next to him and extended my hand. After a slight hesitation he took it and we shook.

"How's it going, Charles?"

"Hi, Fitz. On your way to the great southern state of Texas?" He asked with a trace of a smirk.

I smiled. "Yep, Corpus and then jets, I hope. How about yourself?"

"Back to Gary, Indiana."

I narrowed my eyes, wondering if he had a problem at home. "Emergency leave?"

He shook his head. "Nope, I DOR'd. After a few days with my family I go to Great Lakes Naval Training Center for a year as a yeoman," he said wiggling his fingers over a make-believe keyboard.

"But. . . . "

"I had enough," he interrupted. "I told you this black skin isn't as thick as you thought."

"Maybe not, but it's tough enough to see this through. What happened?"

"I was doing all right until I had a run-in with an instructor at Corry, a LCDR Seymour. After our night cross-country he made what he figured was a cute comment. 'Haley,' he said smiling, 'I almost didn't check you off. You people don't show up much at night . . . Ha, Ha, Ha.' I suppose it doesn't sound like a big thing, but it was sort of the straw that finally broke this weary camel's back. For the first time, I struck back."

Charles lowered his voice an octave. "'Yassuh,' I said blinking my eyes, 'I understands, yassuh, I sho do. When you white folks puke, you know what I mean, dont'cha, suh? That's, uh, re-gurg-i-ta-tion? Well, you know, suh, when that white, yellow, and green slimy stuff starts a comin outta yo mouth? Well, I hasta strain my biiiig, black eyes to make out yo face . . . yassuh, I shorely do.'

"Present company excluded, Fitz." Charles quickly added that of course he didn't put all white people in that context, but there were enough like Seymour to justify the generality. "Anyway," he said, "would you believe Seymour took offense?"

"I can't imagine why," I said with a grin.

Charles smiled back. "OK, so I went a little overboard. We had some words and to make a long story short, I ended up with a SPEEDY Board."

"A SPEEDY Board! I thought SPEEDY Boards are for flying."

"Surprisingly, the Admiral said the same thing. Besides that, he said Seymour had it coming and I could continue the NavCad program. I said, 'No thank you, sir. I've had enough of this white man's game.'" Haley sighed. "Fitz, it's time for me to face reality and go back to Gary to work beside my brothers in the steel mills. That's where I belong."

"No, Charles," I said shaking my head. "You belong here as much as the rest of us—probably more so. And you once told me you love flying. I wish you'd reconsider."

The yeoman called for Seaman Apprentice Charles Haley to come and get his orders.

"Somebody else can do it," he said standing up. "There's a few other token colored guys spread around this Training Command. Let them be the trailblazers. I don't have the stomach for it any-more." Without hesitation this time, he extended his hand. "You're OK, Thomas Q. Fitzgerald . . . " then he added with wink, "For a white guy, I mean. Good luck in Texas and remember the rope trick. You never know when it might come in handy." I rose and grasped his hand.

"I'll remember it well . . . and the remarkable guy who taught it to me. Take care." When we released he walked away without looking back. "What a loss," I said softly.

* * *

When the chief yeoman endorsed my orders to Corpus Christi, Texas, I asked about the paperwork to obtain a bus ticket. He advised me that another Marine candidate, Gawain Winchester Savage, had a car and was leaving the same day. He was looking for a rider to share expenses.

"He should still be at the barracks. Look for a guy a little shorter than you, curly hair and a nose like Abraham," he said.

"I think I know him." I remembered GW was the ex-UDT sailor who cheered me up after my loss to Haley in the smoker. So GW stands for Gawain Winchester, I thought smiling. No wonder he uses his initials. This could be an interesting ride to Texas. As I ran out the door the chief yelled that he'd call the barracks and ask GW to wait.

I caught the shuttle bus on the run and jumped off at the barracks. Cars full of cadets pulled away from the curb in a rush to get started on the three-day weekend. One lone figure loaded boxes in the trunk of a new Ford convertible. Over his wiry frame he wore Levi's with no belt, a tight T-shirt with a pack of cigarettes rolled up in the left sleeve, penny loafers, and no socks. When he turned his wide, drooping shoulders toward me I knew it was GW.

"Savage?" I asked. His shirt was one big sweat stain. GW lowered a cardboard box to the pavement and pulled a bandanna from his rear pocket.

"You're Fitzgerald, right? Got smeared in the smoker by that big colored guy from Chicago."

"Gary," I corrected, "Gary, Indiana."

"Close enough. Nice to see you got over your doldrums," he said, wiping his forehead. "The chief called a few minutes ago. Said you're looking for wheels to Corpus." He stuck out his hand. "Welcome aboard."

I took it and shook once. "Good to see you again, GW, but didn't you tell me I won that fight?"

"I said you should have won that fight. The guy was big and smart, but you had the reach. You could have stayed out of range and peppered him all night, but you waded in and beat up his gloves instead of his face. Anyway, glad to have someone to share expenses. Grab your gear and let's go." He picked up the box and lowered it in the trunk. "Tomorrow's the fourth," he grunted. "I want to spend the night in New Orleans and if we don't get there soon the hotels will be full."

"Sounds good," I said, already on my way to get my bags.

An hour and a half later we were on US Highway 90 driving across the Mobile Bay causeway. We talked about some of our instructors and the more harrowing experiences in the cockpit. GW had a nice smile, but was stingy with it. I learned he was from California and one of nine children. Two of his five brothers were in the Army. His dad served in the Navy during WWII and was now a welder at the Long Beach Naval Shipyard.

"During WWII Pop was a bosun's mate on a battleship," said GW. "He was pleased to finally have a son in the Navy, after my two older brothers were drafted in the Army. When I chose to go Marine Corps he told me, 'Son, you gave up the best military service to be nothing but beach fertilizer.' Pop never forgot the slaughter he saw on the beaches of Tarawa and Iwo Jima." GW chuckled. "But Mom says he still brags all over the shipyard about his son, the soon-to-be Marine pilot. I guess he forgave me after all."

While slowing down to enter the Bankhead Tunnel under the Mobile River, I asked him how he liked his life in the Navy.

"I started as a bosun's mate just like my old man," GW said, after taking a drag on his cigarette. "The bosun does a little of everything: tending anchors, maintaining rigging, supervising refueling operations, all the heavy stuff on deck. It's a good job and it keeps you in shape."

A pickup truck with a shotgun in the rear window passed us. It honked twice and the echo bounced around the tunnel like a Ping-Pong ball.

"When I had a chance to go UDT," said GW, "I jumped at it. UDT is where a sailor can go face-to-face with the bad guys."

"Then why be a pilot?" I asked. "And a Marine pilot at that?"

"After Korea I decided that being a few thousand feet above the waves is better than twenty feet under them, so I applied for flight training. I joined the Navy pretty much to please my old man. Joining the Marine Corps? Well, I'm doing that for me. I'd rather be a flying Marine than a flying sailor."

Here I was on my way to be a Marine aviator, not by any wise planning on my part, but simply because I wanted to avoid blimps and seaplanes. Talk about luck. I knew right there that as a Marine I was going to be in pretty good company.

We emerged from the tunnel and stopped for a red light. Looking straight ahead we saw sprawling live oaks, their tentacle-like limbs weaving a roof over Government Street. GW commented how the majestic, ante-bellum homes seemed to be standing guard over Mobile's main thoroughfare. As we pulled away from the light he told me that the quaint parks with their towering magnolias and trellised walkways composed Mobile's historical Garden District and that this charming little metropolis on the Mobile Bay was one of the oldest cities in the United States. As many times as I had been to Mobile, this was the first time I had seen it during daylight hours, and I was awed by its beauty. Shortly after leaving the city limits we entered the plush low country of southern Alabama and Mississippi. For the next 100 miles GW told me about his duty in the Pacific, especially Japan and Korea. I was enchanted by his description of Japanese women.

"They're sensitive, graceful, and intelligent, which makes them far sexier than the average American broad. Something else," he said tossing me a licentious smile, "they go all out to please a man." GW stared silently at the road. Then he blinked his eyes as though he were waking up from a dream. "Another thing about being a Marine, Fitz, is that they all end up in Japan sooner or later. Man, I can hardly wait to get back there."

GW's uniform lay on the back seat and I noticed his blouse displayed three rows of ribbons. When I asked about the decorations he said they were nothing and changed the subject. As he talked I studied them more closely and recognized a Silver Star, Bronze Star, Purple Heart, and a Presidential Unit Citation, plus a few I wasn't sure about. It was an impressive array of decorations for a 22-year-old sailor.

That evening GW showed me all of his favorite haunts in the New Orleans' French Quarter, including the Famous Door Bar and Pat O'Brien's Collegiate Lounge and Bohemian Taproom. It was at Pat O'Brien's where I met the famous drink called the "Hurricane." An evening of guzzling Hurricanes guaranteed the worst possible hangover known to man. We also patronized The Old Absinthe House and ate a late dinner at The Court Of Two Sisters Restaurant. Visiting about every bar in the Quarter, we talked with bartenders and barmaids GW knew from his many visits there, bantered with a few hawkers and hookers, and retired well after 2:00 a.m.

The next day we motored down the Texas coast toward Corpus Christi. We walked into the headquarters building marked US Naval Air Advanced Training Command, and reported to Captain Forbes, the assignment officer for Marine candidates. While waiting for the captain to process our orders we thumbed through the brochures describing the four training pipelines at the various fields in south Texas. Seaplane and anti-submarine training was conducted at NAS Corpus Christi. Because we were Marine candidates, neither of us worried about that assignment.

On the other hand, we could end up at Cabiness Field where propeller attack training in the propeller driven AD Skyraider was conducted for Marine and Navy candidates. Remembering the crash the first day I set foot on a naval base plus the wreckage Axton showed me at Pace Field, Florida, I wanted no part of an airplane I considered a death trap. I crossed my fingers hoping for NAS Kingsville or NAS Chase Field, the jet fighter training bases.

Captain Forbes opened a folder, studied it a moment, and looked up. "Gentlemen, I have two quotas to fill. One at Cabiness and one at Chase." He looked at GW's record again, and then at mine.

"Cadet Fitzgerald, although your flight grades are about the same as Cadet Savage's, he has a distinguished combat record as an enlisted man. I'm sure you understand it's only fair that he get first choice." I felt cramping in my gut, but nodded my head in agreement. Captain Forbes was right. It was only fair.

"Well, Captain, I'll tell you what," interjected GW rubbing his chin. "When I was working the beaches at Inchon and Wonsan, those flying dump trucks saved my gonads by knocking out North Korean shore batteries. And being once a bosun's mate, dump trucks seem the logical route for me to go. If it's OK with you, sir, I'll take ADs at Cabiness." GW pointed his thumb at my chest. "Send my traveling companion here to Chase." He looked at me and winked. "Sorry, Fitz, but I always wanted to fly Skyraiders."

I could have kissed GW, but that would have gotten both of us kicked out of the program. That afternoon I boarded the shuttle bus for Beeville, Texas, about 50 miles northwest of Corpus Christi. Jets at last!

Chapter 12

When the bus passed through the Chase Field main gate, four Navy Panthers screamed overhead and peeled off for landing. These were the same model jets I saw swoop over the Central Michigan College campus only 18 months earlier. I was awestruck. Soon that would actually be me up there.

Walking up to the barracks steps I heard a loud growl behind me. An MG British roadster with Nebraska license plates skidded to a stop at the end of the sidewalk. The driver wore a WWII flying helmet with the goggles down and the flaps flapping in the breeze like beagle ears. A seatbelt secured his skinny hips to the MG's diminutive frame. I noted a Marine Corps garrison cap on the passenger's bucket seat. Grabbing his goggles with bony fingers, the driver pushed them on top of his cloth helmet and flashed me a spacey grin.

"Hi, Fitz, how's it hang'n?"

"Dufo, I didn't know you were picked up for the Marine program?"

"How about that?" he answered. "Buff did, too. We passed the board before we left Corry. Lucky for us they were short of applicants that week. I lucked out again and got jets, but poor Buff ended up over at Cabiness flying Skyraiders. How about a beer later."

"You bet," I said, giving him two thumbs up.

Dufo pulled his goggles down, slapped his little roadster in low, and disappeared in a swirling cloud of Texas dust.

The OIC of the cadet barracks leaned back in his chair so he could rest his scuffed shoes on his cluttered desk. He was reading a new girlie magazine called *Playboy*. Under his slightly askew gold wings was one lonely and dingy ribbon, the same red and yellow ribbon anybody with 90 days service was authorized to wear. First Lieutenant Jetter was hardly representative of the impeccable Marine pilots I had come across in the Basic Training Command. He put his magazine aside long enough to review my orders. Then he told me to go to the PX and buy a pair of Marine cordovan shoes, a Marine Corps belt buckle, and a Marine Corps garrison cap, the uniform items that distinguished us from Navy cadets.

"If you got any questions," he said from behind his *Playboy*, "ask Yeoman Flatts, the barracks clerk."

I looked at Flatts, sitting behind a typewriter engrossed in a paperback. Without interrupting his reading, he waved a friendly hand, then used it to take a swig of his Coke. Fitz, meet Flatsam and Jetsam, I said to myself.

Later I learned that Jetter was one of those marginal pilots who fell—actually flew—through the crack. The Marine Corps was embarrassed to assign him to a fleet squadron and didn't trust him to be a flight instructor. Hence, the Corps let him spend the remaining two years of his contract baby-sitting Marine cadets. Unlike the Marine officers in charge of the cadet barracks in Basic Flight Training who had teaching and flying responsibilities, Jetter's only duties were to get in his minimum flight hours, check us in and out of the barracks, and occasionally roam the halls to see that our rooms were somewhat orderly.

My three roommates were Marine candidates who had arrived the previous day: Timothy Jordan "TJ" Walden, Jim "Max" Maximilian and as luck would have it, my nemesis, Will Rumford. TJ was former Marine enlisted and a Korean War veteran who looked up at a jet fighter from his muddy foxhole one cold day and decided he'd "rather be up there than down here." Max was an ex-college bum like me, looking for something in life to hang his hat on . . . and Will? Who knew what he was after? Knowing it would rattle Will's cage, I told him about Dufo and Buff being picked up for the Marine program.

"I can't believe they let those two weirdoes in the Marines," muttered Will, while staring at the deck and shaking his head. "First, it's you bouncing in and out like a yo-yo; now it's Dufo—the Dilbert—Hartwood, and that Bungling Buff Brewster, the class clowns. I might have to reconsider going Marine if it's gonna accept twerps and idiots."

"Please do," I said unpacking my gear. "You won't hear any objection from me." Getting no answer, I looked up and saw that Will was staring out the window, his mind a million miles away. That was a first. Will had never allowed me to get in the last word.

"What's there to do in town?" I asked the shirtless TJ while making my rack. TJ was medium build, medium height, and I guessed, medium intelligence. He had no distinguishing features other than a tattoo on his left shoulder that said "Bonnie Sue." I noted he was writing a letter. The envelope on his desk was addressed to Mary Ellen somebody.

"From what I hear there's only one thing to do in Beeville," he said, putting down his pen. "The big event of the weekend is the Saturday night dance at the VFW hall. They call it the local worm wrassle. Girls come from as far away as Kenedy and Goliad."

"I've heard of Goliad," grunted Will while doing push-ups off the windowsill, "but where in the hell's Kenedy?"

"The locals call it Six Shooter Junction, stranger." TJ shot Will with his finger and blew across the tip. "It's 'bout thirty miles up the road towards San Antone. A while back they buried a guy or two a week up thar, from gunfights, strangl'ns, and hang'ns. Reckon you might mind yur manners if you go a callin' in Kenedy, stranger." TJ blew across his fingertip again, twirled his imaginary six-gun into his holster, and went back to his letter writing.

Saturday we accepted Max's invitation to join him in his brand new Mercury and check out the VFW dance. Max was the son of a California state cop and had perfect teeth, steel-gray eyes, and a blond crew cut he kept rigid with frequent strokes from a bar of wax that smelled like bubble gum. Although Marine cadets were probably neater than average, they were not obsessed with personal appearance. Max was the exception. His uniform, bunk, and locker looked like a Marine recruit's on the last day of boot camp—perfect to the last thread. When it came to conversation, however, he rarely offered an observation more profound than a passage from a Dick and Jane primer.

When we opened the doors to Max's new Mercury he held up his hand and pointed at our shoes. "Guys, if you don't mind, could you wipe your feet first?"

After vigorously rubbing our soles on the grass Will and TJ got in the back and I crawled in the right front seat. I took a deep whiff of the new car smell, as yet untainted by the usual cigarette smoke, cheap perfume, and stale beer. Max touched the checklist taped to his dashboard. With his finger on the first item he began.

"Let's see, driver's seat—adjusted; vanity mirror—set; rearview mirror—set." He made an adjustment here, a nod there.

TJ leaned over Max's shoulder. "What the hell are you doing, Max?"

"My before start checklist. Let's see, sun visor—up and secure." Max paused to pull out his Owner's Manual and check a dashboard item.

"But why?" asked TJ.

"Car's new and I don't want to take any chances doing something that'll screw it up. My old man would kill me." He put away the Owner's Manual and went to the next item on his checklist. "Hand brake—set; lights and radio—off; gear shift—park."

"Are we going to town, or what?" boomed Will, kneading the rope-like muscles in his forearms. "I'm thirsty, hungry, and horny."

"Come on, Max, this is ridiculous," I pleaded.

TJ bounced back in the rear seat. "Let's get my car," he said grabbing the door handle.

Max threw up a hand. "Hold it, TJ, I'm almost there. Ignition key—in and twist." The Mercury's V-8 engine roared to life.

"Finally," we all groaned. The Mercury eased out of the barracks parking lot, Max hunched over the steering wheel like Mr. Magoo.

Beeville was a small town at a major crossroads with a dozen churches, four feed stores, half dozen filling stations, and four drive-in restaurants, one at each entrance into town. On Saturday night, cadets, sailors, officers, local farmers, ranchers, oil riggers, and an equal number of local females met at the VFW hall for the weekly "worm wrassle." When we walked in the door I took a deep breath and blew it out slowly. I had never seen so many good-looking ladies in one place.

I counted 36 females on the premises. With only a 50 percent success rate, I thought, looking around at all the smiling faces, I should find 18 ladies willing to make me happy over the next six months. With my limited experience with women, I figured that was probably more loving than most guys got in a lifetime.

I nodded at three girls and a guy all sitting snugly at one end of a table trying to converse over the band's rocking rendition of *Maybelline*. There were four empty chairs at the other end of the table. The guys nodded back and we sat down. One of the girls tilted her head and smiled a greeting. I smiled back.

She was in her early twenties with dark, shoulder length hair and expressive eyes. Her skirt and sweater hugged a trim, shapely figure. One of the other girls resembled her, but was a few years younger with lighter hair. Probably a kid sister, I surmised. The third girl was somewhere between the first two in age, attractive, and probably tall, because her large breasts rested on the table when she leaned over to speak with her friends. When she got tickled her deep, vibrant laugh caused her red tresses to dance on her wide shoulders. While I figured she was enough woman for three men, I suspected Will thought she was just enough for him, alone. It was the first time I saw him stare admiringly at another human being.

The guy at the table was about 19 or 20. From the way he eyed the women scattered around the hall, I surmised he was a friend, but not attached to any one of these girls—probably their transportation. After a minute he got up, tapped the shoulder of a girl at another table, and they whirled away in a fast fox trot. The redhead and the younger girl went to the bar and Will, Max, and

TJ followed. I found myself sitting alone with the girl who had smiled when we sat down.

"Hi," I said turning my chair to face her more directly.

She leaned forward on her elbows. "Hi yourself." Her lips parted slightly, showing two rows of white pearls. "You're new," she said.

"Got here a few days ago. We're NavCads," I said, nodding at Will and TJ.

"No kidding," she said, putting her hand over her mouth. "I would never have known."

Feeling a blush coming on I turned to watch the locals whoop and holler when the band began playing *The Yellow Rose of Texas.* In a minute the girls returned, Will walking behind them carrying a tray of drinks. TJ had joined Max in a stag line leaning against the wall. Obviously smitten with the buxom redhead, Will helped her distribute the drinks. The younger girl started to grab a beer, but the brunette shook her head and gave her a coke. Scowling at her older sister, she scooted back and sulked.

When the band played *The Tennessee Waltz*, I turned to the brunette and motioned toward the dance floor. She nodded and we met at the end of the table. When I took her hand the music faded like it was coming from outside the hall. As we began waltzing to three quarter time she allowed me to pull her close in my arms. I could feel every curve in her body.

"I don't know your name," she said tilting her head back.

As it often did when I talked with an attractive woman, my brain regressed to pre-adolescence. Why not give her a ridiculous name, I thought. Something that would stimulate conversation and maybe get a few laughs. On such short notice, all I could come up with was the first word in the dictionary. "Uh . . . Aardvark," I blurted, "Adam Aardvark." *Geez*!

She said the words slowly. "Adam . . . Aard-vark. I've known an Adam or two, but never any Aardvarks." She narrowed her eyes and a smile formed in the corner of her full mouth.

"Uh, my great grandparents came over from Sweden. The Aardvarks were wonderful farmers." Ant farmers, I said to myself. "And your name?"

"Let's get back to yours. Isn't an aardvark a big anteater?" she asked, her smile drooping slowly.

"You're right, but we spell our name with one 'a' in front, not two."

"Oh, I see," she said, unable to hide her skepticism. "I'm Jean Porter."

Nice, simple name, I thought. "What do you do in Beeville?"

"Nothing."

I pulled back and raised my eyebrows. "Nothing?"

"I live and work in Goliad, not Beeville."

"You mean Six Shooter Junction?" I teased.

"No, that's Kenedy. And it's not called Six Shooter Junction anymore."

"Well, that's good news," I said. She was such a smooth dancer I thought we were floating with the music. I pulled her a little closer, and when her breasts pressed against my chest a tingling sensation ran through my entire body and to avoid embarrassment, I had to back away slightly.

"Goliad's a quiet, little town," she said softly, looking into my eyes. More tingling. "We've never had gun fights and hangings like they did in Kenedy. Well, not as many, anyway." She rested her head against my shoulder.

"Whatever you say." I could smell the shampoo in her hair. A guy can only take so much tingling. "OK," I said, "you live in a nice quiet town about thirty miles up the road. But what do you do? You wouldn't be the daughter of one of those rich oil men," I asked, half hoping.

She lifted her head off my shoulder and laughed. "Lord, no. I'm only a telephone operator—number eighteen."

"Eighteen?"

"Yes, if you want to reach me sometime," she said cocking her head, "just pick up the phone and ask for Goliad, Operator 18. You'll get your nickel back."

And so I did. We talked three times that week and I was still going by the name, Adam Ardvark. I couldn't get up the courage to tell her my real name, now that I had passed myself off as an anteater for several days.

The following Saturday we met again at the VFW dance. I arrived first and when she came in she walked directly to my table and stood with her feet wide apart, head tilted, hands on her hips with her fingers drumming her waist. Actually it was a very sexy pose.

"I asked Frank Jetter, the officer who runs the cadet barracks, if he knew a Cadet Adam Ardvark. He said he never heard of you. What's your real name?" she asked, folding her arms under her breasts and tapping her foot angrily.

When my mouth opened my tongue caught in my throat. "Well, I, uh. . . . "

"You know what?" she said nodding her head. "I think Aardvark fits you perfectly. The way your nose is growing you'll look like just like an anteater before the night's over!"

I figured I had better fess up. In thirty seconds I made a sloppy, but clean confession..

"You're not even an Adam?" she said thrusting her head forward. "I must have sounded like a fool when I asked the lieutenant about you. Good night, Mr. Adam Aardvark with one 'a,' or two a's, or Thomas Fitzgerald, or . . . or," then she said while throwing her hands in the air, "whatever your name is." She spun on her heels and joined her voluptuous redhead friend in the back of the hall.

I called her the next day and after a long apology over the phone she agreed to see me. I borrowed TJ's car and we made up over burgers and fries at a drive-in restaurant. When we pulled in front of her home in Goliad we talked, laughed, embraced, and parted with a long, passionate, goodnight kiss. I had no idea what the future held, but so far the duty at NAS Chase Field was looking pretty good.

Chapter 13

Stage I of advanced training was instrument instruction in the North American T-28 Trojan, a powerful, tandem seat, propeller aircraft. Stage II was 50 hours of jet transition in the TV-2, a tandem seat version of the Lockheed F-80 Shooting Star, the first Air Force jet fighter flown in Korea. Stage III was 50 hours of tactics, gunnery, and bombing in the single seat, Grumman F9F-5 Panther, the Navy's first jet fighter in the Korean War.

On July 20th I began instrument "all weather" training in the Trojan's back seat. A curtain—or hood—lined the inside of the canopy to block out any outside references. Included was high altitude cross country flight from one radio fix to another; radio instrument approaches to 500 feet above an airfield; and precision radar approaches down to 200 feet. When nearing a destination from high altitude we were taught to penetrate—steep, high speed descent—to initial approach altitude. During the descent we followed a beam from a multi-directional VHF navigation facility known as OMNI, or from a Low Frequency (LF) range.

Half way through the syllabus I was under the hood penetrating from 15,000 to 2000 feet on the Corpus Christi OMNI range. While concentrating on tracking the 270-degree inbound bearing to Corpus Christi, my instructor, Lieutenant Crowley, told me to give him the controls and raise the hood. Assuming we had a problem with the airplane, I let go of the stick and unsnapped the release that allowed the hood to pop open. When I looked out of the cockpit I gasped. We were a mere 10 feet above the Gulf of Mexico, our prop churning a rooster tail as though we were a forty foot Chris Craft. Lt. Crowley added power and began a slow climb. While staring at the receding white caps I clasped my arms over my chest attempting to quiet the pile driver pounding against my breastbone.

"You must never get fixated on one instrument and ignore the others," said Lt. Crowley calmly over the intercom. At the sound of his voice I turned my head and our eyes met in the rear view mirror above his instrument panel. "Learn to scan all your instruments," he continued, "so you never lose track of the four big A's: attitude, altitude, azimuth, and airspeed. In another second our gory remains and whatever was left of this airplane would have been on the way to the bottom of the Gulf of Mexico."

I looked down and imagined a dark oil slick spreading across the rolling, six foot swells. "Yes, sir," I mumbled. In all of flight training I had never felt more defeated. The thought that I could have killed us both was gut wrenching. I recalled Ryan's warning: "Tommy, the Almighty doesn't have enough angels to keep you out of trouble."

"OK, Fitzgerald, that's a lesson about the importance of the scan that I'm sure you'll always remember. Now, let's go up and try it again. You have the airplane."

"I have it," I said, grabbing the stick and shaking it halfheartedly. I struggled through three respectable penetrations and approaches, never allowing my eyes to lock on an instrument more than a second before going to the next.

All the way back to Chase Field I couldn't escape the image I saw when I popped the hood an hour earlier. In one stupid blunder, I shattered the hard-earned confidence I had developed over the previous twelve months. After landing we parked the aircraft and walked quietly to the hangar. During the debrief, I merely nodded at his comments, unable to say a single word. When he finished Lt. Crowley stared at me for a moment, then noting it was past secure (1630 hours), asked if I had ever flown an open cockpit aircraft.

"No, sir," I answered somberly, while thinking, so what? I've had enough flying for one day.

"You'll love it," he said. "I'll pick you up at the barracks in twenty minutes."

An hour later we arrived at a grass airstrip. He opened the doors of an old T-hangar and sitting in front of us was a pre-WWII, tandem cockpit trainer known as the Ryan Recruit. It had a shiny aluminum fuselage with fabric wings and control surfaces and a metal rod plus two cables reaching from each wing root to the top of the fuselage. Like the engine of another Ryan production, Lindbergh's *Spirit of St. Louis*, a chrome-plated, cone-shaped spinner covered the hub of her wooden propeller, and formed a point for the bullet nose. Her 125 horsepower, radial engine's five knobby cylinders sprouted through the cowling like cogs on a shiny wheel. A small Plexiglas windscreen was mounted in front of each open cockpit. My depression on a holiday, I could not wait to get this vintage flying machine in the air.

Following a quick brief, I climbed in the front cockpit and he hand-propped the engine while I adjusted the switches and throttle for a quick smooth start. After we were airborne Lt. Crowley gave me the controls. Compared to the high performance T-28 Trojan, the Recruit flew like a motorized kite. We climbed at 70 knots and when we leveled off, cruised at 90. After a few steep turns, a chandelle, and a couple of wingovers—all gentle, low-g maneuvers—Crowley took the controls and demonstrated how you don't need great speed to perform great aerobatics. When he gave it back to me I held nothing back. She responded to my touch as though she were alive, looping and rolling effortlessly, and spinning with the grace of a winged maple seed falling in a light summer breeze. The sensation of every roll, twist, turn, and dive was intensified by the wind over the cockpit and the pull on the seat of my pants. This was old-fashioned flying at its best and I was literally on cloud nine.

It was over too soon. Lt. Crowley told me to head for home and see how she handled in the landing pattern. He yelled over my shoulder to bring it in on the main wheels rather than let it stall in a three-point attitude like I landed the SNJ Texan. I bounced a couple of times on the first try, but then learned to pop the stick slightly forward on touchdown. The low angle of attack killed the remaining lift, encouraging the spirited Recruit to stick to the runway instead of trying to fly again. After that I got her down in good shape four times in a row. I taxied in, spun her around in front of his little hangar, and shut down the engine. For several seconds I caressed the polished teakwood and chromed instrument panel. She was a pilot's dream. Driving home I told Lieutenant Crowley that I was surprised he allowed me to fly his classic airplane after I tried to kill us both only a few hours before.

My instructor sighed deeply. "Look, to fly with the eagles is a good thing, but occasionally we forget we're not eagles, we're only men. We make human mistakes. When you have one of those bad days it's good to get back in the air so you won't forget just how great flying is and how lucky we are to be a part of it. It's sort of like getting back on the horse right after you've been thrown," he said with a grin. "Of course, it doesn't hurt to remember what you did to the horse to make it so darn ornery in the first place."

Like teachers, there are flight instructors who merely do their job and there are those of the highest magnitude. Crowley was definitely among the latter. With my confidence soaring once again, I figured it was time to send Ryan an update.

> Dear Ryan, I'm at NAS Chase Field and in the middle of All Weather training. It's the hardest flying I've ever done. In fact, instrument training could easily be my Waterloo. Today, for instance, I was beginning an instrument approach and left my altimeter out of my scan. The instructor took the airplane just before I would have bored a hole in the Gulf of Mexico. It was the worst moment of my life, even worse than the day I spun your Aeronca. One of my earlier instructors told me the more terrifying the lesson, the better it sticks in your brain. This one stuck like a stamp on flypaper. Later my instrument instructor took me up in his Ryan Recruit, a single wing, open cockpit trainer. Have you ever flown one? Before we took off I was ready to hang up my flight suit, but after

> an hour of aerobatics with the wind in my face, I was ready to go back and give flight training another shot. If I finish instruments without washing out or killing myself I'll be flying jets in a few weeks. By the way, Will's one of my roommates. We still don't get along, but we manage to be civil so as not to irritate our other two roomies. Hope Uncle Trevor and Aunt Connie are well. Your all-weather-flying cousin, Tommy.

* * *

Tired of the boring, regimented routine at the base chapel, TJ and I decided to try one of the churches in Beeville. It wasn't that we were regular churchgoers; we were just looking for a change of scenery. We jumped in TJ's Chevy and being sort of nondenominational, stopped at the first church we saw, a Southern Baptist. The service had already started and while the pastor finished a prayer and launched the congregation into *Amazing Grace*, an usher led us to a front pew right under the pulpit. The deep baritone voice above us shook the rafters, overpowering the collective voices of the congregation and choir. With narrow, sunken eyes and shocks of white hair jutting from his huge, bony skull, the pastor was the epitome of the fire and brimstone evangelist. On the organ's last note, he lowered his head and those beady eyes drilled TJ and me like lasers. I squirmed in my seat.

"Before I deliver my mes-sage to-daaay," bellowed the pastor, "I must com-ment about punct-u-al-i-ty when at-tend-ing ser-vices in the HOUSE . . . OF . . . THE LOORRRRRD."

TJ and I looked over our shoulders and met a hundred pairs of accusing eyes. We smiled nervously and scrunched in our pews, vowing silently never to be late for church again, at least not this one. After we were appropriately chastised he began his planned sermon on the sanctity of marriage. As we left the church, we were surprised to hear many people asking us to return, including the pastor who winked when he shook our hands. TJ and I elected to try it again, but next time we would definitely be on time.

The following Sunday morning, Kevin O'Malley, a former enlisted Marine pal of TJ's, walked in to tell us about his overnight date. TJ asked him if he'd like to join us for church in town.

"Hmmm," he said rubbing his chin. "What kind is it?"

"Baptist," we answered together.

"Baptist, eh. I guess that's better than Methodist or Presbyterian. All that witnessing and predestination stuff. Hell, nothing in my life is pre-planned." I didn't doubt that one bit. "I don't like Episcopal," he said, toeing the floor, "too much like Catholic. Definitely can't do the Catholic route—lots of guilt and always confessing everything." His head popped up. "Is it air conditioned?"

TJ rolled his eyes. "Churches aren't movie theaters, Kev. They can't afford air conditioning. But they had fans and the windows were open, so it was breezy and comfortable." I nodded assent.

"No air conditioning . . . but breezy." He scratched his chin again. "Were any girls there? You know, friendly, good looking . . . eager?" he added with a salacious grin. "I hear Texas girls work up a lot of passion in church, especially Baptists." TJ shrugged and I braced with impatience.

"There were a few young ladies," I said, beginning to wonder if his company was worth the trouble, "but I can't vouch for their passion, availability, or their virginity for that matter. Anything else?" I glanced at my watch. "We don't wanna be late."

"How about pads? On the pews, I mean. I hate to sit on hard pews." Kevin held the small of his back. "I have a sensitive lower spine."

I took a deep breath and let it out slowly. "Yes, Kev. As I recall, there were pads on the seats . . . not on the backs, but on the seats." I'd about had it with this inquisition.

"Hmmmm, padded seats only. That might be OK if the bench's back is curved and the service isn't too long. Do you recall how long it lasted? I've got a one-hour butt when it comes to a sitting in church."

"For Pete's sake, Kevin!" snapped TJ as he began counting on his fingers. "The church is nice and cool, the girls are sweet as honey, and the pews are form-fitted to your sorry rear end. But no, damn it, I don't remember how long the service lasted. Are you coming or not?"

"Let me see. No air conditioning, but there are ceiling fans and it's breezy . . . Baptist and a few girls, but passion is an unknown . . . pads only on the seats . . . the backrests are curved . . . not sure about time. Hmmmm." He looked down at the floor, traced the edge of a tile with his toe, then looked up, cinched his lips, and shook his head. "Tell you what, I think I'll pass this time. But if the girl thing gets encouraging, give me another holler." He patted TJ on the shoulder and left our room, whistling *Onward Christian Soldiers.*

* * *

Monday morning I received Ryan's answer to my last letter.

> Dear Tommy, I expect that instrument training is a lot more complicated than it was when I learned it in '43. We only had the low frequency basics, while you're getting all the latest in VHF radio aids and radar approaches. It may be tough, but without it you'd be dead the first month after getting your wings, assuming by some miracle you make it that far. I shudder to think how close you came to buying a piece of the farm, or in this case the Gulf of Mexico. Lucky for you the instructor wasn't daydreaming in the front seat like some of them do on occasion. Yes, I know all about the Ryan Recruit. How could I not know, it being my namesake? I flew them in primary flight training and found it a great airplane for showing off over some of those private girls' schools around San Antonio. Getting back to that near disastrous instrument flight, I'd hate to see you wash out after coming all this way,

> Tommy, but now I'm even more convinced it's in the cards. Remember, dropping out is better than getting kicked out, or worse, crashing in the Gulf of Mexico, or even worse than that, taking an instructor or a wingman with you. Please come home! Give my regards to Will.
> Your beseeching cousin, Ryan

I sighed deeply. I'd come all this way and he still lacked faith in my ability. All my life I worshipped this man, yet could never earn his respect. I placed the letter in the folder with the others wondering what it would take to convince him I was worthy of the smallest praise. Well, he could berate me all he wanted. I was too close to the goal line to quit now. And if he wanted to give Will his regards, he could do it himself.

* * *

Surprising Lt. Crowley and myself, I turned out to be a pretty fair instrument pilot qualifying for my standard rating right on schedule. I shook Crowley's hand, thanked him again for saving my bacon in more ways than one, and walked across the hangar for jet transition. The first item on my check-in sheet was the safety office. When I entered my eyes were drawn to the posters covering the walls, mostly cartoons depicting the proverbial Dilbert making stupid mistakes. Two clerks busily typed reports while a lieutenant, junior grade (jg), dipped a calligraphy pen in a bottle of ink and printed captions under a stack of accident photos. Lieutenant Carlson, Squadron Safety Officer, leaned on the open drawer of his filing cabinet. While signing my check-in sheet he glanced at my shoes.

"Number one," he said, "go to the PX and buy a pair of over-the-ankle work shoes—boondockers. At the speeds we fly, if you have to eject," he said pointing at my spit-shined, cordovan oxfords, "you'll lose those immediately and have to walk home barefooted. I see you're a Marine candidate. I know how you guys like spit and polish, but you'd better not put any wax on your boondockers. The stuff's flammable."

I wondered if he was serious. I didn't have the slightest intention of trying to spit-shine a pair of buckskin boondockers.

He walked over to his locker and pulled out his green, nylon anti-g suit. "Number two, go to flight equipment and check out one of these." He grabbed the hose extending from the waist, demonstrated how it plugged into the cockpit console, then pointed to the five bladders. "The garment is laced skintight. When you pull g's, air is forced through this hose and into the bladders. The pressure against your stomach, thighs, and shins pushes on the blood vessels and prevents pooling in the lower extremities. That fights blackouts during steep turns, aerobatics, bombing, and gunnery. And always wear a T-shirt underneath," he added, pointing to my chest.

It was obvious that bearing down and grunting like Lt. Axton taught me in C Stage was no longer sufficient. "OK, but why the T-shirt?" I asked. I'd much rather fly without an undershirt in the Texas heat.

"If you have a fire in the cockpit and the nylon in the anti-g suit melts, the T-shirt might protect your torso from serious burns," he said matter-of-factly.

I looked at the strange garment, a body suit with corseted waist and legs, and pictured its melted nylon sticking to my skin like candle wax. My thoughts were interrupted by a muffled explosion followed by the blast of the crash horn and roar of rescue vehicles.

We hurried to the window and saw crash trucks converging on a billowing cloud of black smoke at the approach end of runway 36 (360 degrees—oriented south to north). The clanging of a red phone on the Safety Officer's desk drowned out the commotion spreading throughout the office. Lieutenant Carlson grabbed the receiver and listened, his face grim. He placed the phone back in the cradle, picked up a tool box with ACCIDENT KIT painted on the lid, and yelled at a petty officer to grab a camera.

"We'll finish our session later. A Panther just crashed on landing approach. No chute," he said shaking his head. Since no parachute was sighted, the pilot was most likely dead.

When he left, the lieutenant (jg) walked to the window and while staring at the pillar of black smoke said, "Let this be a good lesson about flying jets, Cadet Fitzgerald. The turbine engine doesn't have the quick response you get from a powerful prop job like a Trojan." He turned toward me, face expressionless.

"Say you're careless and let yourself get low and slow. You feel an airframe buffet. Stall's coming on, right?" I nodded. "OK, you jam the throttle forward." I nodded again. "Well, it's too late. By the time the jet engine's spooled up you've spun in and claimed your private plot on the old cattle ranch. There are two sets of limitations in aviation, especially in jets. We call them envelopes."

"Like the safety zones of angels," I mumbled.

"Say again?" he said, frowning at the interruption.

"Nothing, sir," I said waving my hand. "Please continue."

He held up an inky finger. "First, there's your own limitations based on talent and experience." He popped up another finger. "Then there's the aircraft's limitations—what she can and can't do. You must know those envelopes like you know your own name—that is, if you want to survive." He closed his fist and returned to his project.

I stared at the thinning column of smoke blending with the gray, hazy sky. Envelopes, ejections, shoes torn off my feet, fires with nylon melting all over my body, stalls, spins, and crashes because of the slow engine response. Maybe Ryan was right. I was getting in over my head. Exiting the office, I remembered Ryan's many warnings: "you're in with the big boys now . . . the faster you fly the harder you hit the ground . . . it's getting more and more dangerous as you go along . . . the roads ahead are full of chuck holes . . . you could be dead the first month after getting your wings . . . washing out is in the cards." What was I doing here?

After a few classes of ground school and five sessions in a cockpit simulator, I was ready for my first flight in a jet aircraft. When I climbed into the TV-2 cockpit my instructor, Marine Captain Steve McCracken, helped me strap in. After getting attached to the ejection seat and parachute I noticed a yellow line extending from the left console, continuing up and along the windscreen, and down to the other console. I asked Captain McCracken what it meant.

He rubbed his chin and grinned. "It's supposed to be a warning line."

Great, another warning. "For what?" I asked.

"If you have to eject it's possible that any part of your legs extending beyond that line will hit the edge of the windscreen as you leave the aircraft."

I gulped. "You mean I could lose my knees?"

"Theoretically, but I wouldn't worry about it."

Sitting as far back as possible, my knees were at least two inches forward of the yellow lines. "Do you know if anyone six feet, four inches, has ever ejected?" I asked, hoping he could name at least a couple—and that their legs were still intact.

"I don't know of any, but surely, among all the guys who have ejected from these aircraft, someone must have been that tall."

I mulled over his answer. Did he say, "*all* the guys who have ejected?" How many were there? My mouth opened, but nothing came out.

"Fitzgerald, don't worry about things that will probably never happen. Let's go up and have a good flight." He started to turn around, then paused. "Oh, yes. The envelope for safe ejection is level flight, 500 feet altitude, and 100 knots airspeed. If you eject out of those parameters you might not get out of the seat and deploy your chute in time." I stared at the ejection handles on the armrests. "And one more thing. If you do have to eject, remember Pre, Pos, Ox, Pull."

Oh, oh, I thought. Another one of those ditties. "Meaning?" I asked.

"*Pre* is for Pre-ejection lever—pull that thing right here," he said pointing below my left shoulder. "It jettisons the canopy and positions the leg restraints. *Pos* is for position—sit up straight, head back." He stiffened his back as though he were getting in position. "If you don't sit erect you might injure your spine. *Ox* is for pulling the green apple." He pointed to a green, wooden ball next to my left thigh. It was about the size of a cherry, not an apple. "It activates the little oxygen bottle in your parachute pack; and *Pull,* that's for pulling up the levers on both sides of your seat," he said touching both armrests. "They activate the ejection mechanism. Got all that?"

"Got it, sir." I touched each item as I repeated the sequence: "Pre, Pos, Ox, Pull." He nodded and moved to the rear cockpit.

Finally, I was ready for my jet ride and possibly the loss of both of my kneecaps. With McCracken coaching me on the intercom, I started the engine. We went over the taxi checklist together and I eased the silver jet trainer onto the taxiway. On the way out he reminded me about the takeoff, to expect a few seconds delay from the time I added throttle until the engine was at full RPM.

When I added take-off power I could see what he and the Lt (jg) meant when they cautioned me about slow acceleration. A couple of seconds after I pushed the throttle all the way forward the engine was still winding up like an air raid siren working to max volume. A second later the aircraft began to roll. When the engine reached one hundred percent RPM I felt a gentle, then significant push against my seat as the TV-2 lurched forward and accelerated down the runway. At 90 knots I eased back slightly on the stick and at 100 knots we lifted off the ground with the grace of an eagle. It seemed odd not to hear the T-28's nine huge cylinders banging away in front of me. Because the jet engine was behind the cockpit I heard only the air rushing by the canopy.

When we leveled off at 20,000 feet I had trouble getting accustomed to the hydraulic boost, a kind of power steering, but much more sensitive. Because I was constantly chasing the boosted controls in a futile attempt to keep the wings level, the aircraft was in a perpetual state of wing rock. We practiced a series of climbs, turns, stalls, and some slow flight with the landing gear and flaps down, all the time the wings rocking like I was acknowledging a cheering crowd at an air show. Halfway through the flight McCracken said it was the wobbliest flight he'd ever been on and that I was making him airsick. On landing I discovered that without the windmilling prop to slow you down a streamlined jet needed considerably more runway, something I had best keep in mind. Taxiing into our parking spot McCracken told me that with the exception of the wobbling wings, I did fine.

We spent the next half hour sipping coffee while we went over my weak points, such as the over controlling the ailerons and failing to anticipate the delay in acceleration. He also commented on my strengths, not many, but at least I had one or two, like a good attitude. When he departed I put my hands behind my head, leaned back in my chair and basked in the afterglow of my first flight in a jet aircraft. Incredible, I thought, simply incredible.

After flitting around in pure ecstasy the rest of the afternoon, I went back to my room and fired off a letter to Ryan.

> Dear Ryan, I have to tell you about my first flight in the Lockheed TV-2, the Navy's two-seat version of the F-80 Shooting Star. It was fantastic! A jet is so much different from a prop. Although the engine responds more slowly, when it gets revved up its power is unbelievable. We flew at airspeeds and altitudes that are impossible for the fastest propeller jobs. I'm anxious to get through jet transition so I can fly a real single seat, jet fighter—the F9F Panther. This is the home stretch, Ryan, and I think I'm gonna make it. Wish me luck. Your sky-streaking cousin, Tommy

Before sealing the letter I took Ryan's patch from my drawer and affectionately rubbed the faded threads. Staring absently out the window at the blue sky, I rubbed until a tiny blister surfaced on the tip of my thumb.

About midway through jet transition I was pulling off the

runway when I heard the pilot in the aircraft behind me make a distress call.

"F-flameout on final! Tower, I've got a flameout on final!"

A shadow floated by my cockpit and when I looked up a silver TV-2 passed silently a few hundred feet above me. It was heading toward a cornfield 200 yards beyond the end of the runway.

"DO NOT EJECT!" screamed his instructor who had been flying behind him. "YOU'RE TOO LOW!" Although crash landing a jet is not recommended, he was out of his ejection seat envelope and had no choice except to stay with the aircraft.

"Roger, sir, landing straight ahead," said the pilot in a stress-induced falsetto voice.

I watched him disappear below the trees expecting to see a fiery explosion. But there was none. The instructor orbited over the cornfield and within minutes the ASR helicopter skimmed the flight line on its way to the crash site. I parked my aircraft and rushed to the ready room. Student pilots leaned over the backs of the instructors listening to the squadron radio.

Tower, this is Rescue, a voice crackled out of the speaker. *I see the pilot. He's out of the cockpit and appears unhurt.* Everyone cheered.

"Who is it?" I asked anyone, but all eyes remained on the radio.

This is Rescue, crackled the speaker. *We're now on the ground. As soon as the pilot finishes taking a nervous pee, we'll bring him in.* Laughs and more cheers.

"What's the guy's name?" I yelled again.

"MacKenzie. Ensign Ted MacKenzie," said someone over his shoulder. I reached back in my memory to the Officers' Club at Saufley Field and had an image of a young ensign jumping on the bar to ring the bell.

Wow! said the helicopter pilot. *Look at all the corn in the intakes of that aircraft. I'd guess at least a dozen bushels.*

Ensign Ted MacKenzie did a good job ditching his crippled TV-2. It's not often a pilot can walk away from a crash landing in a jet aircraft. The Navy did have to pay the farmer $2000 for the corn swallowed up by the jet intakes and for the stalks he flattened when he bellied in. I made a quick calculation and figured the farmer got at least 10 bucks an ear.

The afternoon mail brought Ryan's answer to my last letter.

> Dear Tommy, You're two up on me now. First, the carrier landings and now jets. I've never sat in the cockpit of a turbine aircraft, much less flown one. I have heard, however, about the slow engine response you mentioned. Be careful about that. Thinking you have all that extra power could fool you into believing you can use it get yourself out of trouble. Before you know it, BOOM! You're in the bottom of a smoking hole and there's no crawling out of a smoking hole, Tommy. By the way, have you thought about the airlines? You now have the hours and instrument ticket to get yourself a commercial license. You could DOR and hire on as an airborne bus driver with one of the big air carriers. If you have to fly, it's safer and certainly more in your line than jet fighters. By the way, tell Will I saw his mom the last time I was home and she's really worried about him. I don't know what's going on but something's definitely not right. Please forget about being a jet fighter pilot and give serious thought to the airlines. Your forever-worrying cousin, Ryan

I could not believe it. Not even the fact that I was flying jets impressed my hotshot cousin. How I yearned for just one sentence of encouragement from the pilot I respected more than any other. Well, I wasn't about to counsel Will about easing his mom's concerns. Emma need not worry about her pompous son's welfare. As far as I could tell, his ego and his body were strong as ever.

Chapter 14

Will and I were progressing about the same rate, but had different instructors; so our contact was limited to our room and occasionally at the bar. There were still his nasty remarks about my flying ability, even though we had not flown together since qualifying on the *Monterey*. The day of my close call in the T-28 he dropped a DOR form on my rack with my name penciled on the dotted line.

During my last week of TV-2 training I walked in the gym and spotted Will and TJ lifting weights. Will was doing bench presses with 100 pounds of cold steel on each end of the bar. TJ stood by the weight rack curling 25-pound dumbbells. Will had lain off me in our room lately, but this was his turf. If he wanted another confrontation this is where it would be. Why give him the chance, I thought. I started to do a fast retreat, figuring I would do my workout later.

"Hey, Fitzgerald!"

I turned in time to see Will puff out a long exhale while placing the sagging bar on the rack above his head.

"What say we have another go on the wrestling mats?" Raising his head he wiped at the rivulets of sweat channeling down the ripples in his abdomen.

"I would have thought you got enough satisfaction back at Whiting?" I said, arms folded.

"Oh, come on, Fitz-*gerald*. I need some amusement and that skinny body of yours could sure use the exercise."

I looked around the gym. NavCads and sailors had interrupted their routines, waiting to hear my answer. This was the challenge I'd been expecting for weeks and fool that I was, I felt duty-bound to accept. This time, however, I would choose another milieu. Remembering that Will had not fought in the Pre-Flight smokers, I wondered if he boxed as well as he wrestled. Since either way I would end up with plenty of pain and degradation, I opted to try the boxing route. After all, what did I have to lose?

"You're right," I said with a shrug. "I could use some exercise, but this time let's put on the gloves. Last time you messed up my joints for weeks. This way I'll only hurt for a few hours." Will sat up and narrowed his eyes. His hesitation told me I may have guessed right. But if I hadn't. . . .

"It's your funeral," he said slapping his palms on his sweaty thighs. "You get the gloves and I'll secure the ring."

I quickly changed and checked out two pairs of boxing gloves. When I left the locker room Will was in the ring, tugging on the ropes as if he were a pro wrestler warming up his audience. I threw him a pair of gloves, slipped one of mine over my hand and gave the other to TJ.

"You're nuts," whispered TJ while lacing up my glove. "You're gonna get creamed. Maybe I oughta have a corpsman standing by."

"Don't sweat it, TJ. I got a feeling he can't box like he wrestles. I intend to spend the next nine minutes dancing around like Tinkerbell. Who knows, I may even get in one or two lucky pops."

TJ shook his head, finished lacing my left glove, then walked across the ring and helped Will with his gloves. When TJ finished, he volunteered to be our timer. Will shrugged and nodded his consent. I agreed.

"OK," said TJ, "this will be three rounds of not three, but two minutes each. I'll yell 'DING' to signal the beginning and end of each round. You get a one-minute rest between rounds. At least it'll be over pretty quick, one way or the other," said TJ glancing in my direction.

At TJ's signal we walked to the center of the ring and touched gloves. When we separated Will raised his left glove, then his right, then his left again, as though he couldn't decide which hand would be his guard. He moved his feet stiffly, plopping one foot down, then the other, neither coordinated with the movement of his hands. I danced left and right, doing a little two-step that any amateur could penetrate. But Will stood like a statue, seemingly confused as to how to begin.

He's like Frankenstein's monster, I said to myself. Lots of power but composed of alien, uncoordinated parts. I basked in the discovery that I was about to subject this bombastic pile of mismatched sinew to enough discomfort to pay him back in spades. Jabbing repeatedly, I caught him on the nose and forehead, throwing an occasional right to the jaw. Will winced at each blow, but his hate-filled eyes never left mine. I feinted with a right and came back with two more stiff left jabs, catching his jaw both times. I easily dodged his clumsy, telegraphed attempts to counterpunch.

"*DINNNNG.*"

We retreated to neutral corners for our one-minute rest. So far Will had not landed one blow. I looked at TJ and grinned. He raised his eyebrows and then shook his finger, mouthing, "Don't get cocky."

During the second round I kept up the pressure, bobbing, weaving, jabbing, throwing a right cross here, a left hook there. When he heaved an occasional thundering right cross, the shock wave popped my eardrums, but his glove never touched my body. I finally have this miserable jackass where I've always wanted him, I thought, peering at him over my gloves. I knew I couldn't knock him out, probably couldn't even knock him down, but I sure as hell could make him wish he hadn't walked in the ring with me.

KER-BLAM.

My skull gonged like the Liberty Bell on the fourth of July. Blinded by complacency I never saw Will release his lumbering left hook. I stumbled backward towards the ropes, Will plodding after me, arms swinging wildly. Through the cacophony of bells and cymbals rattling in my head I heard Haley's prophetic advice: *Remember the rope trick. You never know when it might come in handy. Remember the rope trick . . . the rope trick . . . rope trick . . .*

Covering my face with my gloves, I cowered against the ropes. Will followed me throwing a barrage of walloping lefts and rights. The guy's power was staggering. My vision blurred and my knees threatened to buckle under me. Once again this obnoxious farm boy was humiliating me. After what seemed like minutes, but had to be a few seconds, I felt his blows weakening. I peeked between my gloves hoping to throw one last, face-saving punch before I crumpled to the canvas. His gloves were dropping lower after each blow. It was now or never.

After Will threw a weak left hook I threw my first counter punch, a left jab. It passed above his drooping guard and caught him squarely on the nose. He looked confused. I threw another. Will blinked over glassy eyes and backed away a step. I threw another jab and a right cross. He stumbled back, mouth open, gloves hanging limply at his sides. I whirled a left hook to his temple. He staggered, caught his balance, and shook his head. Raising his gloves to his belt, he stepped forward. I reached down to the depths of my soul and threw the hardest right cross I could manufacture, connecting on the left side of his jaw.

A hundred needles shot up my forearm as though I shattered every bit of calcified tissue below the elbow. The blow knocked Will backward and he pawed at the ropes for support. With my throbbing right hand dangling at my side I bent my knees, cocked my left elbow and using all of my remaining energy, launched a crushing left hook. Will's long deserved coup de' grace was on its way.

"*DING—DINNNG,*" screamed TJ jumping through the ropes. "Bout's over, guys!" Startled by TJ's voice, I pulled my left hook enough to miss Will's head by a millimeter, the momentum spinning me sideways.

"You guys have had enough." Arms spread, TJ stepped in between us.

With one glove on the ropes and the other on his knee, Will mumbled, "I'm . . . not willing . . . to stop . . . unless he is."

Bent over with both gloves resting on my knees, I labored to

04-UPCH

catch my breath. "I-I have to leave anyway," I said. "Got a simulator hop in half hour."

Will pushed his gloves toward TJ. As I started to leave the ring Will called out. "This isn't over yet, Fitzgerald."

I stared at Will leaning back on the ropes, revulsion boiling out of his swollen eyes. "Yes, I know," I muttered.

Walking toward the locker room I glanced back one more time, wishing I knew what it was that "isn't over yet." I used my teeth to untie the knots in my right glove and carefully removed my injured hand. Slowly I clenched my fist, then spread my fingers. It hurt like the devil, but nothing seemed broken. A little discomfort could never ruin this glorious day of triumph, I thought, smiling.

Will backed off after that day. I knew the animosity was still there, but he didn't come after me like he usually did. I sensed that he was building up to something even more vicious than our little boxing match, which unfortunately seemed to have been all for nothing.

* * *

At the end of October the training officer pronounced me jet qualified. I waved good-bye to the TV-2 ready room rats and walked across the hangar to the Panther squadron. This was the day I had been waiting for since Indoctrination. But remembering Ryan's warnings about the faster you go, the harder you hit the ground, I looked forward to my first flight with guarded enthusiasm.

Following two days of ground school and a couple of sessions in a cockpit trainer I passed the open and closed book exams and was assigned to a four-plane flight. The other two students were First Lieutenant Baker Reems, a Gung Ho Marine, and Commander William Bryant, a WWII and Korean War veteran. CDR Bryant was the squadron's new executive officer. He was learning the syllabus and at the same time transitioning into the Panther from his previous jet aircraft, the F2H Banshee. Our flight leader and instructor was Navy Lt. Robert "Rabbit" Warren, a Korean

War veteran with combat experience in both the AD Skyraider and his current aircraft, the F9F-5 Panther.

"Just consider me another cadet," said CDR Bryant at our first briefing. Rabbit knew better. A Lieutenant does not treat a commander like a cadet, especially his executive officer, unless he wants to blunt his Navy career. With a shaky, 20-year-old NavCad, a rigid Marine officer, and the new executive officer wanting to play student, Lt. Warren had his hands full.

The F9F-5, with its bullet nose and short, tapered fuselage was a beautiful airplane. She had four 20 mm cannons, a roomy cockpit, dual air intakes in the wing roots, and a compact Pratt and Whitney J45-P6 turbine engine discharging 6000 pounds of static thrust. One 120-gallon fuel tank was attached to each wing tip increasing its combat range to over 650 miles. The cockpit sat well forward of the wings allowing the pilot excellent visibility and with the fuselage low to the ground on stubby tricycle gear, the Panther was a stable platform on landing and take off. The rugged F9F-5 Panther was a typical product of the Grumman Aircraft Corporation, affectionately called the "Grumman Ironworks" by naval aviators. It was fast, strong, and dependable. And in a few days, a scrawny kid from Detroit, Michigan was going to strap it on and fly it to the stratosphere.

Because the Panther was a single-seat fighter, my initial flight was solo with no one looking over my shoulder. Lt. Warren, however, was in a chase plane to help out if I got into any trouble. As in the TV-2, we did a series of stalls, turns, climbs, and glides, then I joined on Rabbit's wing for some formation practice. We finished with a tail chase, where I took a tight position behind his aircraft and followed him through a series of low-g maneuvers: aileron rolls, barrel rolls, and wingovers. The high-g maneuvers—loops, Immelmann turns, and Cuban eights—would come later. After a short debrief I returned to my room to once again bask in my good fortune.

While lying in bed that night I relived that flight a dozen times. It was hard to believe, but barring my doing something really stupid, in a couple of months I would be wearing bars and gold wings. I'd progressed a long, long way from the kid plodding across the snow-covered campus of Central Michigan College. I jumped out of my rack and began writing. I couldn't resist the temptation to rub it all in Cousin Ryan's nose.

> Dear Ryan, Today I began the last phase of training with my initial flight in the sleek F9F-5 Panther jet. I can't begin to explain how incredible it is to fly a real jet fighter after the clumsy Lockheed trainer I flew during transition. It was almost as dramatic as going from props to jets. I know you never believed I'd get this far, but I'm here and still in one piece. I wouldn't dream of quitting to try the airlines, now that the training office says that if the weather holds we should get our wings in December. Will flew his first Panther today, also. We don't talk much these days, so I don't know if he was as impressed as I was. Speaking of Will, we had a little boxing match a few days ago. His idea, but I hammered him pretty good. Nothing's changed, though. He still hates my guts. It would sure be nice if you could come to our graduation. Say hi to your mom and dad. Your cousin, Tom, the jet pilot.

Surprisingly, five days later I received Ryan's answer.

> Dear Tommy, You let me down by not taking my suggestion to drop out and go with the airlines. I talked to a friend who flew jets in Korea. He said the closing speeds when jets dogfight is almost twice what we saw in P-47's when hassling Messerschmitts over France. When you collide at those airspeeds there's nothing left but a puff of dust. Even if you make it to graduation, I don't think I'll be able accept your invitation. I'm now part owner of this radio station and with all marketing and the public

> relations stuff it's tough to get any time off. Say hi to Will.
> I'm sure he's doing well. The guy's a born fighter pilot.
> Your disappointed cousin, Ryan.

"I'm the one who's disappointed," I mumbled. "I wanted to see him come down here and eat his words, including the ones he spoke at that airstrip in Kentucky ten years ago. I should have known he'd say no."

* * *

Right after we began our training in the F9F, Will, TJ, and I joined Max in his Mercury and headed for Corpus Christi. TJ knew several of the Marine candidates in the Corpus area, many of whom were ex-Marine enlisted. We were getting together for a Marine Corps candidate happy hour at the Corpus Christi Officers' Club. Advanced cadets were allowed to use the O Club, the scuttlebutt being that the brass wanted us to learn how to behave like real officers and gentlemen when around the wives and VIPs. The trouble was that our role models, the ensigns and second lieutenants, didn't behave much better than NavCads.

Behind us was another carload of Marine candidates driven by Romero Hernandez, a former sailor, who was born in Mexico and raised in California.

We nicknamed him Cisco, after the Cisco Kid, the Hispanic cowboy on TV. Like the Cisco Kid, Romero had black, wavy hair, and a smile revealing sparkling white teeth so perfect they looked like piano keys against his mahogany complexion. He was smart, had a heart of pure gold, and was forever cheerful. It was impossible not to like the guy.

When we walked in the O Club we saw 10 Marine candidates standing at the far end of the bar, including Vince, Buff, and GW. After having a drink and a quick chat with Vince, GW and I rehashed our stay in New Orleans. I asked him how he liked the AD Skyraider.

"Can take a hell of a beating, but keeps galloping like the reliable old war-horse she is, Fitz. I love that machine." When the NavCad behind him cleared his throat, GW rolled his eyes and threw his thumb over his shoulder. "Fitz, say hello to Hotshot Dean Claymore. He's flying Panthers at Kingsville." We shook hands.

"Who's your best stick and rudder man out at Chase?" Dean asked before taking a long pull on his beer.

"I don't know, maybe Will Rumford," I said, nodding toward Will who was sitting at a table with Vince. "He had the least problems in Basic and handles the TV-2 and Panther like they're kiddy cars. Why?"

"Has he whipped any instructors in a dog fight yet?"

"I have no idea," I answered with a shrug.

"Dean, here," said GW with a chuckle, "figures that because he snuck up on his instructor's six o'clock just long enough to say, 'bang, bang,' a few days ago, that he can now whip anybody's ass."

"Whip yours any day of the week," Dean said smugly.

"If you mean in the air, you're dreaming," said GW, his face expressionless. "Even your fancy Panther versus my Skyraider. If you're talking a hassle behind a hangar some night, you're asking for your worst nightmare." GW stood up, hands on his hips. "Which one is it, Hotshot?"

"Just watch your six o'clock, GW," said Dean. He grabbed his beer and went to the other end of the bar.

"Don't turn your back around that guy," said GW, reaching for a cigarette. "He's trouble."

TJ snatched a leather cup from the bar and started to roll the five dice for a game of horses, the traditional Navy method to determine who pays for the drinks. GW put his hand on the dice cup.

"Have you guys ever played a game called Buzz?" Heads shook back and forth in close formation.

"The idea is to count in turn, but no one says a number with seven in it such as seven, seventeen, or twenty-seven, or a number divisible by seven, like twenty-eight, thirty-five, and forty-two, OK?" We nodded our heads.

"We start the game," he said standing in the middle of us, "with the first guy saying one; the next guy says two; the next says three; and so on. When it's the seventh guy's turn, he says 'buzz.' If he says 'seven,' he buys the round." He paused for questions. There were none. "OK, I'll start . . . one." Three guys rattled off two, three, and four in sequence. Buff stumbled on five and next it was TJ's turn.

"Six," he said, turning to me.

"Buzz!" I said, glancing at GW for approval. He nodded.

As the counting progressed, buzz was substituted for numbers 14, 17, and 21. After number 26 it was Will's turn. Instead of saying 27 he yelled, "Buzz." He jerked his head toward Max hoping to catch him sleeping. He did.

"Twenty-eight . . . aw crap!" We cheered and GW announced the bad news, for Max, that is.

Will lifted his beer and chortled, "The round's on you, Max." Max pounded his fist on the bar, reached in his pocket, and pulled out $5 to pay for the first round. The bartender placed a drink in front of each Marine candidate and took Max's $5. The count progressed to 34. Cisco was next.

"Zumbar, senors," he said saluting with one hand and grabbing a handful of peanuts with the other. Before we could object he added, "That's buzz in Espanol, my Ma-reeen amee-gos."

"No good, Cisco," barked Vince. "Zimber, zumber, or whatever doesn't count. You gotta say it in English. If you can say it in Spanish, then I can say it in Italian."

"Spanish can be substituted, but not Italian," interjected GW. "In Texas, Spanish is like a second language."

TJ took us to 41 and Vince, still irritated at Cisco's "zumbar," was up. He allowed his wrath to mess up his math.

"Forty-two," he snapped too quickly. We cheered his error of blurting the multiple of seven times six. More drinks landed in front of each NavCad. Vince paid the tab, scolding himself for getting distracted. "Sure as hell's an expensive way to get a *buzz* on," he grumbled.

The count progressed to 45. Next was a redheaded bruiser with a bullfrog voice and a cherubic smile, Thorsan "Thor" Kreugerman. Thor was a former DI at the Parris Island Recruit Deport.

"Forty-six," he croaked. Thor's sidekick, Roy "Tiger" Stubbs, was up. Tiger was a former amateur boxer and Para-Marine, sort of a Marine commando. Thor and Tiger had consumed a few drinks waiting for us to arrive from Chase Field.

"Forty-sev . . . no, no, wait a minute . . . bras!" Tiger rammed his left fist in the air declaring his call properly amended.

"What's with bras?" growled Thor. "The word's, buzz. We're playing for booze, not broads, you boob."

"Who you calling a boob, you red-headed buffalo?" Tiger shot a punch at his antagonist. Thor grabbed Tiger's arm with his meaty paw. Tiger jerked his arm away and recoiled for another punch.

"Hold it, Tiger," said GW, interrupting a potential bar fight. "Pay first, then hit him."

"Yeah, champ," said Thor with a snide grin. "Pay first and after you get that tight wallet pried open you'll be too exhausted to fight."

Tiger cursed his cohort while he laid a five-dollar bill on the counter. Vince, a math major in college, discovered that four drinks were skewing his ability to recall the multiplication tables. "Forty-nine!" he barked with confidence.

I held up my drink and smiled. "Pay up, Vince. That's the buzz-word squared."

Vince scratched his head. "Dammit! Seven times seven . . . that's forty-nine. How could I have missed that?".

"And you aced aerodynamics?" chided Beau Thomason.

"Pay up again, Senor Fabrizio," ordered Cisco. You just said the buzz-word twice and the buzz-word squared. That's three more drinks, amigo."

"What're you talkin' about? It's not my turn anymore," snapped Vince.

Cisco shook his head. "If you say the buzz-word, you gotta buy."

"Bull!" Vince turned around. "What's the rule, GW?"

GW shrugged. "Sorry, Cisco's right. It's the spirit of the thing. Saying the buzz-word and its multiples while we're playing is a big no-no."

Muttering Italian expletives, Vince dug into his wallet. Later it was my turn again.

"Sixty-two," I barked. Dufo was up next, but was becoming incoherent.

"Fuzz? No-no, uh, Wuzz?"

"Sorry, Dufo," said GW.

"Fuzzy wuzzy?"

"Nope."

"Scuzzy fuzzies?"

"Pay up, Dufo," I said.

"Boozy floozy?"

"No, dammit," we said, shaking our heads. "Pay up!"

While Dufo continued to probe for the password he began tapping a plastic stirrer against the bar like a miniature drumstick.

Tappity, tappity, tappity. . . .

"Uhhhhh, bruising ghouls?" he said, clicking the stirrer on the counter faster and faster. *Tappity-tap-tap-tap-tap-tap. . . .*

Recognizing the warning signal, I backed away slowly.

Tappity, tappity, tappity, tappity, tappity. . . .

"Bubbling boobs?" Dufo continued.

Vince saw me retreating, got the message, and stepped away from the bar, motioning the others to follow.

Dufo's stirrer was now a blur as it fluttered against the bar. *Tappitytappitytappitytappity . . .* Suddenly his fingers froze and a sound resembling ripping canvas echoed throughout the O Club.

"Sorry, guys. It's the tension," Dufo yelled through the stench as we ran for the exit.

Before following the crowd, the bartender flicked the ceiling fan on maximum revolutions. Five minutes later we stuck our noses inside for a quick check. Satisfied it was all clear we resumed our game. The first to sit at the bar, Cisco switched his order to a gin and limejuice.

"I'm outta lime juice," said the bartender. "How about gin and 7-UP."

"OK," said Cisco with a shrug. "Gin and 7-UP sounds fine."

Vince struck at Cisco like a rattlesnake. "Gotcha, Cisco! You said the buzz-word. It's your turn to pay!" Cisco lay his forehead on the bar and banged it seven times.

After an hour we had consumed five drinks each and another was in front of us. The astute bartender rang his bell.

"Bar's closed for you guys," he said. "I need this job too much to get fired because Marines can't count." Grumbling about being cut off, the herd of Marine candidates made its way down the stairs to the dining room. Thank the Lord for wise bartenders.

While in the buffet line I ran into my Pre-Flight class leader, Pete Zarek. He had some problems with carrier landings, but managed to qualify after a few extra FCLP periods. He finished basic training with Ron Warden and they were both flying anti-submarine aircraft at Corpus. Pete had bad news, however, about some of our classmates. Three washed out at Saufley and two more bought the farm at Barin, both because of target fixation. One dove into the ground on a bombing run and another hit the target sleeve during gunnery. Only a few were flying Panthers. I felt lucky to be one of them.

* * *

The closer I came to being commissioned in the US Marine Corps, the more I worried about my tattoo. I was raised in a humble, but orderly household by parents who insisted that everything be in its proper place. The arm of a Marine officer was not the place to display a Navy tattoo. I wondered if I should have it removed. While mulling that over one afternoon, I walked in our room and found TJ lying in his skivvie shorts, reading *The Bridges at Toko-Ri*, by James Michener. I noticed he had a thick bandage taped over his left shoulder.

"What happened to you?" I asked, pointing to the bandage.

"Getting married right after I graduate," he said, eyes glued to his novel.

"What's getting married have to do with that mess on your shoulder?" Blood had seeped through the bandage turning it into an ugly, maroon scab, about three inches long and two inches wide. He lowered his book and pinched off a dog-ear to mark the page.

"I got my tattoo after boot camp when I was dating Bonnie Sue Harding, my high school sweetheart back in Norfolk. I was hot for her body in those days, but she said she was saving it until we got married. When I got home from Korea it turns out she had been saving her body for some sailor and got herself impregnated. When Mary Ellen saw Bonnie's name on my shoulder she says, 'TJ, our marriage cannot be consummated until that woman has been cleansed from your body as well as your soul.' I cleansed Bonnie from my soul when she got knocked up." He shrugged. "Now I'm cleansing her from my body."

"Is it gone?" I asked, thinking I might give it a try.

"Nope, not yet. Takes three or four sessions. The corpsman numbs the flesh and uses sandpaper to remove one layer of skin at a time," he said swirling his fingers over the bandage. "They let it heal for a few days, then we do it again. Should take about two more sandings before he gets through the last layer with ink in it. It'll leave a scar about this big," he added, making an egg-sized oval on his biceps. "It'll look like a bad burn, but it's better than having Mary Ellen gripe about Bonnie Sue—you know—being under my skin." He grinned and went back to his reading. I undressed and left to take a shower.

Before stepping in the shower stall I looked in the mirror. My tattoo was twice the size of TJ's. If I used his method of removal I would have a nasty scar covering half my upper left arm. I decided

I'd leave it alone, at least until they came up with a method that was less obvious and a lot less painful.

I thought about Stump and how he wanted to be a "man of the sea" like his father. Now they were both dead. "At least you had your tattoo to show your dad when you joined him," I mumbled into the mirror. "I'm still mad at you, Stump, for talking me into getting this damn thing." While I held my left shoulder toward the mirror to get a better look, Will walked in.

"Well, well, admiring your mark of manhood, Fitz-*gerald*? I bet you can hardly wait to show that USN tattoo to your USMC squadron mates." With his usual nasty grin, Will stepped in a shower stall and pulled the curtain.

Stump, I thought with my eyes on the ceiling, if you've gained any influence up there, please don't let me end up in the same squadron with that jerk.

* * *

The days I spent in the cockpit of the F9F-5 Panther were my best days in flight training. The aircraft was fast, forgiving, and tolerant of my inexperienced hand on the stick. Being in the same flight with a Navy commander with over 4000 flight hours and a perfectionist Marine first lieutenant, I had to work hard to keep up. On the other hand, Baker Reems was a serious student pilot and Marine officer, a good role model for a NavCad about to become a Marine Corps aviator.

Rabbit took us through more instrument training, dog fighting—officially known as air combat maneuvering (ACM), air-to-air gunnery on a towed banner, section tactics, dive bombing, strafing, and low altitude reconnaissance patrols called "road reccees." A road reccee was legalized treetop flying over the Texas countryside. During all this training I managed to avoid most of the stupid mistakes for which NavCads were known—most, but not all.

Near the end of the syllabus Rabbit was leading me on a tactics flight. I was fighting a sinus headache and thought that breathing 100 percent oxygen on the way out to the practice area might cure the discomfort. I made a mental note to switch my regulator back to normal when we arrived in the training area over the Gulf. Rabbit started us off with some section climbs, dives, tight turns, wingovers, and chandelles. After 30 minutes he told me break off and do a series of loops, barrel rolls, and other overhead aerobatics to warm up for our first ACM engagement.

While approaching the top of a loop at 16,000 feet my oxygen mask grabbed my face as though I were being kissed by an octopus. My peripheral vision closed in on both sides and a tingling sensation spread across my forehead. Approaching blackout, I felt the airframe shudder and sensed I was hanging in my seat straps, whirling in a frightening panorama of sea, clouds, and sky. Was I spinning? If so, was it inverted, upright, flat? I tried to focus on the altimeter. Its needles were unwinding like sweep second hands in reverse, but I couldn't read the numbers and had no idea how far I had tumbled. I sucked on my mask, but it refused to yield a whiff of oxygen. My tunnel vision was getting narrower and narrower.

Garbled messages crackled through my headset. Was that Rabbit calling or just static? With numbing fingers I tried to unsnap my useless oxygen mask, but it was like trying to untie a knot while wearing boxing gloves. Trying to regain control of the aircraft with one hand, I pawed at my mask with the other. Eventually it loosened enough to suck in pressurized air under the seal. It tasted as sweet as the water at a desert oasis.

As my lungs filled with oxygen, I emerged from my narrow tunnel into bright sunlight. I could now see that I was plummeting toward the Gulf in an inverted spin and I tried to remember what the book said about recovery. I drew a blank. Well, do something! I told myself. I moved the stick and rudder pedals into various positions, hoping I would hit upon the right solution. Nothing worked. My rejuvenated brain told me the altimeter needles were sweeping past 5000 feet. I knew I should eject, but my pride wouldn't allow me to admit defeat and leave a perfectly good aircraft. I pushed full left rudder. Still nothing. I sucked in more ambient air and tried full left aileron. Again, nothing. I wasn't going to make it.

With my head about to explode from negative g's, I saw 4000 feet come and go on the altimeter. Holding in full right rudder and aileron, I pushed the stick all the way forward. At 3000 feet the Panther made one final rotation and flipped upright. I was out of the inverted spin, but in a 60-degree dive rapidly accelerating past 400 knots. I grabbed the pre-ejection lever. No, at this dive angle, altitude, and airspeed I would never survive an ejection. I deployed the speed brake, pulled on the stick with all of my strength—and waited for impact.

A salty film covered my canopy as the shuddering Panther scraped the white caps at 580 knots. Easing into a shallow climb I tore off my drooping oxygen mask and deeply inhaled, using the exhale to thank God for being alive. While in my hypoxic gray-out I had lost three miles of altitude in a brutal inverted spin and miraculously recovered. If there were really such things as guardian angels, I had one flying with me that day.

A shadow approached my right wing. It was Rabbit. He tucked in tight, raised his goggles, and peered at my cockpit. "Damn, Fitzgerald. I thought you bought it. Are you all right?"

"Stand by for a second, One." I looked down at my oxygen regulator gauge and saw the needle resting on empty, the selector still on 100 percent. I had forgotten to return the regulator to normal when we started section tactics. The oxygen bottle was bone dry. Because the bottom of the bottle often contained contamination, allowing it to become empty was a safety violation.

"Well, Two, I'm waiting. What the hell happened."

"One more minute, One." I had never earned an unsatisfactory grade in all of flight training. I could say I was distracted, stalled, and was able to finally recover. Not good airmanship, but it would probably save me from getting a down. Then I would use the pressurized air in the cockpit to get me through ACM. But hassling between 15 and 20,000 feet without oxygen was asking for big trouble and I had enough of that already. Besides, floundering around in the sky like a drunken gooney bird was a sure give-away that I had probably been hypoxic. It was time to bite the proverbial bullet.

"One, this is Two."

"About time, Two."

"Sir, I ran my oxygen dry, got hypoxic, and almost blacked out while in an inverted spin." Silence.

"One, did you read?"

"I heard you loud and clear, Two. Regulator leak?"

Was he trying to give me an out? Should I take it? No, whatever the outcome I had to be honest, or I'd lose his respect. "No, sir. I ran my bottle dry on a hundred percent."

"I see. Stay below ten thousand and take us home."

When we were debriefing, Rabbit stood and threw up his hands, his face growing redder by the second. "Fitzgerald, how could you do something so stupid two weeks before graduation?" My silence gave him time to regain his composure. Hands on his hips, he paused to look at the deck, then looked me in the eye. "You know I have to give you a down for the safety violation," he said calmly. "Have you had any unsats? If you have, especially if you've had any for headwork, you may get a disposition board."

"No, sir, this one's my first in the entire program," I answered, thinking that bit of information might tempt him to bend the rule a little. "I was hoping for a clean slate." On the other hand, I didn't want him to think I was begging. "I know I screwed up, sir. I put it on a hundred percent because I had a headache and forgot to return the regulator to normal when I started aerobatics." I was talking too much.

"If you were feeling that bad you should have told me and we would have postponed the flight until tomorrow. You used bad headwork twice today and it could have cost you your life. I hope you've learned from this." He put his hand on my shoulder. "Look, if you don't feel well, don't fly. And when you go to a hundred percent, note it on your kneeboard and monitor the oxygen closely.

You'll live a lot longer." He patted my shoulder. "Sorry, Fitzgerald, no clean slate."

Back at the barracks I flopped on my bunk and relived the inverted spin that almost bought me my four by eight plot of Texas farmland. "Ryan and Will were right," I muttered to the ceiling. "I should get out of this business before I kill myself."

I pounded the mattress. "No, they will never get the satisfaction. I'll see this through or die trying." I hoped it never came to that—the "die trying" part, that is. I closed my eyes and I was in my Panther twirling around and around until I plunged into the rolling swells of the Gulf of Mexico. "God help me," I moaned into the pillow. I swear I heard a voice say, *He did, Fitz,* just before I drifted into a restless sleep.

* * *

In mid-November Kevin and I were driving back to the air station after dates with the telephone operators, 14 and 18. While cruising along in TJ's Chevy, one of the hottest muscle cars of the 1950's, a Hudson Hornet, overtook us as though we were still waiting at the last stoplight. As the Hornet zoomed by, the moonlight sparkled on the strips of chrome trim stretching from bumper-to-bumper. Even the frame around the rear license plate gleamed like polished silver. With her sleek lines, slanted windshield, and low silhouette, the Hornet was the fantasy of all serious car lovers.

But this one was weaving all over the road, the driver obviously feeling no pain. When he pulled up to the main gate smoke poured from under the hood. The Hornet's powerful 308 c.i.d. engine was fed by twin carburetors that had a habit of leaking fuel if not maintained properly. Under the right conditions the seeping gasoline found its way to the manifold and the engine turned into a flamer. Waving away the Marine sentry the driver got out, staggered to the front of the car and pulled up the hood. When he backed away from the flames dancing around his manifold, the flickering light reflected off the face of Captain Grady "Huck" Finn, the most highly decorated Marine Corps flight instructor at Chase Field.

Lying about his age, Captain Finn enlisted in the Marine Corps in 1949, when he turned 16. He went to Korea in 1950 and earned the Navy Cross and Silver Star for heroism, plus two Purple Hearts. When he came home in 1951 he was barely 18 and a bona fide hero. The Marine Corps gave Captain Finn his choice of assignments and he opted for flight training. He finished in record time and returned to Korea as a fighter pilot where he added two Distinguished Flying Crosses, a Bronze Star, and several Air Medals to his array of decorations. When a truce ended the fighting in July 1953, he returned a hero for the second time.

Although twice a hero, Captain Finn was too young in 1953 to buy a drink off base. But this was 1955. Now 22 and old enough to drink legally, he made up for lost time. Another Marine officer, also feeling no pain, got out on the right side. Kev and I exited our car and from a safe distance watched the action. The Marine sentry, anxious to please the celebrated Marine pilot, asked if he should call for a fire truck.

"Hell, no," said Captain Finn, motioning the sentry to back away. Then the two Marine officers opened their flies and while launching into a chorus of the Marine's Hymn, arced two thick streams of urine on the flaming carburetor. Like the loyal Marine sentry we stood at attention, the proper position whenever a Marine hears the sacred bars of his anthem. When their bladders were empty, they zipped up, stuck their heads under the hood, and checked the results. The flames weren't quite extinguished. Captain Finn looked at us gawking from 10 feet away and recognized us as Marine candidates. He pointed at the flames sputtering around the carburetor and bellowed, "Marine Cadets, piss on that engine!"

Kev and I looked at each other and figuring an order's an order, opened our flies and poured away. The Marine Corporal of the Guard, not to be outdone by a couple of cadets, looked to make sure no cars were approaching, unzipped, and joined in.

Now it was our turn to salute our Corps with a chorus of our sacred hymn. Our three-alarm effort worked. The manifold sizzled, the flames fizzled, and the smoke disappeared. We zipped up and backed away from the Hornet.

Captain Finn leaned forward and peering through the rancid mist, nodded his approval. "Well done, Marines." The two officers got in their car, Captain Finn hit the starter, and the engine thundered its pleasure for being rescued from the fires of hell. The Hornet lurched down the road, leaving a cloud of smoke and a puddle of steaming urine next to the sentry post.

Kev and I peered at the Hornet's taillights weaving toward the Bachelor Officers' Quarters. "Ya know what?" I said quietly. "This being a Marine gets weirder all the time. The funny thing is, I'm beginning to like it—a lot." The Marine corporal and Kev, the former Marine sergeant, nodded their heads slowly.

"I hope you do like it," replied Kev with a sigh, "because believe me, you ain't seen nothing yet."

"Amen to that," said the corporal. "Double amen to that."

Chapter 15

Just before Thanksgiving I received a message to call Operator 18. Jean wanted to take me out to dinner for my 21st birthday. I borrowed Beau Thomason's car for the big event. It was an honor to drive Beau's new Oldsmobile 88 Holiday. A born fighter pilot, he was tearing up the banners in jet gunnery the same way he riddled the sleeves back at Barin Field.

Jean and I had a quiet, romantic dinner at a Mexican restaurant south of Goliad. For the first time I was able to legally buy the cocktails and dinner wine. Afterward we walked along the old downtown section and talked about life after I earned my wings.

"What are your plans after graduation?" she asked coyly, keeping her eyes on the moon hanging over the town hall. We were very close, but had never talked about getting married.

"Nothing right now," I answered with a shrug. "Guess I'll wait and see what's over the horizon. How about yourself? I mean . . . well, you know, after I leave."

"Oh, I suppose I'll find me another lonely NavCad to cuddle up to," she said, peeking at me out of the corner of her eye. "Unless, of course, you want to stretch things out, just to see what happens."

"We should keep in touch, that's for sure, but I don't have any idea where I'm going when I leave here," I said trying to be tactful. "I may even go overseas. It could be a long time before we see each other again."

She turned toward me and scowled. "Are you trying to tell me something?"

"I'm just saying I don't know how long it'll be before I get back here. It wouldn't be fair to tie you down." I wasn't handling this very well.

"You mean tie *you* down, don't you?" She looked away.

"No, not at all. You're special to me, Jean. I promise I'll do my best to get back and see you, but it may be months before I'm qualified to fly a cross country in whatever new airplane I'm assigned. It wouldn't be right to ask you to go steady, or anything like that."

"Go steady? That's for teenagers, for heaven's sake. I think the word you're trying to avoid is engagement." A tear trickled out of one eye and she quickly wiped it away. "I'm not trying to rush you, Thomas. I just wish I knew what you wanted."

"I'll be around for a while yet," I said softly. "Let's just see what develops, OK?" If she only knew how much I wanted her, I thought. She was everything I dreamed about in a life-long partner. But marriage? Marriage was more frightening to me than being in an inverted spin, blindfolded with my hands tied.

"If you don't know what you want right now," she said, "you won't know a month from now." She threw up her hands. "But I'm sure not going anywhere, so why not—like you said—see what develops."

"Great," I said kissing her on the cheek. Arms around each other's waists, we slowly walked to the car.

When we arrived at Jean's house, Ellie met us at the door, babbling about something that happened while she and her boyfriend, Bobby-Joe, were at the drive-in movie watching *From Here to Eternity*.

"It was crazy. Bobby-Joe and me were locked in a stimulatin' embrace when I heard this loud rumble that shook the car. I thought maybe it was his stomach, so I pulled back and said, 'If you're hungry, Bobby-Joe, have some more popcorn.' He says, 'That wasn't me. I thought it was you. Let's get back to what we were doing.' Making out's the only thing Bobby-Joe likes better than eating."

"Is that it?" Jean interjected. "A loud rumble while you were necking?"

Ellie shook her head. "Let me finish. We picked up where we left off, but I wanted to catch the scene where Burt Lancaster and Deborah Kerr are doing it on the beach. . . . "

"Ellie!" Jean snapped. "They were not '*doing it*'. They were only. . . . "

"Well, I bet they did it later," Ellie insisted. "Anyway, I peeked over Bobby-Joe's shoulder and. . . . " Jean and I leaned forward in anticipation.

"WHOOOOM!" Ellie swooped her hand in front of our noses and we jerked backward as though we were dodging a rattler.

"This black shadow screams in front of us like a giant bat out of you know where. It almost shook the speaker off our door. Everyone jumps out of their cars, looks all around and says, 'What the heck was that?'"

"And what was it?" asked Jean.

"Nobody knows. It never came back, so in a few minutes we climbed back in our cars and took up where we left off."

It sounded to me like a lot of high school lovers were in the critical phase of making out and were interrupted by the Pearl Harbor attack scene in the movie. I shucked the whole thing off and bade Ellie good night. On the porch Jean and I had another mopey conversation about our future and 45 minutes later I was back at the barracks. When I walked in Dufo was telling TJ about his night hop.

"Start again, Dufo, so Fitz gets it from the top." TJ looked at me and rolled his eyes. "You gotta hear this. I can't believe he's alive to tell about it."

"It wasn't that dangerous," said Dufo. "While I was suiting up for my last solo night hop Captain Finn strolls by and says, 'Hey, Hartwood, how about checking out the flick at the Goliad Drive-In. You know, sneak a peek at what's playing. I may want to go tomorrow night.' He pats me on the back and laughs up a storm. Well, I decided, if I come back and tell him what's playing, the hottest Marine pilot on this air station will really be impressed." Dufo inched closer on the chair and lowered his voice. "I took off, turned north, and pretty soon I see the drive-in movie screen flickering along Highway 59. . . . "

Oh, no, I thought with a shudder. Surely he wasn't. . . .

"So I figured," continued Dufo, "why not sneak by the drive-in and take a peek. The first pass I was too high to see anything."

"Bobby-Joe's stomach rumble," I muttered.

Dufo frowned at my interruption. "Who's Bobby-Joe?" he asked. I motioned for him to keep talking.

"I really wanted to find out what was on that screen, so I decided to take a closer look." Smiling, he nodded at each of us, checking if we were still with him.

"How close is 'closer'?" asked TJ.

"I'm getting to that. When I pulled up I remembered that the elevation was flat and there weren't any obstructions or anything. You know, from flying all the road recces up and down that highway that goes by the theater?" We nodded our agreement. "Right. So I decided to chance one quick look at the screen low and up close."

"Oh, no, you didn't. . . . " whispered TJ.

"I peeled off like I was diving on a target," said Dufo raising his hand high above the table. "Then I leveled off about thirty feet . . . " he swooped his hand toward the table's surface, " . . . and ZOOOOOMED right by the movie screen." Hands on hips, he stared at us with a haughty grin, eyes flashing like rhinestones. "Pretty neat, eh?"

"No! Pretty stupid," I replied.

"Well, it was all for nothing," said Dufo throwing his hands in the air. "I must'a blanked out the movie projector 'cause all I saw on the screen was my own shadow. Never did find out what was playing."

"Dufo, you could'a killed yourself and a hundred other people!" scolded TJ.

"*From Here to Eternity*," I said quietly. "The movie was *From Here to Eternity*."

"Really?" said Dufo. "How'd you know that?"

"Never mind," I answered while unbuttoning my shirt.

The following day there was an inquiry about a jet flying through an outdoor theater, but nobody could provide a tail number or even the type aircraft. The air station commander, Captain Truesdale, dismissed the idea as too outrageous, even for his NavCads at Chase Field. Had to be some crazy Air Force pilot, he said.

* * *

As graduation day approached the last major milestone, our long cross-country, appeared on the flight schedule. Rabbit chose San Diego, California as our destination. The flight out to the west coast went fine. While at the NAS North Island O Club I ran into some ex-NavCad buddies who were now jet fighter pilots, stationed in California. After two nights of partying in San Diego and Tijuana, Mexico I joined our flight in base operations to plan our trip home. The weather was lousy and I listened carefully to Rabbit's instructions for take-off and climb through the low overcast. I would fly on his wing and Baker would fly on the wing of CDR Bryant, the idea being that with the weather close to minimums, taking off in two plane sections would be safer and hasten our join-up on top.

We went out to our aircraft. I took what I needed from my flight packet and slipped it under my seat. After waiting half an hour for the fog to lift we started our engines and taxied to the runway. With his head on a swivel, Rabbit paused to take one more look at the weather. The overcast rested on the peak of a nearby water tower with the forward visibility about a mile—barely good enough for a legal departure. Rabbit radioed CDR Bryant to take a one-minute interval before beginning his take-off roll. We would join up as soon as we broke out of the overcast.

With me nestled tight on his port wing, Rabbit added power and started down the runway. When his nose wheel eased off the concrete I pulled back on my stick. After moving an inch the stick refused to come back any further. When Rabbit's Panther lifted in the air I was unable to get enough back elevator to follow him off the runway.

"Pull up, Two!" he yelled on the radio.

I pulled harder. The nose lifted slightly, but not enough to get airborne. I was rapidly running out of concrete.

Rabbit leveled off at 25 feet and yelled again over the radio. "Pull up, Two, or drop your hook and abort the take off!" There was an arresting cable in battery at the end of the runway for just such emergencies.

Determined to get airborne, I released the throttle and with both hands, pulled on the stick with all of my might. My nose wheel lifted off, but the main wheels stubbornly clung to the runway. I knew I'd bought it, but my plot wouldn't be on the old farm, it would be at the bottom of the North Island Marina.

With the asphalt overrun disappearing under my nose, the main wheels skipped once and bounced into the air. As I closed on Rabbit I took my left hand off the stick to lift my landing gear handle and adjust the throttle. The nose dropped toward the sailboat masts a few feet below us. Too low to safely eject, I had to fly or crash. Using everything I could squeeze from both biceps, I pulled the stick back one more inch, enough to get me back on Rabbit's wing and just in time to be swallowed up by the overcast.

When we entered the clouds muscle fatigue compounded by a hangover brought on vertigo—total disorientation. There was no up, down, or sideways. My befuddled brain told me that instead of a gentle climb with our wings level, we were descending in a graveyard spiral toward the Pacific Ocean. Pulling desperately on the stick, I stole a glance at my instruments to confirm that we were in a climb. When I looked up I had drifted well behind Rabbit's aircraft. It was merely a large dark shadow in the mist. I increased power and inched forward until the shadow took the shape of a Panther.

Another glance down at my instruments verified my wings were level, but when I looked up at Rabbit I swore he was in a steep left turn, spiraling down, down, down, toward the ocean. My two sensors for equilibrium, the inner ears and eyeballs, were locked in verbal combat.

You're spinning, screamed my inner ear. *No, you're not,* shouted my eyeballs as they peeked at my instrument panel. B*elieve those gauges. They're your only chance.*

Uh-uh, yapped my inner ear, *your instruments are faulty. Look at Rabbit. Can't you see he's in a steep bank, spiraling toward the earth? Break away now!*

Negative, negative, countered my eyeballs, bouncing back and forth between Rabbit and my instrument panel. *You gotta have faith in your instruments and your instructor. You're not in a steep bank; your gyro horizon and altimeter are assuring you everything is fine. Believe them!*

No, no, nagged my inner ear. *Those eyeballs are lying to you. It's your inner ears that tell the truth. When you move your head the cilia in my canals sway like hula skirts, giving you direction. Believe them, not your fickle eyeballs. If you don't trust me you're gonna crash, Crash! CRASH! CRAAASSSHHHHH!!!*

Using all the energy I could muster to hold my wing position and fight my severe case of vertigo, I watched Rabbit, crosschecked my instruments, and prayed. As we climbed through the clouds I knew that if I ran out of muscle power and lost sight of my leader, I would have only one option: steer a westerly heading away from any populated areas and eject when I thought I was over the Pacific Ocean. I chanced another peek at my altimeter—5800 feet. If we don't break out in a few seconds. . . .

Deliverance! We popped out of the clouds at 6100 feet and my vertigo disappeared as though it had been turned off with the flick of a switch. The top of the overcast resembled a thick-pile carpet stretching as far as the eye could see. The air above was crystal clear, the sky azure, and the sun bright and warm. It was, without exception, the most beautiful blue sky I had ever seen.

I eased off Rabbit's wing and massaged my arms, one biceps at a time. When I checked the control stick I could not believe what

I had done. Because I had not secured my flight packet properly, it slipped from under the seat and wedged in the small well at the base of the stick, preventing backward movement of more than an inch and a half. I relaxed backpressure. When the nose momentarily dropped I grabbed my packet then pulled back on the stick to regain my wing position. Rabbit watched my aircraft bobbing up and down like a porpoise.

"What's going on, Two? You have a control problem?" He leveled off, his dark goggles glaring at me over his oxygen mask.

"No, sir," I answered. "Just a problem with cockpit management. I'll explain when we land to refuel." I carefully secured my flight packet on the right console and rejoined my leader in a proper free cruise position—neat, but loose. I held the stick with my left hand and worked the fingers in my right to relieve the still burning muscles in my forearm. In my rear view mirror I saw CDR Bryant and Baker Reems emerge from the clouds. Within minutes they were on Rabbit's right wing and our flight of four began climbing to a cruising altitude of 25,000 feet.

When we landed at Deming, New Mexico I told Rabbit what had happened. He shook his head and grunted disappointment at my carelessness, but refrained from giving me a lecture. I guess he thought I had enough misery for one day. As I crawled in the cockpit for our last leg home, I noticed the steel control stick was bent at its base about an inch, an impossible feat so said the maintenance chief back at Chase Field.

Chapter 16

With graduation on the horizon we wanted to so something to top off our training—something memorable. On Friday, December tenth, Max, TJ, Will, Dufo, and I sat in the Chase O Club at happy hour, discussing the few remaining flight requirements before getting our wings. Out of the blue, Max made an observation.

"Do you realize we'll be splitting up in less than two weeks and we still haven't done something significant as a group . . . to sort of, well . . . bond us all together. I just had a thought. How about a trip across the Rio Grande?"

"Mexico?" grumbled Will. "Never been there and I doubt I'm missing anything."

"Well, I have," I said lifting my beer. "I went to Tijuana on my cross country and it was mostly souvenir stands, smelly food carts, and urchins begging for money and cigarettes. We'll get enough of that when we get to the Far East."

Max would not be deterred. "I don't mean a border town like Tijuana, I'm talking about a classy city—Monterrey. I hear down there the tacos make your throat tingle. And the senoritas! Man, they are hotter than the tamales and jalapenos, combined. Monterrey couldn't be more than three hours away. We could make it our swan song. I'll drive."

"Better count me out," said Dufo. "I got circumcised on Wednesday."

"What?" I said. "Why in the hell would you do that?"

"After I get my wings, I might get married to a girl back home and the flight surgeon suggested I get Bronco Billy clipped before the wedding. Even though it's covered with a gauze bandage a couple of inches thick, it's pretty sensitive."

I cringed, thankful my parents had taken care of that little detail immediately after my birth. "Circumcision at our age must be painful," I said.

"Not bad . . . as long as it doesn't get hard," said Dufo. "If Bronco Billy gets on his saddle, it might break the stitches, so the Doc gave me this spray." He held up a soft plastic vial like one of those squeeze-bottles for underarm deodorant. "If I feel one coming on I unzip and spray liberally at the root. Bloop . . . Bronco Billy turns into Wimpy Wally. No strain, no pain."

"Great! Then there's no problem," said Max pushing his chair back in anticipation. "Bring your little bottle and join us. Come on, guys. Let's take a quick trip to Monterrey, Mexico."

After two more drinks our inhibitions faded away and we decided Max had a good idea. We rushed back to the barracks to pack an overnight bag and Dufo ran by the dispensary to pick up an extra vial of "limp-aid." Two hours later we had crossed the Rio Grande and were driving through Nuevo Laredo. So far we hadn't seen any senoritas, only kids, vendors, and a few rowdy vaqueros. Max said the pickings would be better in Monterrey.

"Monterrey's gotta wait," I said. "I'm hungry. Let's find a place to eat." Everyone agreed.

Max eyed a cabstand and pulled up next to a beat up, 1940 Plymouth held together with rust, fence wire, and adobe mud. TAXI was hand-painted on a caved-in front door. The driver leaned out his window trying to read a newspaper under the dim streetlight. When I rolled down my window I detected an odor somewhere between fresh baked tortillas and the foul vapors from digested refried beans.

"Que pasa, Senor," I said in my fractured, high school Spanish. "El restaurante, por favor? Cerveza? Vino?"

"Dancing, too," said Max. "Ask about girls and dancing."

"Eh, salon de baile? You know—senoritas?" I made curving gestures with both hands. The driver peered in the car and smiled.

He put his paper down and started his car. A cloud of black smoke poured from under the engine and when he shifted gears it sounded like someone dropped gravel in a garbage disposal. He motioned for us to follow him.

After driving over a mile through back roads and alleys we stopped in front of an opening in a whitewashed adobe wall. The taxi driver pointed at the wooden gate. "Salon de baile!" he said proudly. "Vino . . . mucho buena senoritas." He unfurled two rows of jagged, yellow teeth and held out his hand.

"He wants a tip," said TJ. I reached in my pocket and handed the driver a dollar through the open window.

"Ahhhh, gracias! Buena suerte, senors." He stepped on his accelerator and black smoke masked his departure.

I got out of the Merc and pounded on the big wooden gate. A pair of dark eyes peeked through a slot in the wood. Two tough-looking hombres with slick hair-dos and dressed in black trousers and ill-fitting dinner jackets opened the gate. They looked up and down the alley, then motioned for us to quickly drive inside. When I got back in the car Max followed their directions up the gravel driveway. The gate closed behind us.

TJ leaned forward and tapped my shoulder. "What are we getting into here, Fitz?"

"Probably a turd sandwich," I whispered.

I was first out of the car. I stepped up to the entrance and walked into a small, dimly lit cocktail lounge. A jukebox played scratchy music and a couple dancing on the small dance floor were so entangled I couldn't tell where one person stopped and the other began. Round, glass topped tables and deep cushioned booths lined the outside walls.

Max smiled and said, "Neat, eh, guys? Booze, food, and broads. I told you it'd be great."

The place was about half full. Some couples were nestled in booths engaging in some mutual groping and fondling. A voluptuous, middle-aged hostess in a long sequined dress led us to a table in the corner of the room. As we took our seats four ladies appeared out of nowhere. They varied in age from 17—probably younger—to 40 plus, and wore spike heels, short, tight skirts, and halters. Their makeup didn't quite mask the acne on the young and the pockmarks on the old. TJ smiled at me and mouthed, "whorehouse." I nodded.

We ordered beer and a plate of cheese nachos loaded with jalapenos. The girls asked if they could have something to drink. To our chagrin, Max said, "Sure, ladies. Name it."

"Four Chevas sours," said the one next to Will, while caressing his thigh with her long, brown fingers. I scanned the prices over the bar and figured that Max's generous offer would cost us about 12 bucks, probably for garnished tea.

Dufo's hostess, Carlotta, was pouring over him like hot fudge. I saw her hand reach under the glass table. Oh, oh, I said to myself. If she takes hold of Dufo's thickly wrapped member she's gonna think she's grabbed a donkey. I was right. Carlotta's eyes flashed with impassioned anticipation.

"Ohhhhh, Magnif-ico!" she crooned. From the agony displayed on Dufo's face, he was suffering big time from the involuntary reaction between his legs. He pulled out his little plastic bottle, stuck it down his crotch, and sprayed as though his shorts were on fire. Carlotta pulled back and giggled.

"What you doeeng? Is that theeng gonna make you even *beeger*?"

"No, no," said Dufo, tears welling in his eyes. "I'm trying to make it smaller."

"Woweee," mocked Rosita, leaning over me. "He has to make eet *smaller* for you, Carlotta? For me he would have to make eet *beeeeger*?"

"Oh, Rosita," said Carlotta shaking her head, "beleeve me, eet is beeg enuf alreeeady."

Rosita looked at me and bussed my cheek. "I like you guys. You reeeally fan-tassss-tico." While nuzzling my neck, she drew her hand up my thigh and Rhino snapped to attention. I either had to give him a green light or borrow some of Dufo's spray.

Our beer and nachos arrived. I gobbled down a handful, chug-a-lugged my beer and wiped my mouth. It was decision time.

"Guys, either we stay here or move on to Monterrey. What's it gonna be?"

Dufo was fighting off his hostess as she tried to get at his uncommonly large and uniquely shaped organ. Rosita, not wanting Carlotta to have all the fun, was now sitting beside Dufo, inching her hand upward along his thigh. Poor Dufo was almost out of spray.

"I say we move on . . . PLEEEASE," cried Dufo wiping his eyes.

Will's hostess had her hand under the glass table tugging on his zipper. "Look," he said grinning like a high school kid, "if we're going, we have to go now, because in one minute I'm gonna be beyond the point of no return."

I looked around for Max. He had been dancing with a red-hot senorita but they had disappeared. We couldn't get anywhere without our driver. There was a stairway near the bar and I assumed it led to the pleasure closets. I figured it also led to the toilets.

"You guys pay our bill and I'll find Max," I said. I walked over to the bar.

"Toilet?" I asked. No reaction. "El bano?" The bartender nodded his head toward the stairs.

When I reached the second floor the first two doors on the left were marked *Senoritas* and *Hombres*. Heated words in English and Spanish passed through the first door on my right. One of the voices was Max's. I stepped into a cubicle about the size of a walk-in closet and found Max putting on his trousers and his hostess sitting on the edge of the bed in a sheer negligee. She kept shoving out her hand while angrily jabbering in Spanish with some American obscenities mixed in.

"Oh, hi," said Max. "She says I owe her twenty bucks, but I told her I thought we were doing it for love." He frowned when I rolled my eyes at his unbelievable naiveté. "She was all over me downstairs, Fitz. This wasn't my idea. It was hers. I'm not giving her any money." He rammed his zipper home and pulled on his shirt. "Let's go," he said.

I placed my hand on his chest. "Give her the money, Max. This a whorehouse, not a cantina. If you don't pay for your pleasure we may not make it outta here."

"Not on your life." He pushed my hand away and walked toward the door. The girl jumped up and yelled something toward the stairway. I pushed Max through the door and we sailed down the stairs three at a time, the girl in hot pursuit. At the bottom of the staircase we dodged the grubby bartender and ran into TJ and Dufo. Will was tail end Charlie, hopping along behind while struggling with his zipper.

"We gotta vamoose!" I said. I pushed aside a bartender and hurriedly followed Max and Dufo to the car. Two hombres were close on our heels. Something struck the back of my head and my knees gave way. As I reached to break my fall, Will grabbed my arm and shoved me toward the Mercury.

"You're gushing blood, twerp. Jump in the car before you pass out."

Will ran ahead and put his shoulder into the heavy wooden gate. One side moved six inches before it stuck fast against the gravel. With the help of adrenaline and his daily workouts, Will heaved it several more feet. Before he could get it all the way open, two hombres screaming, "Veinti dolla, veinti dolla,"tried to tackle him. Will knocked one down with a sweeping backhand, dodged a wild swing from the other, and jumped in the back seat, locking the door behind him. Two more goons appeared from nowhere and pounded on the roof, screaming "Yanqui owe, veinti dolla, veinti dolla." I pulled my hand from behind my head. It was covered with blood. Max put his finger on his checklist. I knocked his hand away, smearing blood on his spotless dashboard.

"Forget it, Max! Get us out of here, NOW!"

He hit the ignition and jammed the accelerator to the floor. We barely moved as the spinning wheels dug deep trenches in the soft gravel. Something crashed against the roof. A chunk of adobe tumbled over the windshield and off the hood. The back window shattered, peppering Will, TJ, and Dufo with bits of safety glass.

Max eased off the accelerator until the Mercury found traction. We crashed through the partially open gate and into the alley ahead of an avalanche of flying debris. Spinning wildly onto the main road Max steered toward downtown Nueva Laredo. When he saw a sign for Monterrey he took his foot off the accelerator.

"The hell with Monterrey!" yelled Will. "Get us across the Rio Grande into friendly territory."

Max floored the Mercury and we raced through town dodging cars, bikes, vegetable carts, and pedestrians. When we roared through an ALTO (stop) sign we almost hit a car marked POLICIA. Within seconds it was on our tail, siren wailing like a banshee.

"Turn right and do a couple of wooferdills through alleys," shouted TJ, glancing behind us. "It worked for me once in Manila."

Max whipped the Merc into the next alley, knocked over two ash cans and a cart full of tamales, then erupted out of a row of buildings smashing crates and piles of boxes as he spun around to regain traction on the main street. The police car was still on our tail but losing ground. Max repeated his maneuver twice and when he burst out of the third alley the police car was gone.

Will slapped Max on the shoulder and pointed right. "Turn here! The river's down this hill."

Max whipped the wheel, almost made it around a taco stand and sped down a steep incline toward the Rio Grande. Holding a towel against the back of my neck, I turned and looked out the broken rear window. An angry vendor held up his fist, mouthing a string of obscenities drowned out by the roar of the Merc's V-8 engine.

"Slow down, Max," I yelled, "before we attract more cops." Max eased up on the accelerator and we crept up to the border station at 10 miles an hour. When the guards saw a Yankee car that looked as though it had been caught in a demolition derby, they looked at Max suspiciously and asked if he had been involved in an accident on Mexican soil.

"Oh, no, Senors," Max answered politely. "Some drunked-up vaqueros did this while we were eating dinner in a cantina. The police took a report. They told us they'd find the culprits and make them pay for the damage." The guards laughed, no doubt at our assumption that the Mexican Policia would bother looking for the culprits, let alone send us money for damages. Still laughing they waved us across the Rio Grande and we drove into Laredo, Texas.

A mile north of Laredo, Max pulled over and we inspected his battered Mercury. One headlight and both taillights were smashed; the windshield was spider webbed on the passenger side; the side and rear windows completely shattered; the roof and hood caved in with a corner of brick peeking through the ceiling upholstery, and half a concrete block was imbedded in the trunk. Dents, scrapes, and gashes ran from bumper-to-bumper. With tears streaming from his eyes, Max got in the car, ripped the checklists off his dashboard and threw them out the window.

Max didn't get much sympathy. It was his idea to go to Mexico, his idea to drive, and his idea to cheat his whore. On top of that, he was the only one who got laid. All the way back to Beeville I held a towel against the back of my throbbing neck while Dufo, Will, and TJ picked glass from their clothes, throwing the pieces out the empty back window frame. So much for bonding and our swan song south of the border.

* * *

As we approached graduation, the tail end of our training was mostly "clean up" hops from bad weather days or incomplete flights. We needed a diversion so we created a game called "formation driving." NavCads who owned cars often met at the Yellow Rose Drive-In Restaurant about a mile northwest of Beeville. After getting our burgers and shakes, we would chomp away while doing automotive formation tactics.

Beau took the lead in his blue and white Olds 88. Cisco's Olds was on the left wing, while Will in his Buick and TJ in his Chevy were the two-plane section on Beau's right. Since Max's Mercury was still in the body shop he relented to be Will's co-pilot. While in formation Beau gave arm and flashing light signals to direct his "wingmen" to cross from one side to another. Sometimes TJ moved his Chevy to the slot position and the four automobiles formed a diamond, mimicking the Blue Angels. Dufo darted around our diamond in his little MG, acting as the solo member of the team. Surprisingly, we never so much as dented a car, at least not ours. While doing some free cruise maneuvers we did knock over a trashcan or two and a few carhops were forced to drop their trays and run to avoid "midair" collisions.

Formation driving was not easy. It was tricky to maintain position while the leader roamed all over the parking lot, often placing his flight in trail, so he could squeeze through some pretty tight spaces. I rode as Beau's co-pilot, keeping one eye on our wingmen and the other peeled for the local police. But Beeville's three patrol cars were usually busy elsewhere, either driving the mayor to some barbecue or quelling a domestic disturbance at a local ranch. That doesn't mean they ignored our little "air show," especially when we became bolder and "flew" down the highway. If I sighted one of their familiar green and white cruisers we immediately split up in different directions, sort of like the Blue Angels' fleur-de-lis. It was another one of those NavCad things that gave base commanders and Texas authorities ulcers.

* * *

Ten days before graduation I stopped at the O Club for a pack of cigarettes and decided I might as well enjoy a beer before retiring to my room. While the bartender poured me a draught Will walked in.

"Quiet night," he said, scooting onto a barstool.

"Yeah," I agreed, sipping my Budweiser. "What's on your mind?" I knew he didn't join me to be sociable.

"We finish in less than two weeks and we have some unfinished business," he said while signaling the bartender.

"So what's unfinished? After our last go around in the ring I thought we might be evened up," I said hopefully.

"Not quite."

I held my mug to my lips, wondering what he had in mind: more wrestling, a no-rules fistfight—what else was there?

Will lifted his beer and paused. "We could put this to rest with one final contest. When it's over we'll know who's the twerp and who isn't." He took a deep slug of his beer.

I looked at the muscle-bound, physical fitness nut sitting next to me. The last thing I wanted to do was give him another chance to pulverize my body.

"I concede," I said. "Let's play that you ended up standing over my broken body screaming like Tarzan, thumping your hard, hairy pecs in triumph."

"As usual you misjudge me. That's not the kind of a contest I had in mind."

"So, what exactly do you have in mind?"

"Got any solos left?" he asked.

I had two more X's to fill in to complete the Panther syllabus. One tactics hop with Rabbit and one alone where I could do about anything I wanted. "Only one," I answered. "You?"

"Two. We have the same number of flight hours, pretty close anyway. Why don't we get the training NCO to see if he can schedule our solos at the same time? We'll meet somewhere and have a winner-take-all dogfight."

"You're not serious," I said quietly, looking around to see if anyone was listening to his insane proposal.

Will stared into the mirror behind the bar for a second before facing me. "Dead serious," he said. "We'll choose a rendezvous point like Cuero, forty miles northwest of Victoria. It's isolated enough to be safe from the eyes of instructors. Whoever stays on the other's tail in a good firing position for five seconds wins."

It was the boldest of ideas and also risky, but if it ended this ridiculous rivalry it was probably worth it. On the other hand, it could have far reaching consequences. Even if we didn't get caught, and it was an even bet that we would, the loser of this dogfight between peers would suffer far more humiliation than if he wore a black eye for a few days.

Ryan was right about Will. He was a damn good pilot. I watched him waltz through gunnery and CQ at Barin Field and I knew from talking with Kevin O'Malley that he had also breezed through the Panther ACM syllabus. And to my knowledge he had not tried to kill his instrument instructor, had not taken off with his flight packet immobilizing his control stick, nor had he burned his oxygen bottle dry and spun out of the sky like a ruptured duck. Even though I knew he outclassed me and that we were two inexperienced NavCads who had no business in a dogfight with each other, my pride was my master. Refusing would be as bad as losing. Regardless, I tried one more appeal to his common sense.

"You realize of course, that we'd be taking an awful chance at killing ourselves or getting caught. Either way our careers would end before they got started."

"I can understand your reluctance," he said ignoring my concerns. "The guys will understand." He drained his beer and started to get up.

I took a deep breath and puffed away my common sense. "Wait a minute," I said touching his arm. "If we do this, how do we know who's the real winner? Either one of us could claim he had a shot and be miles out of position."

"Gun cameras. I have a friend, a sailor I work out with at the gym. He's in ordnance and could load the cameras on my call. I'm sure he can get the film developed without anybody knowing but the three of us."

"Might be workable," I said cautiously.

"Good. I can talk to the schedules clerk and get our solos on the board for Friday." He signaled the bartender for another beer.

"Is there anybody you don't know?" I asked.

Will shrugged. "He owes me from a bet on how much I could bench press. We'll meet at fourteen hundred hours over Cuero. Let's say twenty thousand feet, clouds permitting."

"How about a tactical frequency of two forty-two point six megahertz," I said. "It's way down the list of alternate frequencies. Should be safe from unwelcome ears."

"Done," he said.

"We need call signs," I said, pulling out my pen and jotting down the specifics. After all, this was the only brief we would have.

Seeing me take notes, Will did the same, then rubbed his chin. "Why don't you be Custer, the boldest of Civil War heroes. He was born in your home state, right?"

"Guess he was, at that," I said, recalling that Custer was also the most notorious loser in American military history.

"I'll be Lincoln," he said thumbing his chest. "Like Abe, I was born in Kentucky and love wrestling . . . not boxing," he added with a grin that disappeared quickly. Sound fair?"

"OK," I said, ticking off the items. "Over Cuero, angels twenty, fourteen hundred hours on freq two forty-two decimal six. Lincoln and Custer. Got it." We simultaneously drained our beer mugs as though it was a final seal of approval.

"There's a condition," I said wiping my mouth. "I want the answer to one question."

Will rolled his eyes. "And what, pray tell, might that be?"

"From that first day we met at Whiting you've been on my back. Surely it's not that fight under Ryan's airplane. Hell, that's ancient history. Why the vendetta?"

Will set his empty mug on the counter. "Vendetta? You have a wild imagination."

"Like hell I do. Explain what's been going on or you can go up there Friday and play with yourself."

Will sighed. "All right. You asked about Ma the first day we met at Whiting, remember?"

"Yeah, and you never answered."

"My old man didn't leave a cent of insurance. Ma had to sell off everything except the house, a plot for her gardening, and a couple of acres for me to build a house, should I ever want it. My Uncle Pete on Ma's side—he's the county sheriff—helped her set up two annuities with the little money left after paying off all Pa's debts. One annuity was to see her through until she qualified for social security and the other to get me through college. But school was more than they planned for and after a couple of years my funds ran out. She wanted to dip into her own pocket but I couldn't let her do that. When I mentioned to Ryan I was gonna quit school and go to work he told me that since I was broke, liked to fly, and had two years of college I should look at the military aviation programs. So here I am."

"It was something like that with me," I said. "No money and looking for something I could hang my hat on. How'd your dad die, by the way?"

Will picked up his beer and looked across the bar into the mirror. "Accident," he said.

"What kind of accident?"

"Just an accident."

I thought it was strange that he wanted some accident to remain a mystery. "OK, but I still don't see what any of this has to do with me."

"Your whipping me that day and him finding out I was gonna go on a plane ride behind his back caused me to have one hell of an accident, myself. He gave me a few bumps off and on before that—well, more than a few—but nothing like he gave me that day. You saw the cast and bruises in the feed store, but you didn't see the cracked ribs and missing tooth."

Ryan was right about Fulton, I thought. The guy was a monster.

"Whenever my bruises showed, Pa told everybody I fell while swinging on the hay lift." Will shook his head and grinned. "The neighbors musta thought I fell off that hoist every week or so. You'd think all those God-fearing folks would have figured it out after a while."

I supposed that Will considered Aunt Connie and Uncle Trevor some of those, "God-fearing folks."

"Pa never let Ma go anywhere, so when she met up with her *accidents* he never had to tell stories about her bruises. But he was careful they didn't show anyway, because Uncle Pete would've killed him if he knew. We never told him—something I'll always regret—so all that time her own brother didn't know his sister was getting beat up by her own husband several times a month.

"But as Pa got older I got stronger. One day I drove his truck to the store to get Ma some medicine and groceries without his permission. When I was moving hay in the loft that afternoon, he climbed up and lit into me with a horse bridle. That's the day he met up with his own *acciden*t. The bastard fell off the hay lift and snapped his neck like a toothpick—just like that," he said clicking his fingers.

"I'm sorry he was so brutal, Will, but I still don't understand. . . . "

"For Pete's sake, Fitzgerald, you just don't you get it, do you?" He looked away and shook his head. "No, I guess you wouldn't. Anyway, things at home may not have been like Sunny Brook Farm before that day we fought at the airfield, but at least they were tolerable. After the fight my world came apart. And all because a scrawny city kid got in one lucky punch! Well, let's see just how lucky you are on Friday." He emptied his beer mug and slammed it on the bar. "Cuero at angels twenty. You better be there, nose wart." He spun off his bar stool, and departed.

I stayed at the Club another half hour trying to digest what he had told me. Would beating me in a silly dogfight somehow free him from his hatred? All those beatings—both him and his mom. That must have been horrible. Wait a minute. Surely he didn't mean that he . . . Nah, in my neatly arranged life those things just didn't happen. As I often did when something was too horrible to contemplate, I shook it off and concentrated on the task at hand.

The notion of a shoot-out at the OK Corral was crazy, but well within the mindsets of two novice aviators, young enough to consider themselves immortal. On Thursday night I checked Friday's flight schedule, half hoping his friend would not come through. But there we were, scheduled for individual tactics hops taking off at 1345 and landing at 1515. Will notified his friend in ordnance. The sailor assured Will that he would personally load and unload the gun camera film and have it developed by late Friday afternoon. We ate a light lunch and suited up for our flights.

At 1358, I was at 20,000 feet monitoring UHF frequency 242.6. Cuero was four miles below me, but so far, no Will. Using our agreed call signs I tried to raise him on the radio.

"Lincoln, this is Custer, over?"

"Custer, Lincoln here. I'm within a five-mile radius of the rendezvous area, angels twenty. Say your position."

"Soon to be on your six o'clock," I chuckled.

"Watch out, Custer, here come the Indians!"

I put my head on a swivel, up, down, left, right, and over my shoulder. But I saw nothing. I checked my altimeter. Nineteen thousand, eight hundred feet. I eased my nose up. I didn't want to give my adversary even 200 feet of altitude advantage. But where was he? Finally I spotted him at my 8 o'clock high, at least 1000 feet above me, perfectly positioned for a gunnery run. I slapped the stick left in a tight, three-g turn.

"What are you doing with that altitude advantage, Lincoln?" I grunted.

"Sorry about that, Custer. I had to climb to maneuver over a cloud."

Bullshit, I said to myself. There isn't a cloud anywhere near us. "Cheating already, huh, Lincoln?"

"You got . . . to . . . be . . . flexible, Custer."

Will's voice trailed off in a long grunt as he increased his g's in the tight turn. I continued my left turn at full throttle hoping to spoil his sight picture, but he was closing in at my 7 o'clock. Damn! Two minutes into the fight and I was about to be blown away. Cursing my complacency, I pulled harder, the airframe buffeting its objection to the excessive g's. The Panther was on the edge of the envelope, but I was getting inside his turn. I couldn't let up. As he slipped by a valid firing position a series of expletives invaded my headset.

After two more turns we closed head-on in a 90-degree bank over Cuero. Seeing we were nose-to-nose I pushed away slightly to provide a margin of safety, but he pulled in to keep us on a collision course.

"What the hell's he doing," I mumbled. I pushed away again and in a fraction of a second we met canopy-to-canopy at a closing speed of over 800 knots, missing each other by a mere few feet.

KA-THUMP. The shock wave bouncing between us stopped my heart in mid-beat.

"That was too close, Lincoln," I called on the radio.

"Did I hear a chicken go cluck, cluck, cluck?" answered Will. "You can quit any time, nose wart."

Without answering I sucked on my oxygen and held my turn, stretching my neck as far back as the vertebrae allowed. He was exactly opposite our circle. It was a brand new ball game, neither of us having an advantage.

Trading airspeed for altitude, we pulled up on opposite sides of a loop. Seconds later we met on top, belly to canopy, going opposite directions. I glimpsed the bottom of his fuselage for only a milli-second before we dove down the opposite sides of the circle, rapidly regaining our airspeed. As I increased backpressure on the stick I felt a buffet in the airframe. I was on the edge of an accelerated stall, but I had to continue holding maximum g. When we met at the bottom he was slightly below me. He snapped his wings hard right, missing my aircraft by inches. If he loses energy in that turn, I told myself, this could be my chance. Now all I had to do was use my limited knowledge of ACM to take advantage of the edge he gave me.

Wings level, I rammed full throttle and entered another loop. On top I arched my neck backward hoping to pick up his silhouette against a wide bank of stratus clouds forming below us. Will was nowhere in sight. Was he on my tail? I glanced in my mirror. Nothing at my six o'clock position. Where in the . . . ? I found him.

Will had been unable to follow my loop and attempted to cut across the arc to catch me in the backside of my maneuver. That put him 1500 yards off my tail in a 60-degree bank and well out of firing position. Bottoming out of the second loop with a solid airspeed advantage I entered a climbing left turn, hoping he would try to follow me. He did. Watching him slide well outside the radius of my turn, I knew I had the speed and altitude advantage to maneuver back to his 6 o'clock. But he increased his rate of turn. I pulled harder on the stick.

Will had to be flirting with the edge of his aircraft's envelope. He would have to reduce his angle of bank or depart from controlled flight. My stick back in my lap, my heart pounded as I held maximum g and began to close on his 6 o'clock position. In spite of the g-forces tugging on my jowls I forced a smile. I had him cold.

A shudder rippled through the airframe. My wings jerked left, then right and the Panther's nose abruptly dropped off the horizon. Dammit! I had pulled too hard and entered an accelerated stall. When I regained control Will was gone. Lowering my nose to regain airspeed, I searched the horizon. There he was above me, descending in a steep bank and coming at me head on like a bullet. I placed him in the center of my windscreen and increased my bank to 90 degrees, putting us canopy-to-canopy.

KA-RUMP! Will's aircraft was no more than a dark blur as it passed me at a closing rate of over 900 knots. For 15 minutes we climbed, turned, banked, dived, and zoomed, often coming dangerously close in head-on runs; but neither was able to get on the other's 6 o'clock for a clean firing position. My g-suit was sopping wet and every muscle screamed for relief from the continuous high-g maneuvering. It had to end soon. At full power we were using our fuel at a tremendous rate and only a few minutes remained before we would be forced to break off our contest and head home.

In our next engagement we found ourselves in a steep climb, rotating around each other's canopies, neither of us experienced enough to know what to do next. Any second one of us had to fall out of the sky. For whatever reason Will's Panther fell first. It bucked once, dropped its right wing, and plunged out of control in a tight spiral toward the earth, five miles below. Afraid he would escape again, I kicked full right rudder forcing my nose downward and took up hot pursuit, hoping to be in firing position the second he regained control of his aircraft. With me 100 yards off his tail, Will stopped his gyrations and stabilized his Panther in a near vertical dive. My heart raced as I maneuvered my Panther to place my gun sight's pipper (center point) on his fuselage. Gleefully I rehearsed in my mind our agreed upon radio call declaring a victory: *Bang, bang, bang, you're dead.*

The straight-winged F9F-5 was not designed to fly beyond the speed of sound. In fact, it got pretty ugly when the airspeed approached compressibility, the near supersonic condition in which the increasing shock waves interfere with control of the aircraft. As we neared this critical airspeed I felt a quiver in the airframe, but I was determined not to break off this engagement. Ignoring the tremors, I allowed my Panther to close on his 6 o'clock. When 75 yards off his tail I stuck my pipper on his tailpipe and placed my finger on the trigger, anxious to get the five glorious seconds of gun camera film needed to verify my victory.

Just as my trigger finger stiffened on the control stick the quiver changed to a bone-jolting vibration. My Panther was trying to shake itself into oblivion. Will's aircraft, now a blur in my windscreen, snap-rolled right and disappeared. I pulled back on the stick. The nose tucked under a couple of degrees. Now in an even steeper dive, my airspeed increased rapidly. I pulled harder. The nose tucked under a few more degrees. I glanced at my airspeed indicator, and was barely able to read Mach (M) .91—ninety-one percent of the speed of sound. That was well beyond the critical M of .875, the airspeed at which the effect of the ailerons and elevator began to deteriorate. Within seconds they would be useless.

My chest collapsed as if the pressure differential around my canopy were sucking out my whole insides. I glanced out the windscreen at the onrushing landscape and back at the bouncing airspeed indicator, now reading M .95. Foolishly I had ignored all warnings about envelopes and safety zones. I was running out of airspace and diving too fast and too steep to safely eject. Then a strange voice boomed through my headset.

Dive brake and power, Fitz!

"Huh?" I said out loud.

Dive brake and power before it's too late!

Was that Will who made that call? Teeth rattling as though I was straddling a jackhammer, I yanked the throttle back to idle and with my thumb, flipped the dive brake switch. When the steel hatch under the fuselage extended into the airstream the vibration increased causing my heart to skip a beat, but it quickly diminished. As the airspeed decreased below M .875 the buffeting disappeared altogether. I was passing 1500 feet. Recovery was still doubtful.

With all of my strength I pulled the nose toward the blue sky in the top of my canopy. The altimeter continued to unwind: 1400 . . . 1200 . . . 900 . . . blue sky crept into my windscreen . . . 600 . . . 500. With the altimeter holding steady at 325 feet and the airspeed 600 knots, I zoomed over a host of fishing boats on the Coleto Creek Reservoir. I eased backpressure on the stick and let out a long, grateful exhale. When I saw the altimeter show an increase in altitude I scanned the horizon to see if Will was anywhere in sight. Except for a few scattered clouds, the sky was empty.

"God, please let him be up there somewhere," I prayed. I pressed my mike button.

"Lincoln, what's your position, over." No response. "Lincoln, are you out there?" Come on, Will, answer me, I said to myself. I lifted my goggles, wiped the sweat from my brow, and scanned the landscape hoping I would not see the ominous column of black smoke.

But there it was. A black, oily cloud spewing from a wooded area a few miles east of my position. Fighting the lump rising in my throat I banked left and rolled out on a heading of 090 degrees. "Oh God, let me be mistaken," I prayed again, while circling the smoke billowing from the trees. But when I looked down at the pile of burning rubble I knew I wasn't mistaken. "Will, I'm so sorry," I mumbled, "How could we have done something so incredibly stupid?" While preparing my Mayday call I was interrupted by a radio transmission.

"Hey, Custer, where in the hell are you?"

A rush of relief enveloped by body and I craned my neck looking for the source of the radio call. "Is that you, Lincoln?"

"Yeah. Say your position, Custer "

"I'm between Victoria and the reservoir orbiting what I thought was your crash site. Damn, it's good to hear your voice. What's your position?"

"Say again, Custer?"

"I said I'm southwest of Victoria orbiting some black smoke at a thousand feet. Are you all right?" Silence.

"Lincoln, I repeat. Are you OK?" More silence. Is he in some kind of trouble? I wondered.

"I'm fine, Custer. Did you say you wanted my location?"

Relieved he was OK, I pressed my mike button. "Yeah, Lincoln. Where are you, anyway?"

"Check your six o'clock, Custer. Here comes Sitting Bull!" I glanced in my rear view mirror. Will was 25 yards off my tail holding a perfect firing position.

"Bang, bang, bang, you're dead, Custer, just like you were at the Little Bighorn?" He accelerated and I felt a thump as his Panther zoomed under my tail and pulled up in front of me in a victory roll.

"Lincoln, you rotten, sneaky bastard!"

"All's fair in Indian wars and dogfights, Custer. Man, that felt good."

Angry with myself for being so naive I turned south toward Chase Field.

"I'm low on fuel," I said softly. "We'd better head home."

Will pulled up along side me and raised his goggles. "Hey, you sound like you're getting dorky on me, Custer. Come on now, take your whipping like a man. I'll lead us home. After all, nose wart, I am the victor." He pointed at his chest, signaling he had the lead, lowered his goggles, and pulled ahead. "Stay a couple miles behind me, Custer, we don't want anybody to catch us flying in formation."

We proceeded back to Chase Field, Will basking in his glory and me limping behind, just like we did so many times when we were kids.

When safely on the ground we performed post-flight inspections of our aircraft. Relieved that at least there was no visible airframe damage from our high-g maneuvering, we walked into the maintenance shack. The sailor from ordnance was standing nearby. Will walked over and whispered in his ear to go ahead and develop his gun camera film, but not to bother with mine. There wouldn't be anything on it. The beefy sailor threw Will a thumbs up and they both laughed.

I suggested that just to be safe, we both recommend on the yellow sheet that maintenance perform a close inspection of our aircraft for overstress, "due to a high-g pull out during routine aerobatics." Will agreed. It was not uncommon for NavCads to write that note on yellow sheets. Maintenance hated to read it because an overstress gripe required a thorough airframe inspection before the airplane could be signed off to fly again. It was a pain in the neck for the mechanics, but it took our honesty and their diligence to ensure our airplanes were safe to fly.

Later in our room, Will told Max and TJ about our duel in the sky and how his "kill" would be confirmed when the gun camera film was developed. He was going to have one telltale frame enlarged and hang it in our room. "Too bad," he said, "I can't hang it in the ready room where everybody can get a good look."

"How'd you catch him with his pants down?" asked Max.

"At the end of our last engagement," Will said proudly, "I caught him hiding in the trees and simply blew him away." TJ and Max congratulated Will for his airmanship.

"Let me tell you what really happened," I said. "We were rolling canopy-to-canopy in a steep climb when Will stalled and fell away in a spin. I pulled a Chinese wingover and got on his tail just as he recovered." I explained how I was zeroing in on his 6 o'clock when we both slammed into compressibility. "About that time I saw Will depart controlled flight again and disappear. After I regained control I was barely able to pull out of my dive, and was afraid that Will might have augured in somewhere. While orbiting what I thought was his crash site, he snuck up behind me and declared a victory. It was a lousy trick."

"I agree," said TJ, nodding his head. "Will took unfair advantage."

"Uh-uh," countered Max. "In combat there's no such thing as fairness. Will was just foxier than Fitz, that's all."

"To tell the truth, guys," said Will, "after I broke off to his right I thought I was coming apart. When I finally got my speed below compressibility I pulled out 400 feet over a junkyard east of Victoria. My Panther came close to being a novelty in a muscle car bone yard. I hear Fitz-*gerald* calling out his position and when I looked up, there he was like an apple waiting to be picked. What the hell, I said to myself, a kill's a kill. When it was over I felt more exhilaration than I've ever felt in my life. I tell ya, I love flying so much it scares me."

I loved it, too, but my feelings about our hassle were more akin to fear than euphoric exhilaration.

TJ and Max waved good-bye and left for the O Club. Later, on our way to the shower I told Will about the warning I received from the safety office regarding pushing the two envelopes—ours and the airplane's.

"I got the same pitch when I checked in. So what?" answered Will, stepping into the shower stall. "You have to tickle the edge of those envelopes if you want to be better than anybody else."

"Maybe," I said, "but we didn't just 'tickle' the envelopes, we punched through with both fists. Actually we violated three envelopes when you count an angel's safety zone Stump told us about back at Saufley."

Will yelled above the sound of running water. "Well, Stump's guardian angel sure wasn't around when he bought the farm at Saufley, was he, Fitz-*gerald*?"

It was a cheap shot, but I let it go. "Getting back to the envelopes," I said, soaping my chest, "we were crazy to. . . . "

"So what if it was crazy," he interrupted. "Pulling all those g's, passing canopy-to-canopy with a closing speed of close to a thousand miles per hour, scrambling out of near non-recoverable dives—I tell you, the feeling was mind-blowing. It was like I was wringing out my soul as well as the aircraft. The old Grumman Ironworks lived up to its reputation. I think that airplane's indestructible."

"Indestructible or not, I say we were damn lucky." I stuck my head in the hot, rushing water.

"Hey, Fitzgerald."

"Yeah."

"I owe you one for calling out, 'Dive breaks and power,' or something like that? You know that call might have been a life saver."

I shut off my water, wondering if I heard him right. "Say again."

"Before you called, 'Dive breaks and power,' I was about to hit the panic button. As much as I hate to admit it, I think your call saved my butt."

"Brace yourself," I said, stepping out of the stall. "I didn't call you on the radio. In fact, I heard those very words myself and thought it was you. Do you suppose. . . . "

Will turned off his water. "Oh, come on. Not that angel crap again."

"How else can you explain it?"

"That's easy," he said pulling back his curtain and pointing his finger through a cloud of steam. "You called me on the radio and you won't admit it."

"I swear on Stump's grave, I-did-not-make-the call!"

Will grabbed his towel and massaged his head. "Why can't you admit a simple radio transmission? Besides, I can't have a guardian angel. I'm a nonbeliever, remember?"

"Doesn't matter. We were close enough together for mine to be doing double duty."

Will rolled his eyes and shook his head. "I'll tell you what. If I buy the farm before you—and that's highly unlikely—I'm gonna petition to be your lousy guardian angel. You think you got troubles now? Wait till I get on your back. Now, what do you think about that?"

"But you claim you're not a believer."

"I'm not. But for the chance of staying on your back and making you miserable, I might reconsider."

Both smiling, we walked back to our room. After putting on our skivvies, we dropped on our racks for a quick nap. The dogfight left us both exhausted. I sat up on one elbow.

"You know what, Will?"

"What now?" he said, eyes closed. "More angel malarkey?"

"After all these months at each others' throats it turns out we're pretty evenly matched. You're the wrestler, I can box a little, and we're a photo finish in a dogfight. Did you see the movie, *Casablanca*?"

"What about it?"

"Remember when Ingrid Bergman's airplane takes off for Paris? After watching it disappear in the fog, Humphrey Bogart and the cop, Claude Rains, decide to forget their differences, team up, and fight the Nazis. As they walk off in the night Bogart says, 'You know, this could be the start of a beautiful friendship.'"

Will turned on his side and faced me. "Fitzgerald, what in the hell are you driving at?"

"Well, we're sorta like them. Only instead of the Nazis, we're teaming up to fight the Russians."

"How are you ever gonna kill any Russians, being such a silly romantic?" He waved his hand once, then laid it across his eyes. "Now, clam up. I'm tired."

"I'm serious, Will. Your vendetta and my pride almost did us in this afternoon. If we don't team up we might kill each other. I don't know about you, but I learned a lesson today I'm not gonna forget."

"I'll remember it all right," he said dreamily. "Next time we're near vertical and canopy-to-canopy, I'll make you stall out first."

"That's not the kind of lesson I was talking about."

"I know that, Fitz. Let's get some Z's, OK?"

I looked at Will curiously. His eyes were closed, his deep breathing indicating he was near sleep. So it's finally 'Fitz,' not Fitz-*gerald* anymore, I thought as I lay back and closed my eyes. Well, it may not be beautiful friendship yet, but at least that's a start.

Chapter 17

On the morning of December 12th the administration office called the barracks with a list of names scheduled for a graduation ceremony on the 19th of the month. All four of us were included, plus Beau, Kevin, and Dufo. We were excited to be getting our wings in time for Christmas. That afternoon the senior Marine Corps flight instructor called us in to pick up our orders. We sat in the conference room and waited anxiously to learn where we would spend the next couple of years, and more important, what we would fly.

"Gentlemen," began Major Gillingham, "I know you've each submitted your three assignment preferences. But remember that the Marine Corps is rebuilding its attack community and the needs of the Corps always come first."

Beau, Will, and I requested the same three duty assignments. In order of preference we asked to fly jets with the First Marine Aircraft Wing in Japan, fly jets with the First Marine Brigade in Hawaii, or fly jets with the Third Marine Aircraft Wing in California. They were all exciting places with loads of beautiful women and plenty of jet squadrons—fighter or attack—to go around. But when the major made his comment about the "needs of the Corps," I had a nasty feeling we were about to be sent to some corner of the globe to fly an airplane that was a footnote in the Marine Corps inventory. Beau's name was the first called.

"Marine Corps Auxiliary Air Station, Edenton, North Carolina," said Gillingham. "Marine Attack Squadron-Two fifty-five. . ."

I knew it! I've sure never heard of . . . where was that . . . Edenton, North Carolina? Where in the blazes was Edenton, North Carolina?

" . . . flying the AD-4B Skyraider." Major Gillingham cleared his throat, trying to dislodge the guilt I suppose, and handed Beau his orders.

We stared at the major, chins hanging on our breastbone. Beau Thomason, the hottest jet pilot the Navy had produced in recent memory was being exiled to some swamp in North Carolina to fly a vintage, propeller driven dive-bomber. I could only guess what Beau was thinking. If they sent Beau to a swamp to fly prop jobs, where were they going to send me?

Major Gillingham stood in front of Beau, his outstretched hand holding a large manila envelope. "Remember what I said about the needs of the Marine Corps, Cadet Thomason. I'm afraid the Corps needs prop attack pilots at Edenton."

Beau nodded slowly, then looked back at us and smiled. It was strained, but a smile nevertheless. "An airplane's an airplane, guys." He took his orders from Gillingham's hand and thumbed through the packet of official documents.

After three more Marine candidates received their assignments—one good, two horrible—I heard my name. "Fitzgerald, you're going to Marine Aircraft Group-Thirty-five at MCAS Miami, Florida."

I didn't know the Marines had an air station in Miami, but that didn't seem too bad. It wasn't Japan, Hawaii, or California, but at least it wasn't Edenton. As I rose to receive my packet I envisioned women in bikini bathing suits lounging on hot, sandy beaches. This could be an OK assignment, I decided. A glamorous place like that had to be loaded with jet fighters.

"Sir," I asked as I accepted my orders, "does MAG-35 have Panthers, Cougars, or Furies? I'd be happy with any one of those jets."

"MAG-Thirty-five," said the major stoically, "is re-forming its squadrons with the new. . . . " My heart skipped a beat. Was I going to fly the new supersonic, delta winged, F4D Skyray?

" . . . AD-6 Skyraider."

KER-PLOP! His words dropped on my head like a coffin lid. This soon to be designated jet fighter pilot was going to fly the big, slow, ugly, oily, dirty, unforgiving prop job known as the AD Skyraider. I stared at the package in the major's hand as if it contained orders to fly blimps in the Congo. Why were we asked to submit three preferences for duty stations when they meant absolutely nothing? I imagined the headquarters wienies reading our requests to fly jets then rubbing their hands and giggling before they typed our orders to fly vintage prop jobs.

Wallowing in self-pity, I listened to the other assignments. Will, Kevin, Cisco, Dufo, and TJ also got orders to Miami. At least I had good company. Max, of all people, was assigned to swept wing Grumman Cougars at MCAS El Toro, California and Baker Reems was going to Hawaii to fly Furies. Max's orders were a mystery, but Baker I could understand. He was Mr. Squared-away Marine and a superb officer and pilot. His was the only assignment that made sense.

After TJ accepted his orders, Gillingham picked up his roster and placed it in his briefcase. He nodded at the sprinkling of smiling faces, then at the rest of us, the misty-eyed NavCads headed for Skyraider country.

"Remember Marines, the needs of the Corps come first. I know you guys going to ADs don't believe this now, but you'll learn to love the airplane. It's the best aircraft for Marine aviators to do what matters most—provide close air support for our ground troops." I never would have believed that the pitch I gave to the Marine Candidate Selection Board would come back to haunt me.

"Good luck to all of you." Major Gillingham turned and left the room.

Some followed him joyfully out the door, those who got jets of course. But most of us remained seated, solemnly staring at orders that would take us back into the world of propellers and tail wheels. TJ wasn't upset about flying the AD. He raved about the great work they had done for the troops in Korea and how it would be an honor to pilot that beloved old workhorse around the sky. Well, good for him. I'm afraid my feelings about ADs were far less than honorable.

Walking back to the barracks, Kevin tried to brighten the horizon. "You know, we might end up in the same outfit. If GW, Vince, Thor, and Tiger join us, we'll be the hottest squadron in the Corps. That wouldn't be so bad, would it?"

Kevin could be right, I thought. If we all ended up together we'd have one great squadron, for sure. But we'd still be flying props, not jets. When we got back to our room I decided to sit down and write one last letter to Ryan. I had to tell him about my orders to AD oblivion. He would probably be pleased.

> Dear Ryan, I received my orders today. You can put aside your fears about me flying jets in the fleet. I was assigned to AD Skyraiders, a big, clumsy, prop driven dive-bomber. It looks like a mutated P-47 Thunderbolt, the airplane you flew in Europe. I had my heart set on flying jets from the day I signed up to be a naval aviator. What a letdown. At least I've been assigned to Miami, Florida, the land of the two-piece bathing suit. That's some consolation, I suppose. Will and I get our wings on December 19th. You always said Will would make it, but in spite of all your insults, pessimistic predictions, and discouraging counsel, I made it, too. I know you can't be here to witness the miracle, but at least you'll know the date you'll be eating that humble pie. Your soon-to-be-winged cousin, Tom.

* * *

By the next day I was no longer sulking and rode to Corpus with Will, Max, and TJ to pick up our new Marine Corps uniforms. After loading up TJ's Chevy we stopped on the outskirts of Corpus and ate lunch at a favorite NavCad hangout, a drive-in called Ziggy's Body Exchange. While eating our burgers I posed a question.

"What do you think was the most challenging part of flight training?" The guys sat back in deep thought. Not Max. Deep thought was not his forte.

"All Weather Training in the T-28," he said without hesitation. "Good thing I figured out the gouge or I would've washed out."

"What gouge?" I asked. The jukebox across the room bellowed out The Four Lads' rendition of *Moments To Remember*. It brought to mind some of my less than wonderful moments to remember in the T-28 Trojan, such as how I almost buried Lt. Crowley and myself in the warm waters of the Gulf of Mexico.

"Flying instruments in the back seat of the Trojan was just too hard," said Max, "so when I got confused or felt vertigo coming on I'd lift a corner of the hood and peek out, get my bearings, and finish the approach." He took a bite of his burger and after washing it down with his coke, added proudly, "Worked every time."

"Max, you're a damn fool," scolded Will. "What's gonna happen when you're on the gauges in that California smog, or it's a pitch-black night over the ocean and you get disoriented? There won't be anything to *peek-out-at*!"

"I'm not worried," said Max with a shrug. "By the time that happens I'll be experienced enough to handle it. I just needed a little help getting started, that's all."

Of course he wasn't worried. Max never worried about anything in his entire life except how to tell his parents when he smashed up his new Mercury in Mexico. We finished our lunch and headed back to Chase.

Chapter 18

On December 16th, only three days before graduation, I laid out the tropical khaki and green service uniforms on my bunk and opened up the large box of accessories. I was lost. Here I was, about to be commissioned a brand new second lieutenant in America's finest, the United States Marine Corps, and I had no idea how to put my uniform together.

There were three service uniforms—one khaki and two green—a raincoat, an array of globe and anchor emblems, two sizes of second lieutenant bars, and a couple of web belts. The service uniforms each had a hip-length blouse, plus the green one had a battle jacket that stopped at the waist similar to the one General Eisenhower made famous in WWII. In addition, there were dress blues and a few guys had the dress whites. Not knowing where to begin, I asked Lieutenant Jetter for some help. Without looking up from his *Playboy Magazine* he said, "I'm busy. Go ask one of your ex-enlisted buddies." Lieutenant Jetter always lived up to my expectations.

When I walked in our room TJ and Kevin were attaching emblems to their khaki service uniforms, the one we were told to wear at graduation. I laid my blouse on TJ's bunk and watched as they attached each accessory. TJ gave me tips on how to place the emblems at the proper angle, how to correctly position the small bars on the shirt collars, and where to place the large bars on the blouse's epaulets. Later Will walked in, stripped to his shorts and T-shirt and did 50 push-ups. Then he pulled out his uniform and took advantage of TJ's guidance.

"Pretty soon it'll all be over," said TJ, buffing a gold bar with the tail of his T-shirt. He held it up to the light and admired the gloss.

"What'll be over?" I asked.

"Our NavCad career. We'll soon be naval aviators ready to go to war." TJ attached the gleaming bar to his khaki shirt collar and picked up another. I eyeballed the placement and did the same with mine. "This time next year we could be duking it out with MiGs or dropping napalm on commie bunkers. Who knows what's waiting out there?"

"I'll tell you what's waiting for us," I said. "Bigger and better things, that's what. If there's one thing I've learned about naval aviation it's that when you think you've done it all, there's something bigger and better over the horizon. I think we'll. . . . "

"Bigger maybe," interrupted Will, "but definitely not better. A Panther has lines like a space ship compared to an AD Skyraider. That monster's about as streamlined as a concrete block." He sat down on his bunk and leaned against the wall. "Look. I love flying airplanes more than anybody in this room. And like Beau said the other day, 'an airplane's an airplane.' It's just . . . well, I have misgivings about ADs. When I was in Primary, I saw an AD after the pilot ran it out of fuel and bought the farm trying to make it to Pace Field."

"Yeah," I said, "I saw it, too. I'll never forget the seat lying there with the pilot's gore spread all over the cushions."

"That's the one," said Will nodding his head. "My primary instructor told me that when you get low and slow in an AD the results are as predictable as when you poke a stick in a hornet's nest. I don't mind flying the Skyraider, in fact I'm looking forward to taking on that ugly bastard, but there's not a thing I know about that aircraft that tells me we're going to something better. No, sir, it's bigger all right, but definitely not better."

"Come on, Will," argued Kevin. "Jets don't like to get low and slow either. We had two guys buy the farm right here at Chase for that very reason. Whether we're flying props or jets, the Grim Reaper is waiting for us to do something stupid."

I shook off a chill, remembering Ryan's own words of warning about the Grim Reaper waiting to pounce the minute our guardian angel turns his head.

"In my case," Will said, while buffing one of the large gold bars for his blouse epaulet, "destiny, fate, Grim Reaper—whatever. I don't intend to make it easy for that scrawny old guy to snatch me up. Anyway, we may be going to something that's a greater challenge, but don't tell me the AD's better than a Panther. That's pure B-S."

"Well, I like ADs," said TJ. He slipped on his blouse to adjust its belt length. The tip had to extend between two and four inches from the buckle. "I can hardly wait to get that lumbering battlewagon in combat and drop a load of napalm on some ChiComs or Ruskies. That's why we did all this, to learn how to kill the commies threatening our grunt Marines. Like the major said, the old AD is the best tool for the job."

"I'm with TJ," said Kevin. "The AD may be big and ugly, but so is a tank. You just can't find a better club to beat up on bad guys. We gotta face it. Our jet flying is history, at least for a while. Instead of a stove pipe under our butts, we'll have a 3000 horsepower windmill sitting on our nose."

"Not me," countered Will. "I have one more day of glorious jet flying. My instructor said the weather had to be good for my last solo aerobatics hop. 'No sense tempting fate a few days before graduation,' he says. It's been rainy for a couple of days, but tomorrow it's gonna be cavu, so I should get it in, no sweat."

"What's 'cavu'?" queried Kevin.

"C-A-V-U means ceiling and visibility unlimited," Will explained. "That's test pilot talk to you amateurs." Recently Will had read the book, *CAVU*, about Lockheed test pilots. "Since it may be a long time before I see the inside of a jet cockpit, I intend to put that product of the Grumman Ironworks through every maneuver known to man." He pinned a gold bar on his blouse's other epaulet and gave it a pat. "There, I'm ready for the big event."

Max walked in with the afternoon mail. He handed a letter to

Will who ripped it open, threw the envelope on his bunk, and anxiously began reading. After sniffing the seductive fragrance on Mary Ellen's envelope, Max tossed it on TJ's rack and blew on his fingers. "Whew! Too hot to handle, TJ. Better let it cool off a little."

TJ snatched the envelope and dragged it under his nose. "Ohhhhh, that Mary Ellen." After savoring the familiar scent for a few seconds he tore open the envelope. "Hey, guys," he said after reading the first paragraph, "she says since Bonnie Sue's no longer under my skin the consummation of our wedding vows will make the record books. Ten more days, guys, ten-more-days."

The first part of Mother's letter was the usual stuff, the latest news about our neighbors, Dad's big project to fence the back yard, and her bouts with arthritis, but my heart fluttered as I read the last paragraph. Ryan might attend our graduation. Something about him being in Texas on business that day and that he may include Beeville in his itinerary. When I looked up to share the news with Will he was staring at his letter, his face pale as the bed sheet. He folded the single typewritten page, stuffed it in his pocket, and left the room.

TJ grinned and said, "Will musta' got a Dear John."

I picked the envelope from his bunk. "I don't think so, TJ. This came from the Bullhead County Sheriff's Department. The sheriff's his uncle, but this looks official."

"Could be a letter of congratulations," offered Max.

"Nobody acts like that after being congratulated," said Kevin looking out the window. He nodded at Will sitting on the barracks steps staring at a flight of Panthers lifting off the runway. Something was wrong.

I threw on my Levis and left the room to join my boyhood pal, our differences having been sweat out during our dogfight. I sat on the steps next to Will and handed him the envelope. "News from home?" I asked.

Ignoring my question, Will took the envelope and stuffed it in his pocket. He plucked a weed from the lawn and while sucking on the stem, leaned backward on his elbows to watch a flight of

Panthers joining-up above us. "Did you ever get the feeling when you go up by yourself that you're escaping every rotten thing down here?"

"Yeah," I answered. "It's a special freedom only people who fly can understand." With my head tilted back I silently critiqued the sloppy rendezvous. I could almost hear the instructor yelling at his three students, "Come on, close it up, close it up! You're making me look bad over the airfield."

I turned toward Will who was staring intently at the aircraft. "I got good news from home," I said. "Ryan might be here when we get our wings."

"Well, how about that?" he said with a chuckle. "The three of us together again. And at an airfield, just like eleven years ago."

"Not exactly. I think we're a lot farther along than we were eleven years ago, don't you?" He didn't respond. "About what you just said," I continued. "I remember Ryan telling us that his little Aeronca would get us up where nothing else matters.'"

"Exactly," he said. "There's you, the airplane, and the endless sky. Nothing else matters at all. And that stuff he said about pilots dreaming they can fly like birds? I've had at least a hundred like that." He patted my shoulder and stood up. "Congratulations on your wings, Fitz."

"And to you as well," I said over my shoulder. When I didn't hear the door open I turned around.

Will was standing at the threshold with his hand on the doorknob, looking at me. "Fitz, as far as those times when I . . . well, it didn't mean anything, OK?" He yanked on the doorknob and walked in the barracks.

What was that all about? Some kind of apology? And why the congratulations now? It couldn't wait a couple of days when they pinned on our wings? Leaning back on my elbows I stared at the four Panthers fading into the twilight. "Yep," I said softly, "something's definitely wrong."

* * *

The next morning was cavu, exactly as Will had predicted. Being close to the holidays, it was a light-flying day. Our requirements completed, TJ suggested we hang around the Panther ready room. "We can welcome Will when he gets back from his last flight," explained TJ. "Maybe it'll cheer him up." Max and I nodded agreement.

When we entered the ready room all the morning flights had launched, so we sat down and swapped stories with the duty officer, Lt (jg) Harper. While telling us about a hard landing he made aboard the USS *Essex*, we were interrupted by the squawk box.

Ready room, maintenance.

"Go ahead," said Harper, picking up his pen.

After this flight Panther one four will be grounded.

"What's the problem?" queried Harper, taking notes.

Yesterday a cadet pulled ten g's and didn't write it up. Needs an airframe check for overstress.

The duty officer turned around and scanned the schedule board. "That plane's already checked out. Why didn't you catch the pilot this morning when he signed it out for his flight?" he asked, irritated at the foul up.

Didn't find out until just now. We'll make sure the pilot downs it when he comes in, but pull it off your list just to make sure, OK?

"Roger that." Shaking his head Harper scribbled another note on his clipboard.

TJ poked my shoulder and pointed at the flight schedule. Will was flying Panther, one four. "Remember him saying how he was gonna wring her out today?" he said raising his eyebrows.

I shrugged. "If it feels shaky, TJ, he'll bring her home."

"Not until he gets in this hop," added Max. "He has to have it X'd off or he won't get his wings with us on the nineteenth."

Now I was worried. "Sir," I said approaching the duty officer's desk.

"What is it, Fitz?"

"How about calling Will and warning him about one four's overstress. He's on an aerobatics hop. He shouldn't be pulling a lot of g's in a wounded bird."

"Good idea." Harper made several calls on the base radio using the squadron frequency then the emergency channel, but there was no response. TJ and I began to pace the ready room. Max drummed his fingers on the table.

The duty officer switched the base radio back to squadron frequency and slapped his pen on his desk. "Will you guys relax? We don't even know if the aircraft's been damaged." He gave us a reassuring smile. "I doubt a cadet could put a wrinkle in a Grumman Ironworks product, anyway."

Unable to sit still, TJ, Max, and I left the ready room and headed for the coffee mess. Fortified with coffee and donuts we climbed the stairs back to the ready room. Five minutes later the blast of the crash alarm caused me to choke on a slug of coffee. We sprang out of our chairs and ran to the line of windows overlooking the flight line. There was no telltale black smoke and not a crash truck, ambulance, or helicopter was in sight.

"Probably a drill," said TJ, shading his eyes from the sun.

The phone rang. Our eyes snapped to the duty officer's desk. Expression grim with the phone cradled in his neck, Harper scribbled on his pad. "Right away, Lieutenant," he said and hung up.

"What's the word, sir?" I asked.

"Don't jump to any conclusions, but a cowboy on the King Ranch saw a jet go down ten miles south of Alice." With that he tore the notes from his pad. "Got to give this to Ops," he said over his shoulder on the way out the door. "Watch the phone."

My eyes switched from the door to the schedule board. I stared at the fourth entry: Pilot: Rumford; Aircraft: 14; Mission: Solo aerobatics; Time: 0745—0900. Over the take-off time, the initials, WR, indicated where Will had checked himself out. I glanced at the clock: 0905. He was overdue.

"Come on, Fitz," said TJ, watching me stare at the flight schedule. "They don't know if it was even a Navy aircraft, let alone a Panther." We sat down and waited.

By 1000 we learned that all of Kingsville's F9F's were accounted for, including a solo aerobatics hop like Will's that returned half an hour late. We watched the morning launch file back in the ready room, the pilots and instructors sitting at tables in the rear of the room to debrief. Of the nine Chase Field Panthers flying that morning, only Will's had not returned. We engaged in clipped conversations, anxiously waiting for more information. At 1010 Harper announced that the witness was sure the aircraft was a Panther. Since Will didn't answer any radio calls, Ops concluded the aircraft seen going down was his. A team was already on the way to the site. TJ and I decided to shift our vigil to the safety office.

"The witness," the safety clerk read from a progress report, "is a cowboy employed by the King Ranch. The guy's a Korean War vet and familiar with US Navy aircraft. Claims he heard a loud bang overhead, looked up, and thought he saw two jets, then decided it was only one, a Panther in a vertical dive. It hit a hillside and exploded about a mile or so from where he was tending his longhorns. One more thing . . . no chute."

When he said, "no chute," TJ looked out the window. There was a smattering of white, cumulus clouds in the sky. "The bang the cowboy heard," he said, "might have been the ejection seat. The parachute could have blended in with the clouds. Will might be out there waiting to be picked up."

"We'll know soon," I said. "By now the accident investigation team is at the crash site."

After half hour sifting through the Panther's smoking hole, one of the investigators radioed back that the cockpit was empty, no pilot and no ejection seat. That was great news. Will was out there somewhere. We went back to the ready room and waited.

At 1220 an operations clerk walked in and handed Harper a dispatch. "It's about NavCad Rumford," he said.

We rose to our feet. "Is he OK?" we asked in unison.

His face expressionless, Harper scanned the message.

"Well?" queried TJ, impatiently.

Harper shook his head. "Sorry, guys. They found his body half mile from the crash site still in his seat. Must have been out of the ejection envelope." Too stunned to speak I backed against a sofa and sat down.

* * *

TJ and I stood outside the radius of the whirling helicopter rotor-blades. Two corpsmen lifted a long, canvas bag, placed it gently on a stretcher, and rolled it into the ambulance. They closed the doors and the gray vehicle slowly drove off the flight line. We watched as a helicopter crewman took the battered, sod-impacted ejection seat and passed it to an officer who carried it toward the hangar.

"It doesn't make sense," I said shaking my head. "He was one of the best student pilots to go through Chase Field."

TJ placed his hand on my shoulder. "You heard him say he was gonna try everything in the book. I knew Will since he soloed back at Whiting Field. He never flew a hop where he didn't push himself to the limit. This time he pushed too hard."

"Maybe he didn't push too hard," I said. "Maybe the airframe had been damaged from the overstress. Or maybe there was another airplane involved."

"Those are very big maybes," said TJ, lifting his hand from my shoulder. "We'll have to wait and see what they find. But what difference does it make? Will's dead. Whatever they find won't change that. Come on. We gotta go back to the barracks and pack up his gear."

The next day I went to the hangar looking for Lt. Warren. I found him on the flight line checking a Panther he had flown on a maintenance test flight minutes earlier. Leaning on the nose, he scribbled comments on the maintenance form.

"Lieutenant Warren?"

"It's Rabbit," he said, putting his pen in his flight suit pocket. He stuck out his hand and we shook. "You'll be a lieutenant in a couple of days and my Marine friends tell me there isn't much space between a Marine lieutenant and a Navy lieutenant," he said smiling. He was being gracious. A Navy lieutenant was equal in rank to a Marine Corps captain.

"What's on your mind, Fitzgerald?"

"You were in a Skyraider squadron. What's it like?"

"Oh, yeah, I heard you got ADs. I know how you wanted to fly jets in the fleet, Fitzgerald. Sorry about that. I'm also sorry to hear about Rumford. I understand he was your roommate. Chased him on a check flight once. He was an arrogant kid, but a damn good pilot. Two days before he got his wings . . . well, that stuff happens."

"I'm finding that out," I said.

"Now, about the AD. See this baby right here?" He patted the nose of the sleek jet fighter.

"Yes." I looked woefully at the Panther's smooth lines and sighed. Damn, I was going to miss flying jets.

"She's got no torque, so use of the rudder in flight is minimal. She's got a quiet cockpit and she's built for speed."

Come on, Rabbit, I scolded silently. Stop teasing and tell me something about the Skyraider I can look forward to.

"Compared to an AD, though, a Panther's engine responds like a snail and it has the payload of a Piper Cub." He stuck his head in the engine intake like he was hunting for something.

"And?" So far he didn't offer anything I didn't already know.

He pulled his head out of the intake, made a note on his form, and continued. "An AD's a Sherman tank with wings. She's tough as hell and carries enough ordnance to wipe out a battalion. That monster could fly through a barn door, ram through the other side, and be hardly worse for the wear."

"I've heard all that, but what's it like to fly one?" I asked, impatient with what sounded like a commercial by Douglas Aircraft Corporation.

He scratched his head, smiled, and pointed at my feet. "Because of the torque, exercise that right leg a lot," he said chuckling, "and get a good supply of hemorrhoid ointment." When I narrowed my eyes, he added, "She's a dive bomber. Pulling all those g's everyday, your anal sphincter's gonna look like a tractor tire with snow chains. Good luck, Fitzgerald." Rabbit shook my hand and returned to his form.

That night I had a call from Mother and Dad, congratulating me on getting my wings. They figured if they waited until the next day I'd be out celebrating and they'd never catch me. Mother did pass along that Ryan probably wouldn't make it after all. It looked like the trip to Dallas was cancelled, she said, adding that she was sure I would understand. I told her about Will and what was supposed to be a cheerful phone call ended with tears all around.

The next day seventeen cadets and three officer students met in the base commander's conference room for a graduation ceremony. Captain Truesdale welcomed the girlfriends, wives, and parents who had traveled hundreds of miles for this momentous occasion. Jean met me at the door. We hugged, then exchanged small talk while a yeoman brought in our commissions and laid out the wings that would soon be on our left breast. This was the day I had pursued for 17 long, arduous months. I looked at the room and the small gathering of people around me. It seemed so anticlimactic, considering the tremendous effort it took to get there. But I was there and that's all that counted.

Baker Reems and Ted MacKenzie walked in, then Cisco, Max, TJ, Dufo, Beau, Kevin, and Fred Engle. We all talked briefly about the tragedy that befell us two days before. Although this should have been a happy occasion, because of Will's loss, the mood was somber.

"It's nice to see a Fitzgerald carry on my legacy."

My head snapped toward the door. Standing with his arms folded, wearing his A-2 leather flight jacket and a broad smile was my cousin, Ryan. Convinced he would not show up, my mouth hung open, but quickly widened to a beaming smile.

"Doing a radio promotion with one of our sponsors based in

Dallas," Ryan said with a shrug, "so I thought I'd drop in."

"Mother warned me you might not make it," I said, finding my voice, "and when I didn't hear from you I was sure you'd be a no-show."

"Almost was. The Dallas trip was off-and-on so many times I didn't want to make any promises. When our sponsor finally made up his mind it was too late to write. Can't stay long, though. I have a radio interview in Ft. Worth this afternoon."

"Well, in a few minutes you'll be looking at the hottest Skyraider pilot in the Marine Corps," I said.

He wrinkled his forehead. "No more sobbing about not getting jets?"

"Nahhhh . . . Jets are for playboys," I lied with a wave of my hand. Although I was resigned to flying the big Skyraider, jets would always be my first love.

Ryan nodded his head with satisfaction. "Good attitude, cousin."

I introduced him to Jean. After they shook hands, she joined TJ and Max while Ryan and I moved to a corner to talk. "Did you hear about Will?" I asked.

"Yep, poor Emma's about done in by it. Seemed to me that since Fulton got himself killed five years ago, Will and his ma shared something that went beyond kinship, but Ma and Pa said they were merely clinging to all they had left." Ryan sighed deeply. "When he had to quit college I'm afraid it was me who suggested he try flight training. I guess that's something I'll have to live with."

"That was his choice, Ryan. He loved flying and was good at it."

"They find out what happened?"

I shrugged. "The airplane was overstressed on a previous hop, but not written up. That could have been a factor."

"Damn!" Ryan said, shaking his head.

"But it could also have been hypoxia or disorientation," I added quickly, "or he just plain pushed the envelope. We may never find out what really happened."

"Any other airplanes involved?" Ryan asked.

"Maybe and maybe not," I said. "A NavCad from NAS Kingsville was up on a solo at the same time. My spies tell me he's Dean Claymore, a guy who loves to sneak up on your six o'clock and scream victory. But he claimed he wasn't anywhere near the King Ranch and the accident board believed him. I'm not so sure. Anyway, the board's official position is that Will was alone when he went in. You know, Ryan, from the day he became a NavCad Will had to prove he was a better pilot than the rest of us, especially me. Hell, until recently I was convinced he hated my guts. He constantly pushed himself and his aircraft—tickling the envelope, he called it."

"I think Will hated himself, not you, Tommy. You have to understand that after you left that summer you guys got in the fight, Fulton beat up on Will even worse than he had in the past—and pretty often, too. Ma thinks he also beat on Emma. When Will got older and stronger, he may have gotten mad and fought back—do you get what I'm driving at?"

"I-I think so," I said, recalling the conversation Will and I had at the O Club bar.

"And there were rumors," continued Ryan, "that the county was gonna reopen the case. I heard the prosecutor got a call from a local farmer whose handyman did odd jobs for Fulton. The handyman was mucking the stalls that day and heard a commotion in the hayloft. When he looked up he saw Will and his pa going at it like crows over road kill. Supposedly the guy didn't want to be involved, so he backed away from the stalls and ran for the barn door. He heard a thump and when he peeked around the door he saw Fulton lying motionless on the ground under the hay lift. Will was staring down at his pa with a horse bridle in his hands. The guy was afraid to say anything for years. For some reason the old geezer developed a conscience a few days ago and mentioned it to his boss."

"But that doesn't prove that Will. . . . "

"Now hear me out," Ryan interrupted with his palms up. "Suppose he did kill his pa—by accident or whatever. Most likely it was to protect himself or maybe, Emma. Regardless, he would have been carrying around a lot of guilt. You said yourself he turned into an ornery cuss. Maybe this was one way he could unburden himself and at the same time provide his ma with some insurance money. Pilots have been known to do things like that before, you know."

I shook my head vigorously. "Will ejected. That proves he didn't, well . . . commit suicide, if that's what you're saying."

"So maybe he decided he couldn't go through with it, but waited too long to get out," Ryan said with a shrug.

"I can't see it. He wanted those wings more than anything else in the world. This was his last flight in a Panther. More likely he was wringing her out and accidentally pushed through the envelope. Or maybe something snapped because of the overstress on the previous flight. In either case he's the kind of guy who would try to save the airplane rather than leave it. He might have waited too long to get out, but not because he was gonna commit suicide, for Pete's sake."

"OK, cousin, whatever you say. Remember what I told you the day you tried to wreck my Aeronca?"

"Yes. Some pilots have dreams about flying like birds and believe that's what heaven is all about—doing things you dream about for eternity. Matter of fact I've had a couple of dreams like that, myself."

"Right. Well, maybe Will's getting all the flying he ever wanted right now, and without a care in the world. But enough of this. Let's talk about today. Congratulations on getting your wings. I always knew you'd make it." He folded his arms and flashed his devilish grin.

I was incredulous. "Oh, come on! You never once wrote a line of encouragement. Instead of your confidence all I got were put-downs and pleas to quit and come home. I was only ten when we spun out your Aeronca, yet you acted like it made me a lifetime loser." I struggled to keep my voice down. "Damn it, if you thought I could make it, why didn't you give me some support?"

Ryan sighed. "As far as my attitude eleven years ago, well, I was a little messed up when I came home from the war. It took me a while to get civil again. And the letters? I was afraid you got into this flying business for all the wrong reasons. I saw too many friends buy the farm because they were out to prove something to somebody else, not because they wanted to become a pilot. I didn't want to be responsible for the same thing happening to my kin. I figured if my letters were enough to convince you to quit." He paused to hunch up his shoulders. "Well, cousin, you shouldn't have been here in the first place."

"But you. . . . "

Ryan cut me off again. "It's like I told you in the letter. If all you want is to fly airplanes, go with the airlines. Being a fighter pilot is a different ball game. You shouldn't even consider it unless you *really, really* love it. You have to love it so much that you feel it boiling in your veins. Not because you think it's an exotic adventure, or that gold wings will attract women like flowers attract butterflies. You must love flying fighters so much it consumes all of your waking hours and then you dream about it at night."

"Fine," I said nodding my head, "but what about you? You hadn't even flown once before you joined the Air Corps, so how could you have known you'd love it so much. Why couldn't you accept that I, too, could learn to love flying and be as good a pilot as yourself?"

"I was beginning to think just that, at least the loving part. Most of your letters expressed the excitement that I knew in training. But your last letter—the wimpy one where you moaned about not getting jets? When I read that one I was almost convinced I had been right all along. A fighter pilot doesn't worry whether the beast under his saddle is a jet or a prop, he just wants to be in an airplane that pulls g's, shoots bullets, and slings bombs. Listening to you now, I'm convinced you understand that. As a matter of fact, I think you just might be as good as me someday. Do me a favor and tear those letters up, OK?" He offered his hand and after a slight hesitation I grasped it and we shook.

"Are you telling me I passed the test?" I asked.

"With flying colors," he answered with a broad grin.

We shook vigorously and embraced. After a few moments sharing news about our families we joined Jean and the others.

In his opening remarks Captain Truesdale said that each of us wore a $75,000 flight helmet (the amount of money spent to train one cadet). He added that earning our gold wings made us a very special breed of American warrior who protects his countrymen from above. I looked at Ryan and he acknowledged with a wink. The Captain continued with some uninteresting news about world politics and how, as carrier pilots, we would be the spearhead of America's fighting forces. I tried to be attentive but could not help but stare at the empty seat at the end of the row, the one Will would have occupied.

"Why in the hell doesn't he get on with it?" I whispered to TJ. Remarks at military ceremonies are often like church sermons. The officiant does not think the message can be meaningful unless the audience receives the full benefit of his or her wisdom.

When Captain Truesdale finally ran dry the adjutant called us to attention and the pinning began. As he attached the shiny, gold badges identifying us as naval aviators, he droned on about the significance of the day, often repeating himself. The Navy produced over 3,800 aviators in 1955 and it's hard to be original, I suppose, when you officiate at a graduation every other week. When it was over we congratulated each other and could not resist fondling our new wings to make sure they were real.

Jean had to get back to her switchboard in Goliad and left right after the ceremony. TJ let me use his car to drive Ryan to Operations. On his Beech Bonanza's white fuselage, boldly displayed in bright red script was his slogan, *Flyin' with Ryan on WJPK 654 kc.* When he was safely airborne he rocked his wings a few times before disappearing in the Texas haze. While I stared at the horizon I wondered about Ryan's letters. Did I make it through flight training because I was determined to fly fighters, or to prove Ryan wrong? Maybe it was my refusal to give Will the satisfaction of seeing me DOR. Perhaps it was all three.

* * *

TJ, Max, Dufo, and I had one more task to complete that afternoon. We climbed into TJ's Chevy and headed for the train station. The only sound on the deserted platform was the whisper of steam escaping between the engine's giant wheels. In a few moments two porters rolled Will's casket out on the platform. The military escort, one of Will's college buddies and a Pre-Flight classmate who had finished flight training at Cabiness the week before, followed them. With a black armband over the left sleeve of his Marine dress blues he followed behind the squeaky cart, quietly guiding the porters as they negotiated the ramp leading to the baggage car. When aboard they transferred the plain, gray casket onto a temporary catafalque and the escort solemnly covered it with an American flag. I walked up the ramp, saluted the casket, and handed the escort a set of gold wings and two gold bars.

"Please make sure Will takes these with him," I said quietly. "He earned them." The escort nodded and placed them in his briefcase. I started to leave, then reached in my pocket and pulled out Ryan's old patch. It did its job getting me through flight training but it probably should have been Will's, not mine. He was a far better pilot than I would ever be. I turned and held out my hand. "Add this," I said. He took the frayed patch worn glossy by my constant rubbing, dropped it in his briefcase, and took a seat by the bulkhead. After rendering Will a farewell salute, I left the baggage car.

"It's eerie," I said softly while stepping beside TJ and Max on the platform.

"How so?" said TJ.

"Will's mom sold the farm except a little section she was saving for him. Now he's coming home to claim it."

"The proverbial plot on the old farm. That is spooky," said Max as we watched the huge doors roll shut like curtains ending a Shakespearean tragedy.

While the train rolled out of the station I marveled at the irony. Will had been carrying an awesome load all that time, yet he sailed through flight training as though it was child's play. Burdened with nothing but ineptness, I struggled continuously from day one and it was I turning to the next page, not Will. I should have been more perceptive. People don't become jerks without other people and events giving them a little help. But as Ryan said, maybe he's soaring with the eagles now and free of all his burdens.

Standing on that platform I had the strangest feeling. There was a warm breeze from above—a downdraft—as though something were hovering right over me. I looked up at the blue sky, but saw only clouds. In a few seconds the breeze was gone. Could it have been . . . ? Nah, I thought with a chuckle. That's crazy.

After we returned to Chase Field we joined our fellow graduates at the O Club to celebrate our new status as naval aviators. Following a solemn toast to Will Rumford we threw our glasses into the fireplace, cheered loudly, and settled down for some serious drinking. We were officers today, but would have to wait until tomorrow to become gentlemen.

While celebrating I received a call from GW. He and our other buddies at Cabiness were joining us in Miami: Vince, Thor, Tiger, even Buff. "And guess what?" he added. "Dean Claymore, the big shot Panther pilot from Kingsville, got orders there, too. When he found out he was gonna fly Skyraiders instead of jets, the guy about had a coronary. See you in Miami, Fitz."

* * *

The next day Jean drove me to San Antonio to catch my airplane to Detroit. Several flights had been canceled because of bad weather over the southern part of the country and the terminal was jammed with angry, frustrated passengers. We held hands and ambled along, not saying much, just enjoying our final moments together. She looked up at me with moist eyes.

"You won't be back."

"Of course I will."

"No, you won't. You'll start dating those bathing beauties in Miami and forget about me."

I took her hands in mine. "Forget Operator Eighteen? Never." We embraced and after we separated I guided her over to a bench and we sat down.

An elderly man noticed my uniform and walked over to pay his patriotic respects. "Where you stationed, soldier?"

I rose from our bench, took a deep breath and slowly exhaled. "Sir, I'm not a soldier. I'm an officer in the United States Marine Corps and a naval aviator." I pointed to my globe and anchor emblems and my new gold wings. "In a few days I'll report to my first squadron in Miami, Florida." I smiled, satisfied that I had set him straight.

"Good for you, son." He reached up and patted my shoulder, then glanced at Jean. "Your lady friend here will have lots of competition, though. That place is loaded with good-looking babes. Well, good luck, soldier." He waved and walked on. I suppose to some people, every person in uniform is a soldier.

"See?" said Jean after I sat down.

"Forget what that old coot said. Miami's just another city."

"No, it isn't. All the glamorous people go to Miami. I'm a country girl from Texas. There's no way I can compete with them."

"How about the hundreds of cadets cycling through Chase Field? It's you who'll do the forgetting."

"Forget these last six months?" she said angrily. "Hardly." Folding her arms she turned her head away .

"Please, Jean," I pleaded. "Let's not part like this." I touched her shoulder.

While Jean dabbed at her eyes an attractive stewardess carrying an overnight bag was walking briskly through the concourse. She stopped to look at the posted takeoff times, and then glanced at her watch. When she looked up she smiled at me with a pair of deep brown eyes. Then she quickly turned and continued on her way.

Jean noticed me eyeing the stewardess and scowled. "Already it starts."

"Come on, Jean," I said, reaching for her face. She pulled away and we spent the next few minutes in silence.

When they announced my flight I took her hand and led her through the gate to the boarding ramp. After a kiss and long embrace, we broke apart and held hands, our arms outstretched. "I'm gonna miss you, Operator Eighteen," I said slowly backing away.

She nodded. "I'll miss you, too, Adam Ardvark."

We both forced a smile. Our hands parted and I turned to climb the boarding ladder. When I reached the top I waved, then entered the cabin door of the Lockheed Super Constellation.

My seat was next to the window on the terminal side and I looked for Jean's face among the families and loved ones. She was standing to the side of the crowd with her hands in her coat pockets staring at the large aircraft. I waved, but she didn't see me. She continued to gaze at the airplane until the wind from the propellers forced her to back away. I turned to greet my seat partner and when I looked back out the window she was gone.

"Good-bye, Jean," I whispered.

"Care for a pillow, Lieutenant? It's a long flight to Detroit." I looked up at the same brown eyes that smiled at me in the terminal, and nodded.

"Better stay strapped in after takeoff," said the stewardess while handing me the pillow and a blanket. "We're not sure what's waiting for us up ahead."

I snapped the seat belt snugly across my lap. "I'm looking forward to bigger and better things," I said with a smile. As soon as the words were out of my mouth, I had a vision of myself climbing into the cockpit of a big ugly Skyraider . . . and groaned.

The stewardess cocked her head. "Sir?"

I looked at her out of the corner of my eye. "Make that just bigger," I said.

The End

90000
9 780738 814278